Popular Complete Smart Series

Complete Canadian Curriculum

Contents Grade 4

Mathematics

English

Social Studies

Heritage and Identity: Early Societies, 3000 BCE – 1500 CE

People and Environments: Political and Physical Regions of Canada

Science

Answers

* The Canadian penny is no longer in circulation. It is used in the units to show money amounts to the cent.

1

Numbers to 10 000

- Write, compare, and order whole numbers to 10 000.
- Identify the value of a digit in a 4-digit number.
- Round 4-digit numbers.

Count and write the numbers. Then write the 4-digit number on the sign.

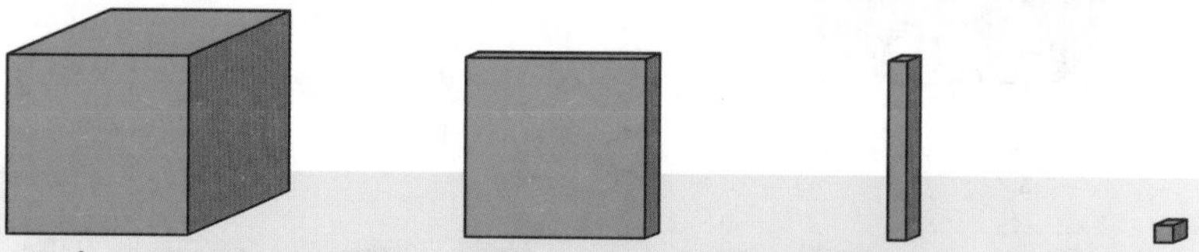

1 thousand 1 hundred 1 ten 1 one

①

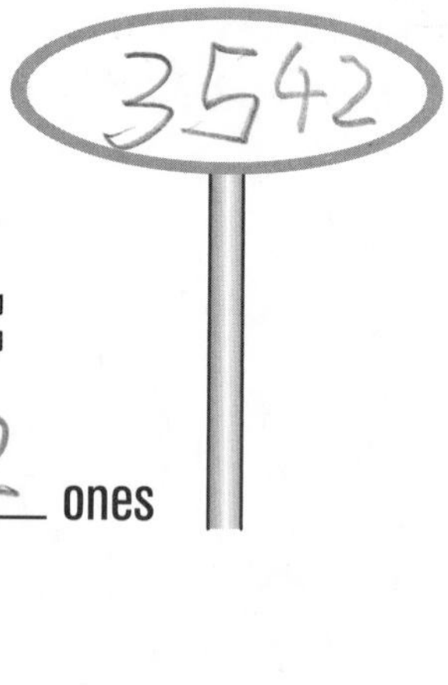

3542

3 thousands 5 hundreds 4 tens 2 ones

②

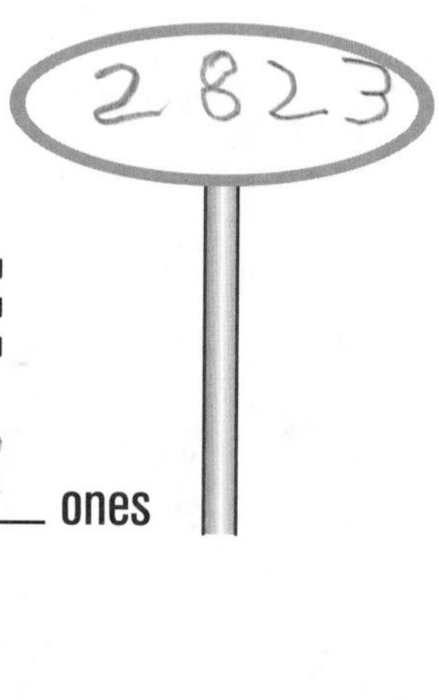

2823

2 thousands 8 hundreds 2 tens 3 ones

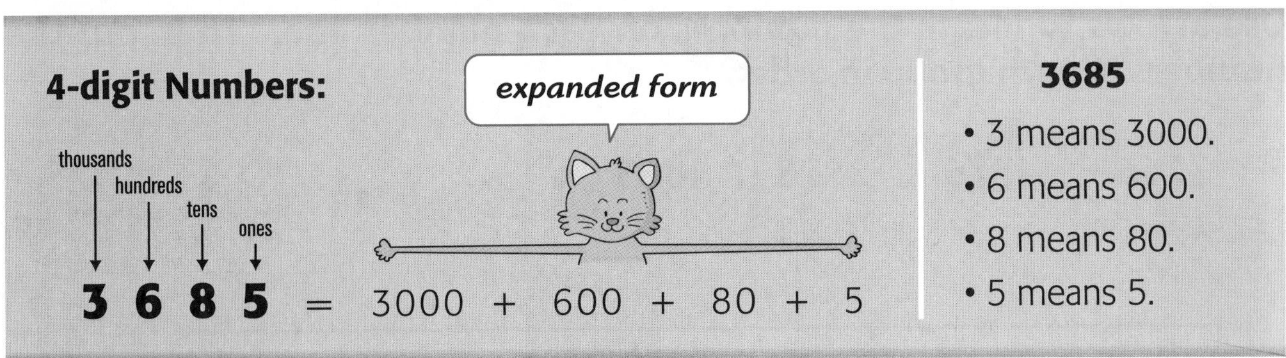

4-digit Numbers:
thousands
hundreds
tens
ones
3 6 8 5 = 3000 + 600 + 80 + 5
expanded form
3685
• 3 means 3000.
• 6 means 600.
• 8 means 80.
• 5 means 5.

Fill in the missing numbers.

③ 3257 = 3 thousands ____ hundreds ____ tens ____ ones

④ 9064 = ____ thousands ____ tens ____ ones

⑤ ____ = 7 thousands 2 hundreds 6 tens

⑥ ____ = 6 thousands 8 tens 4 ones

⑦ 5816 = 5000 + ____ + 10 + ____

⑧ 3649 = ____ + 600 + ____ + 9

Use the given digits in each group to form the greatest 4-digit number, the least 4-digit number, and one 4-digit number that is in between.

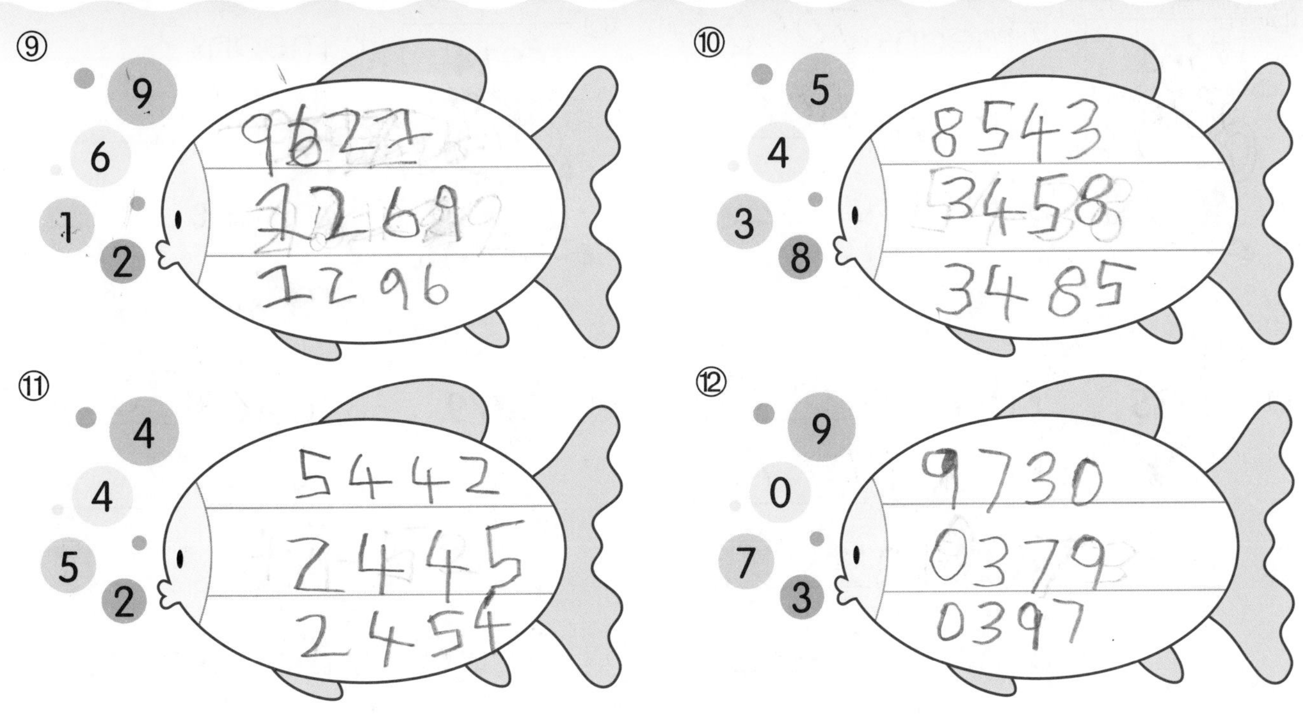

Use arrows to locate the numbers on each number line. Then put the numbers in each group in order.

⑬ **3766 4276 3825 4063**

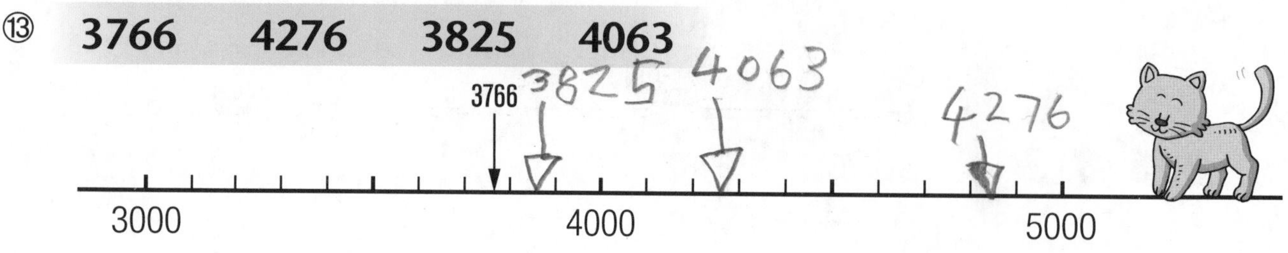

From greatest to least: ______________________

⑭ **5161 5611 5116 6511 6151**

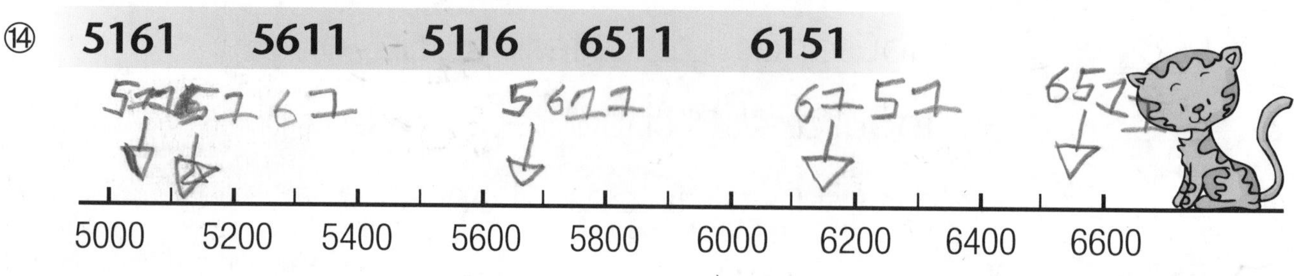

From least to greatest: ______________________

Write the meaning of each digit.

⑮

7 means 7000.

5 means 500.

6 means 60.

3 means 3.

⑯

6 means 6000.

9 means 900.

1 means 10.

4 means 4.

⑰ **2485**

2 means 2000.

4 means 400.

8 means 80.

5 means 5.

⑱ **3879**

3 means 3000.

8 means 300.

7 means 70.

9 means 9.

Round 3547 to the nearest

ten.	hundred.	thousand.
3547 ← 7 > 5, round up	3547 ← 4 < 5, round down	3547 ← 5, round up
3550	**3500**	**4000**

Round the numbers.

Round to the nearest

		ten	hundred	thousand
⑲	6527	6530	6500	6000
⑳	3865	3870	3800	3000
㉑	4129	4130	4100	4000
㉒	9476	9480	9400	9000
㉓	5031	5030	5000	5000
㉔	7750	7750	7700	7000

Write the numbers.

㉕ 

Four hundred sixty-five dollars

$ 465

㉖ 

Seven hundred ninety dollars

$ 790

㉗ 

Six hundred fifty pieces

650 pieces

㉘ 

My score is 5267.

Ted's score: 2000 more than 3267

Addition and Subtraction of 3-Digit Numbers

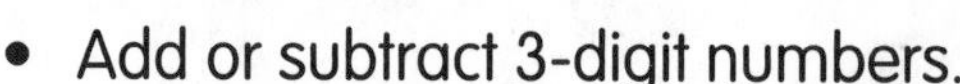

- Add or subtract 3-digit numbers.
- Estimate and check the answers.
- Solve word problems.

Mom, I'll buy this outfit for you once I've saved up $204.

Do the addition.

① $\begin{array}{r} 384 \\ +\ 165 \\ \hline \end{array}$

② $\begin{array}{r} 279 \\ +\ 62 \\ \hline \end{array}$

③ $\begin{array}{r} 147 \\ +\ 258 \\ \hline \end{array}$

④ $\begin{array}{r} 324 \\ +\ 181 \\ \hline \end{array}$

⑤ $\begin{array}{r} 504 \\ +\ 176 \\ \hline \end{array}$

⑥ 79 + 254 = ______

⑦ 317 + 317 = ______

⑧ 243 + 188 = ______

⑨ 555 + 46 = ______

Round each number to the nearest hundred. Do the estimate. Then find the exact answer.

⑩ $\begin{array}{r} 305 \\ +\ 286 \\ \hline \end{array}$

Estimate

⑪ $\begin{array}{r} 413 \\ +\ 174 \\ \hline \end{array}$

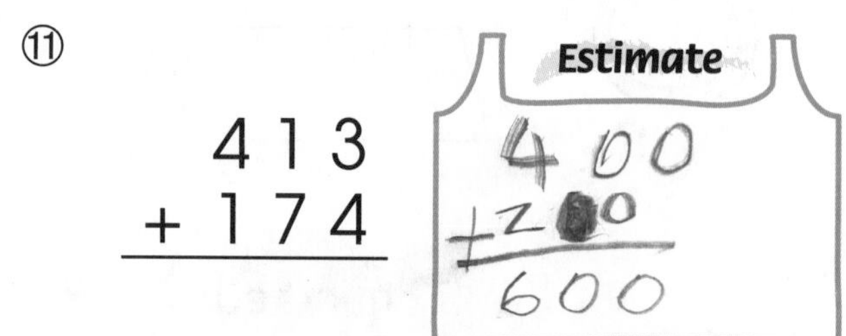

Estimate

⑫ 225 + 166 = ______ **Estimate** ______

⑬ 568 + 125 = ______ **Estimate** ______

Do the subtraction. The answers show the Popsicle sticks the children have collected for art class. Then answer the questions.

⑭

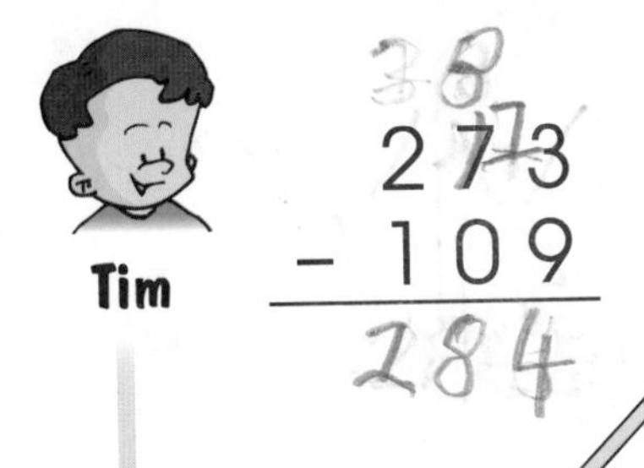

Tim: $273 - 109 =$ ____

Elaine: $345 - 216 =$ ____

Adam: $410 - 277 =$ ____

Tiffany: $600 - 371 =$ ____

Gary: $405 - 135 =$ ____

David: $764 - 298 =$ ____

Louis: $514 - 333 =$ ____

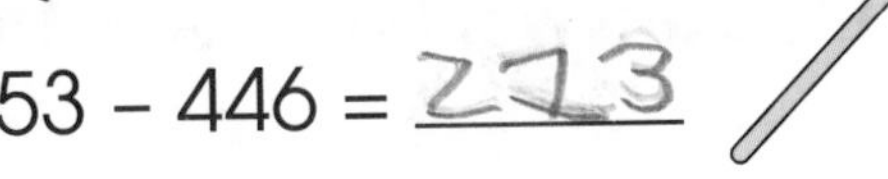

Nancy: $653 - 446 =$ ____

Gloria: $822 - 567 =$ ____

Sam: $914 - 481 =$ ____

⑮ Who collected the most? ____

⑯ Who collected the fewest? ____

⑰ Who collected 100 more sticks than Elaine? ____

⑱ Who collected 300 fewer sticks than Sam? ____

⑲ What is the difference between the number of sticks collected by David and Gary? ____ sticks

Round each number to the nearest ten to do the estimate. Then find the exact answer.

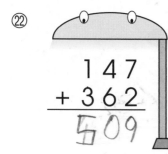

⑳

```
  365
- 134
-----
  231
```

Estimate

400
+200
500

㉑

```
  437
- 254
-----
  223
```

Estimate

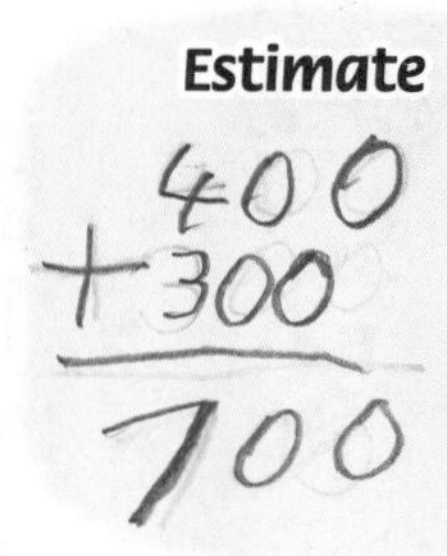

400
+300
700

㉒

```
  147
+ 362
-----
  509
```

Estimate

100
+400
500

㉓

```
  314
+ 289
-----
  693
```

Estimate

300
+300
600

Check the answer to each question. Put a check mark in the space provided if the answer is correct; otherwise, put a cross and find the correct answer.

㉔

A 452 – 183 = *269* ✓

B 713 – 467 = *256* ✗

C 804 – 379 = *525* ✗

D 685 – 296 = *289* ✗

E 300 – 166 = *143* ✗

F 584 – 376 = *208* ✓

Check

A

```
  269
+ 183
-----
```

B

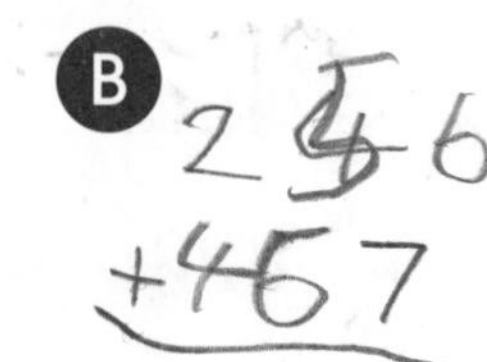

246
+467

C

425
+379

D

389
+296

E

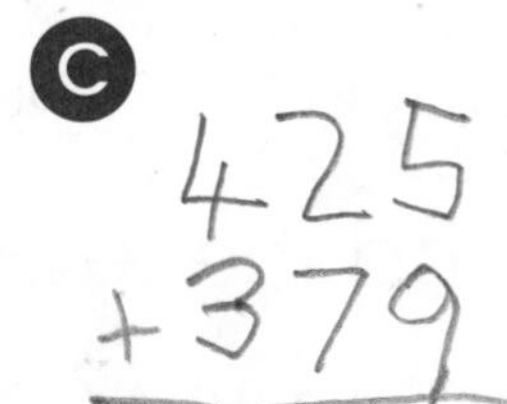

134
+166

F

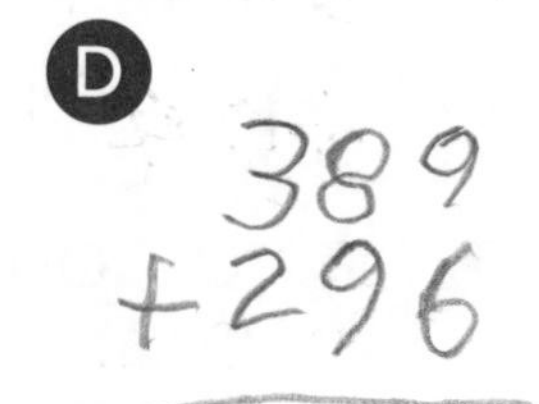

208
+376

Mr. Rice works in a fitness centre. He recorded the number of people attending the yoga classes in the past three months. Help him complete the table and answer the questions.

㉕

Month	January	February	March
No. of Men	389	225	278
No. of Women	463	448	486
Total	852	673	704

㉖ How many men attended the yoga classes from January to March?

389 + 225 + 278 = 432 432 men

㉗ How many women attended the yoga classes in January and February?

463 + 448 = 977 977 women

㉘ How many more women attended the classes in January than in February?

852 + 673 = 7525 7525 more

㉙ How many fewer men attended the classes in February than in January?

389 + 225 = 604

604 fewer

㉚ *Mom, the regular price of this yoga outfit is $204. It is on sale now. The price cut is $29. Do you know how much it costs now?*

$204 + $29 = $234

$ 234

3

Addition of 4-Digit Numbers

- Add 4-digit numbers with or without grouping.
- Use different methods to find answers in a faster way.
- Solve word problems.

There are 2462 spectators watching me.

Do the addition.

① $\begin{array}{r} 2561 \\ +\ 4108 \\ \hline 6669 \end{array}$

② $\begin{array}{r} 3793 \\ +\ \ 204 \\ \hline 3997 \end{array}$

③ $\begin{array}{r} 4412 \\ +\ 3074 \\ \hline 7486 \end{array}$

④ $\begin{array}{r} 1859 \\ +\ 2016 \\ \hline 4865 \end{array}$

⑤ $\begin{array}{r} 475 \\ +\ 3141 \\ \hline 4516 \end{array}$

⑥ $\begin{array}{r} 3881 \\ +\ 4914 \\ \hline 8795 \end{array}$

⑦ 3474 + 1135 = 4609

⑧ 2463 + 4185 = 6648

⑨ 749 + 1320 = 2069

⑩ 3668 + 331 = 3999

Find the total number of jelly beans in each pair.

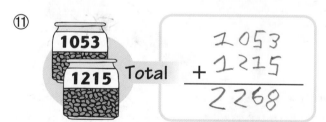

⑪ 1053, 1215 Total

$\begin{array}{r} 1053 \\ +\ 1215 \\ \hline 2268 \end{array}$

⑫

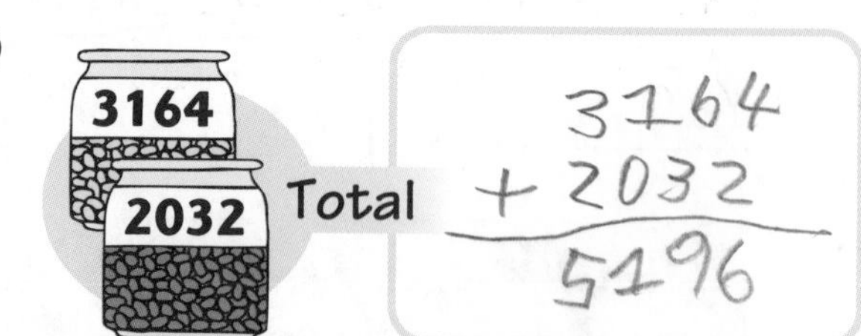

$\begin{array}{r} 3164 \\ +\ 2032 \\ \hline 5196 \end{array}$

⑬

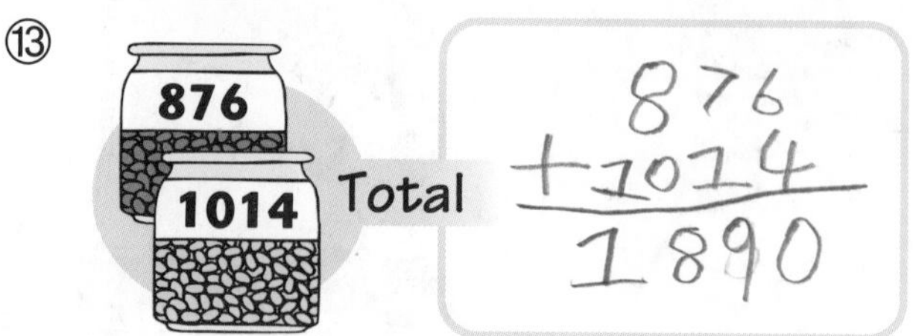

$\begin{array}{r} 876 \\ +\ 1014 \\ \hline 1890 \end{array}$

⑭

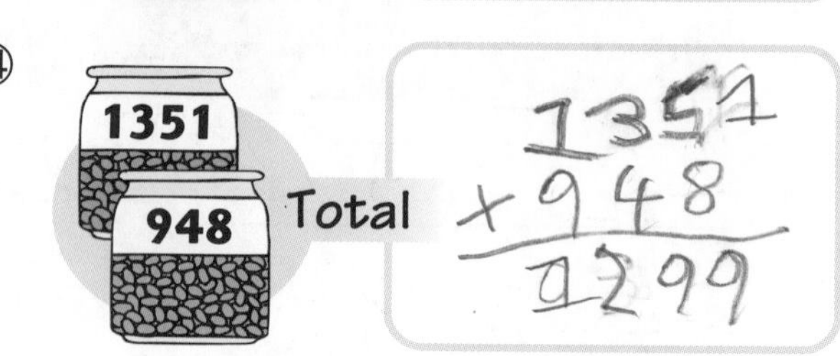

$\begin{array}{r} 1351 \\ +\ 948 \\ \hline 2299 \end{array}$

Do the addition. The answers show the clothing produced by a factory last year. Then answer the questions.

⑮

A: $\begin{array}{r} 451 \\ +\ 1342 \\ \hline \end{array}$	B: $\begin{array}{r} 1016 \\ +\ 147 \\ \hline \end{array}$	C: $\begin{array}{r} 2111 \\ +\ 1093 \\ \hline \end{array}$
D: $\begin{array}{r} 866 \\ +\ 213 \\ \hline \end{array}$	E: $\begin{array}{r} 1244 \\ +\ 2082 \\ \hline \end{array}$	F: $\begin{array}{r} 624 \\ +\ 1015 \\ \hline \end{array}$
G: $\begin{array}{r} 1142 \\ +\ 2364 \\ \hline \end{array}$	H: $\begin{array}{r} 3316 \\ +\ 1433 \\ \hline \end{array}$	I: $\begin{array}{r} 529 \\ +\ 2730 \\ \hline \end{array}$

⑯ How many pieces of A and B were produced in all?

_______ pieces

⑰ If the number of leather jackets produced was 402 more than that of D, how many leather jackets were produced?

_______ leather jackets

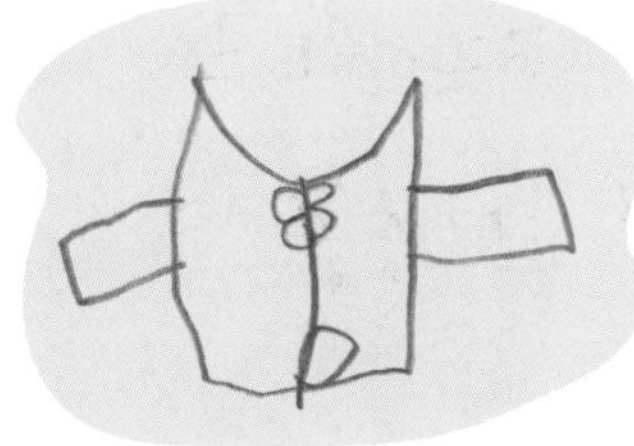

⑱ If the factory shipped C and E to R&M store, how many shirts were shipped to R&M store in all?

_______ shirts

I sometimes use this method to find the answer in a faster way.

e.g. 4217 + 1914 = 6131

1st Add the digits in each place separately.

5000 + 1100 + 20 + 11

2nd Regroup.

6000 + 100 + 30 + 1

Use the above method to do the addition. Then use vertical addition to find the answer again.

⑲ 3529 + 1346 = ______

1st 4000 + ______

2nd ______

⑳ 4714 + 1637 = ______

㉑ 3588 + 4091 = ______

Find the missing numbers.

㉒

```
   3 _ 6 _
 + _ 5 8 2
 ---------
   6 0 4 7
```

㉓

```
   _ 3 3 _
 + 1 7 _ 4
 ---------
   4 0 5 0
```

㉔

```
   1 _ 7 3
 + _ 5 _ 9
 ---------
   4 1 9 2
```

Sometimes we can write a number in a different way which helps us find the answer faster.

e.g. 3992 + 1629 = 5621

Rewrite:
1629 = 8 + 1621

3992 + 8 + 1621
= 4000 + 1621
= 5621

Use the above method to rewrite one of the numbers. Then find the answer.

㉕ 1995 + 1628 = ________

Rewrite 1628 = ____ + 1623

㉖ 4998 + 3774 = ________

Rewrite

㉗ 3996 + 2577 = ________

Rewrite

㉘ 1425 + 1994 = ________

Rewrite

㉙ 4836 + 2995 = ________

Rewrite

㉚ 7058 + 993 = ________

Rewrite

Solve the problems.

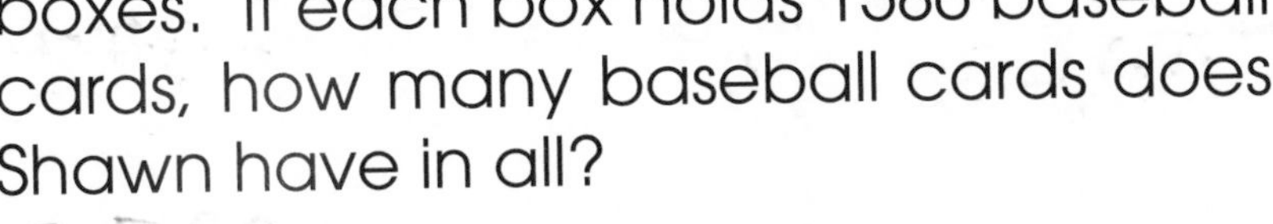

㉛ Shawn puts his baseball cards into two boxes. If each box holds 1586 baseball cards, how many baseball cards does Shawn have in all?

________ baseball cards

㉜

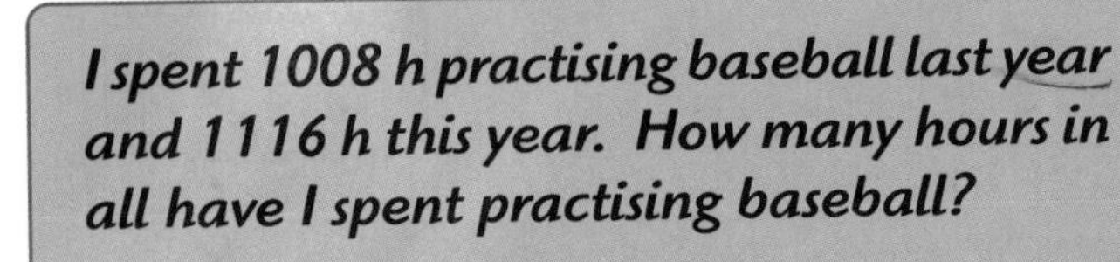

I spent 1008 h practising baseball last year and 1116 h this year. How many hours in all have I spent practising baseball?

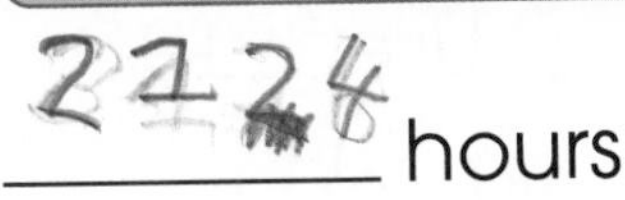

________ hours

4

Subtraction of 4-Digit Numbers

- Subtract 4-digit numbers with or without borrowing.
- Use different methods to find answers in a faster way.
- Solve word problems.

Mom, can I have a puppy?

Do the subtraction.

① $\begin{array}{r} 3965 \\ -\ 1824 \\ \hline \end{array}$

② $\begin{array}{r} 8763 \\ -\ 4621 \\ \hline \end{array}$

③ $\begin{array}{r} 3642 \\ -\ 1535 \\ \hline \end{array}$

④ $\begin{array}{r} 2984 \\ -\ 192 \\ \hline \end{array}$

⑤ $\begin{array}{r} 3068 \\ -\ 1952 \\ \hline \end{array}$

⑥ 9683 – 2265 = ________

⑦ 5032 – 1710 = ________

⑧ 4522 – 486 = ________

⑨ 6274 – 1065 = ________

Find the number of screws left in each box.

⑩ 

Used: 1066

Left: ________

⑪ 

Used: 844

Left: ________

⑫ 

Used: 1065

Left: ________

All the furniture is on sale now. Find the sale price of each item. Then answer the questions.

⑬

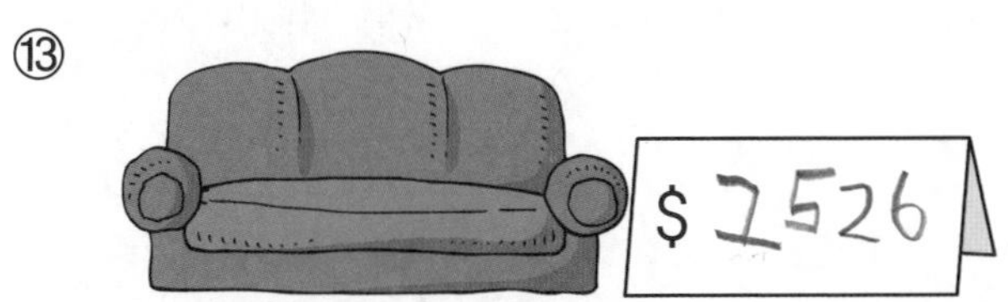

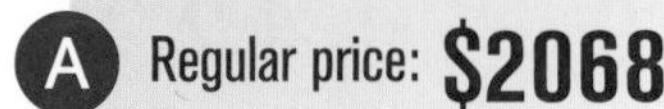

A Regular price: **$2068** Save: **$542**

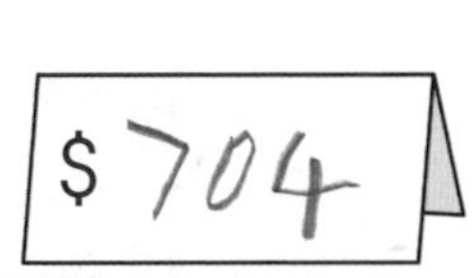

B Regular price: **$1008** Save: **$304**

C Regular price: **$1259** Save: **$216**

$930

D Regular price: **$1144** Save: **$214**

E Regular price: **$1659** Save: **$496**

F Regular price: **$2888** Save: **$629**

⑭ What is the price difference between the armchair and the couch?

1526-704 = 822 822

⑮ What is the price difference between the tables?

1043-930 = 113

⑯ Susan wants to buy E, but she has $322 only. How much more money does she need?

1163-322 = 841 841

⑰ If F is further reduced by $425, what will the new price be?

2267-425 = 1844 1844

e.g. 4245 – 2816 = ______

Align the numbers.	Subtract the ones.	Subtract the tens.	Subtract the hundreds.	Subtract the thousands.
	3 15	3 15	3 12 3 15	3 12 3 15
4245	4245	4245	4245	4245
– 2816	– 2816	– 2816	– 2816	– 2816
	9	29	429	1429

4245 – 2816 = **1429**

If you can't take away, borrow 1 from the column on the left.

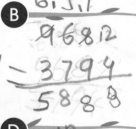

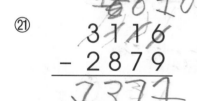

Do the subtraction.

⑱ 4068 – 2779 =

⑲ 5493 – 3897 =

⑳ 5000 – 2864 =

㉑ 3116 – 2879 =

㉒ 7235 – 5868 =

㉓ 6294 – 3395 =

㉔

A 4651 – 2688 = ______

B 9682 – 3794 = ______

C 2586 – 787 = ______

D 6103 – 4594 = ______

E 7337 – 6586 = ______

F 8064 – 2585 = ______

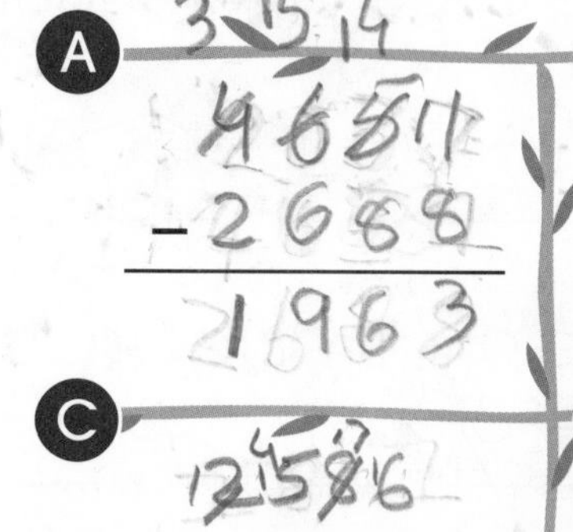

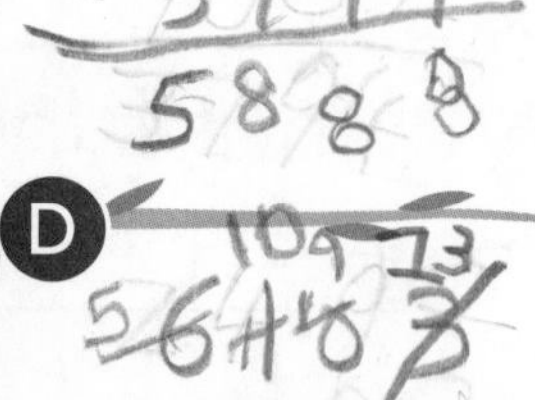

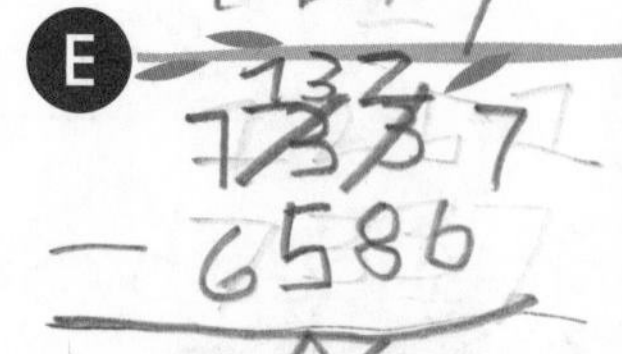

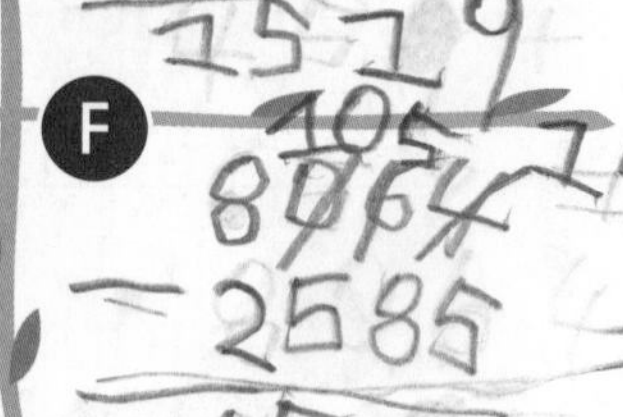

A B C D E F

e.g. 6819 – 3998 = 2821

- Add 2 to 3998, it is 4000.
- 6819 – 4000 = 2819
- Since 6819 has subtracted a number which is 2 more than the actual number, we need to add 2 back to 2819 to get the final answer.
- 2819 + 2 = **2821**

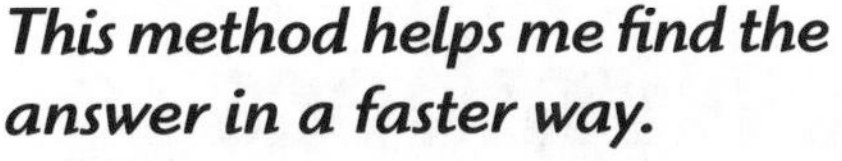

This method helps me find the answer in a faster way.

Use the above method to do subtraction. Then use vertical subtraction to find the answer again.

㉕ 4763 – 2997 = 1766

- Add 3 to 2997, it is 3000.
- 4763 – 3000 = 1763
- 1763 + 3 = 1766

4763
– 2997

㉖ 6287 – 4996 = 1291

- Add 4 to 4996, it is 5000
- 6287 – 5000 = 1287
- 1287 + 4 = 1291

Solve the problems.

㉗ *A big box holds 1682 dog biscuits. If my dog eats 372 biscuits, how many will be left?*

1682 – 372 = 1310   1310

㉘ *Tim walks me every day. Trail A is 2885 m long. If trail B is 394 m shorter, how long is trail B?*

2885 – 394 = 2517   2517

5

Addition and Subtraction of 4-Digit Numbers

- Add or subtract 4-digit numbers.
- Check and estimate the answers.
- Solve word problems.

Find the answers.

① $\begin{array}{r} 1257 \\ +\ 2684 \\ \hline \end{array}$

② $\begin{array}{r} 3239 \\ -\ 1088 \\ \hline \end{array}$

③ $\begin{array}{r} 5234 \\ -\ 2766 \\ \hline \end{array}$

④ 8462 – 7593 = ______

⑤ 1423 + 6811 = ______

⑥ 3527 + 1732 = ______

⑦ 5024 – 4666 = ______

⑧ 547 + 8365 = ______

⑨ 3009 – 1148 = ______

⑩ 2465 + 1838 = ______

⑪ 2101 – 598 = ______

⑫ 4173 – 2368 = ______

⑬ 4207 + 1188 = ______

Put "+" or "–" in the circles.

⑭ $\begin{array}{r} 3275 \\ \bigcirc\ 1823 \\ \hline 5098 \end{array}$

⑮ $\begin{array}{r} 3465 \\ \bigcirc\ \ 869 \\ \hline 2596 \end{array}$

⑯ $\begin{array}{r} 4067 \\ \bigcirc\ 1538 \\ \hline 5605 \end{array}$

⑰ 3287 ◯ 1652 = *4939*

⑱ 3817 ◯ 1386 = *5203*

Find the sum and difference for each pair of numbers.

⑲ 2083 1689

⑳ 3249 5287

See how many people went on the rides last week. Round each number to the nearest hundred. Then estimate the total and answer the questions.

㉑ A

No. of Adults: 1364 (about ______)

No. of Children: 2876 (about ______)

Total: about ______ people

B

No. of Adults: 4065 (about ______)

No. of Children: 1759 (about ______)

Total: about ______ people

C

No. of Adults: 2411 (about ______)

No. of Children: 2035 (about ______)

Total: about ______ people

㉒ About how many more people went on B than C? about ______ more

㉓ About how many more people went on C than A? about ______ more

Use addition or subtraction to check the answers. Put a check mark in the spaces provided if the answers are correct; otherwise, put a cross and write the correct answers.

㉔ Tom's Questions

A 3657 + 1898 = *5555* (✓)

B 4101 – 2583 = *1418* (✗)

C 7056 – 3849 = *3217* (✗)

D 5244 + 858 = *6102* (✓)

E 6183 – 4795 = *1388* (✓)

A
```
  5555
- 1898
```

㉕ Linda's Questions

A 4250 – 2783 = *1467* (✓)

B 1864 + 3918 = *5882* (✗)

C 6274 – 5996 = *268* (✗)

D 3201 + 1899 = *5100* (✓)

E 4283 – 2888 = *1295* (✗)

Solve the problems.

26

a. Calvin the Clown has a bag of stickers. If he gives 1692 stickers to the girls and the rest to the boys, how many stickers do the boys get?

2885 – 1692 = 1193

1193

b. If a box can hold 480 more stickers than a bag, how many stickers can it hold?

2885 + 480 = 3365

3365

27

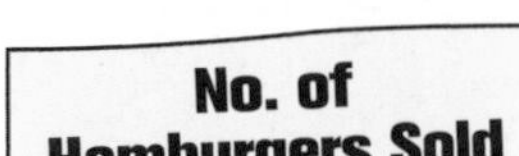

a. How many hamburgers were sold in the past two weeks?

4765 + 3688 = 8452

8452

b. How many fewer hamburgers were sold this week than last week?

4765 – 3688 = 1077

1077

28

Tim, I had 145 candies at first. I took some from your bag and put them into my bowl. Now I have 1000 candies. Do you know how many candies I took from you?

1000 – 145 = 855

855

6

Multiplication (1)

- Multiply to 9 x 9.
- Multiply 2-digit numbers by 1-digit numbers without carrying.
- Solve problems involving multiplication.

There are 48 chocolates.

Do the multiplication.

① $9 \times 3 = $ 27

② $6 \times 6 = $ 36

③ $4 \times 5 = $ 20

④ $2 \times 9 = $ 18

⑤ $7 \times 8 = $ 56

⑥ $5 \times 3 = $ 15

⑦ $4 \times 9 = $ 36

⑧ $6 \times 7 = $ 42

⑨ 3 x 3 = 9

⑩ 6 x 5 = 30

⑪ 4 x 8 = 32

⑫ 7 x 7 = 49

⑬ 6 x 9 = 54

⑭ 9 x 7 = 63

⑮ 8 x 2 = 16

⑯ 5 x 0 = 0

⑰ 3 x 7 = 27

⑱ 8 x 6 = 48

Find the missing numbers.

⑲ 9 x 6 = 54

⑳ 5 x 5 = 25

㉑ 8 x 3 = 24

㉒ 7 x 9 = 63

Count and write the number of centimetre cubes in each rectangular prism. Tell how many more cubes are needed to fill each prism and find the volume. Then answer the questions.

㉖

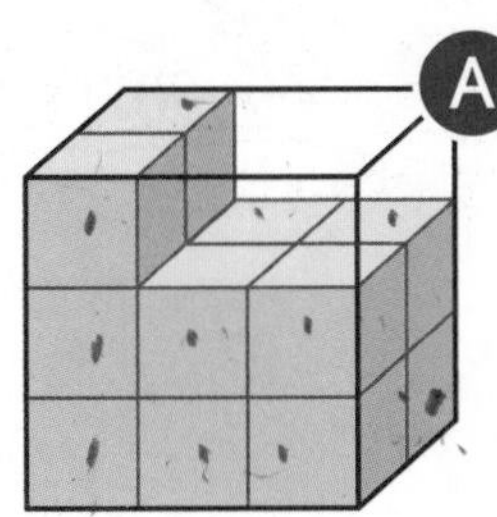

- ____ centimetre cubes are used.
- ____ more centimetre cubes are needed.

Volume of A = ____ cm^3

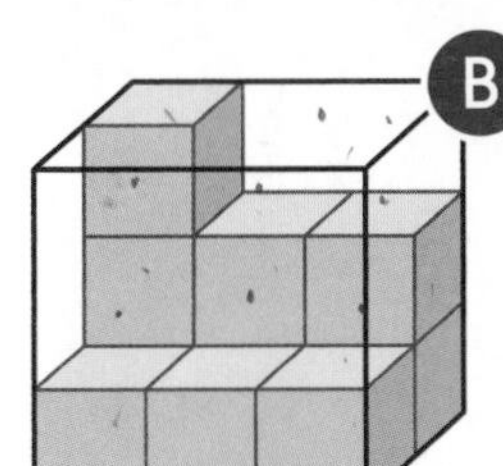

- ____ centimetre cubes are used.
- ____ more centimetre cubes are needed.

Volume of B = ____ cm^3

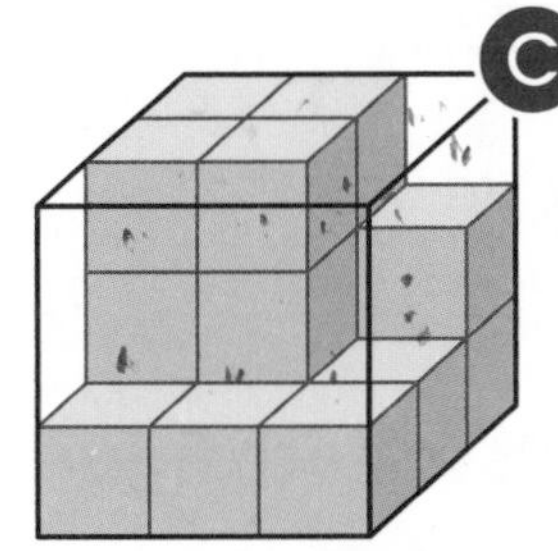

- ____ centimetre cubes are used.
- ____ more centimetre cubes are needed.

Volume of C = ____ cm^3

㉗ *Which prism has the greatest volume?*

㉘ *If I use the cubes in A and B to build a new prism, which prism do I build?*

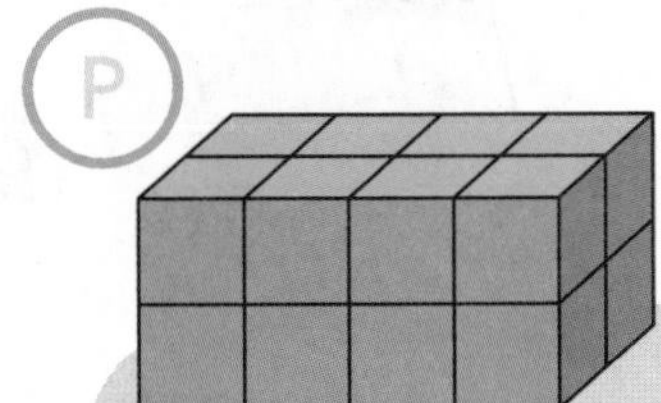

Solve the problems.

㉓ How many days are there in 4 weeks?

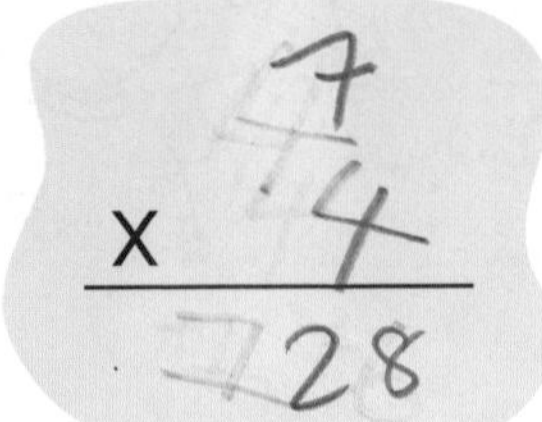

____ days

㉔ A mug costs $3. How much do 8 mugs cost?

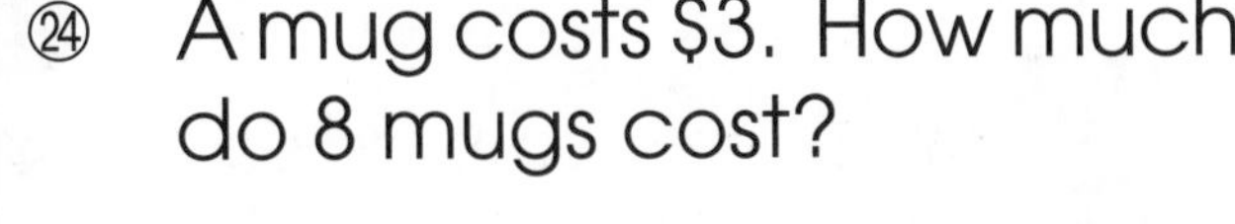

㉕ How many balls are there in 6 boxes?

㉖ How many boxes of juice are there in 9 packs?

㉗ Tim buys 5 robots. How much does he need to pay?

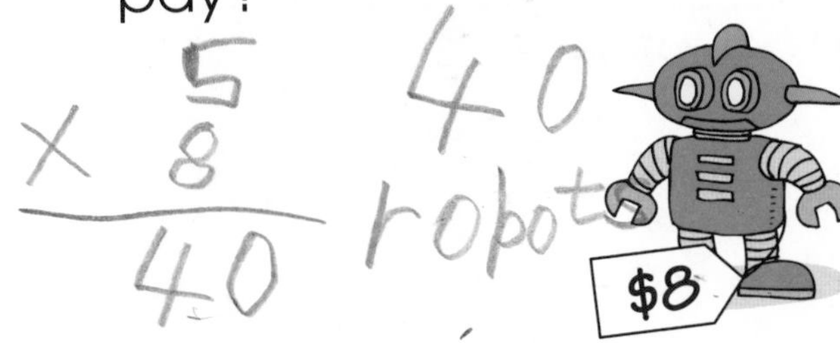

㉘ What is the total weight of 9 bags of potatoes?

㉙ What is the total thickness of 5 books?

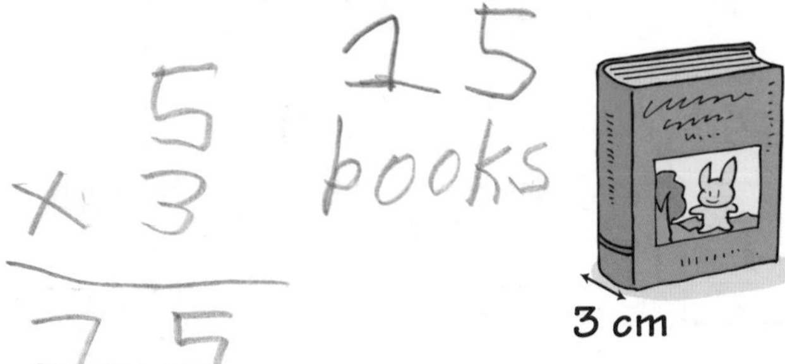

㉚ What is the total value of 8 nickels?

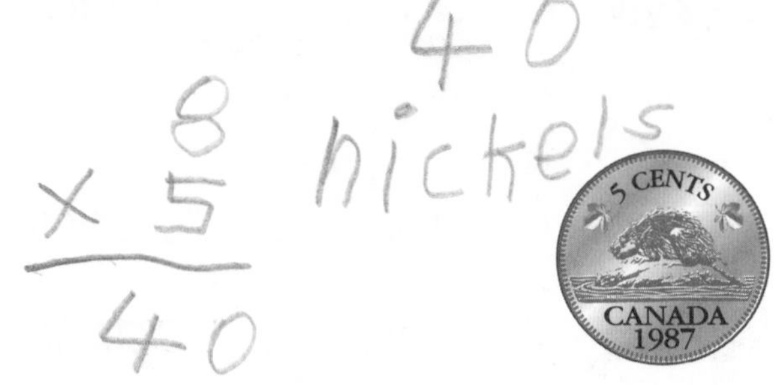

Multiply 2-digit numbers by 1-digit numbers:

1st Multiply the ones.

2nd Multiply the tens.

e.g. 43 x 3 = **129**

1st	2nd
43	43
x 3	x 3
9	129

Do the multiplication.

㉛ 12 x 3 = 36

㉜ 24 x 2 = 48

㉝ 31 x 7 = 217

㉞ 32 x 4 = 128

㉟ 51 x 6 = 306

㊱ 82 x 3 = 246

㊲ 60 x 9 = 540

㊳ 74 x 2 = 148

㊴ 41 x 5 = 205

㊵ 63 x 3 = 189

Find the totals.

㊶

3 cans: 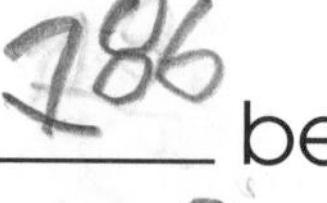 186 beads

4 cans:  248 beads

㊷

21 cm

6 ribbons: 126 cm

9 ribbons:  189 cm

㊸

40

4 bags: 160 candies

7 bags:  280 candies

㊹

2 boxes: 106 straws

3 boxes: 159 straws

Solve the problems.

45 

a. How many party hats are there in 4 packs?

21 × 4 = 84   84

b. How much do 20 packs of party hats cost?

20 × 5 = 100   100

46 

a. How much do 11 dozen roses cost?

11 × 9 = 99   99

b. How many roses are there in 3 dozen?

3 × 1 = 3   3

47 

a. The number of cows on Joe's farm is 2 times as many as Sam's. How many cows are there on Joe's farm?

34 × 2 = 68   68

b. The number of chickens on Sam's farm is 3 times the number of pigs. How many chickens does Sam have?

23 × 3 = 69   69

48 *If I eat 32 chocolates every day, how many chocolates do I eat in 4 days?*

32 × 4 = 128   128

7

Multiplication (2)

- Multiply 2-digit numbers by 1-digit numbers with carrying.
- Solve problems involving multiplication.

Do the multiplication.

① 37 × 8 = 296

② 52 × 7 = 364

③ 45 × 9 = 405

④ 73 × 4 = 292

⑤ 64 × 5 = 320

⑥ 28 × 6 = 168

⑦ 49 x 7 = 343

⑧ 63 x 8 = 504

⑨ 55 x 3 = 165

⑩ 38 x 2 = 76

⑪ 17 x 6 = 102

⑫ 44 x 9 = 396

Find the total weights.

8 bags: 360 g

⑭

4 cans: 312 g

⑮

9 packs: 108 pieces

Find the total costs.

⑯

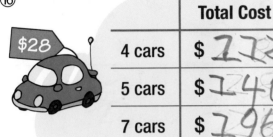

	Total Cost
4 cars	$ 112
5 cars	$ 140
7 cars	$ 196

⑰

	Total Cost
3 dolls	$57
7 dolls	$133
8 dolls	$152

⑱

	Total Cost
3 robots	$162
6 robots	$324
8 robots	$432

⑲

$35

	Total Cost
2 pigs	$70
5 pigs	$175
9 pigs	$315

Round each number to the nearest ten. Then fill in the blanks.

⑳ about 80 cookies

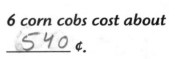

There are about 560 *cookies in 7 cans.*

㉑ about 90 ¢

6 corn cobs cost about 540 *¢.*

㉒ about 20 flowers

There are about 180 *flowers in 9 bouquets of flowers.*

Fill in the missing numbers.

㉓
```
    4 6
x     9
-------
  4 1 4
```

㉔
```
    3 6
x     8
-------
  2 8 8
```

㉕
```
    5 9
x     6
-------
  3 5 4
```

㉖
```
    7 2
x     7
-------
  5 0 4
```

㉗
```
    7 5
x     9
-------
  6 7 5
```

㉘
```
    6 3
x     5
-------
  3 1 5
```

Solve the problems.

㉙ 

How many baseball cards are there in 9 packs?

252 baseball cards

㉚ 

Mrs. Green buys 8 packs of pencils for her students. How many pencils does Mrs. Green buy in all?

96 pencils

㉛ 

Uncle Sam buys 5 boxes of pop. How many cans of pop does Uncle Sam buy in all?

120 cans

㉜ 

Baby Bob uses one bag of diapers each month. How many diapers does Baby Bob need in half a year?

528 diapers

e.g. There are 12 red marbles and 15 blue marbles in a box. How many marbles are there in 4 boxes?

Sometimes we need to do some calculation in our mind first.

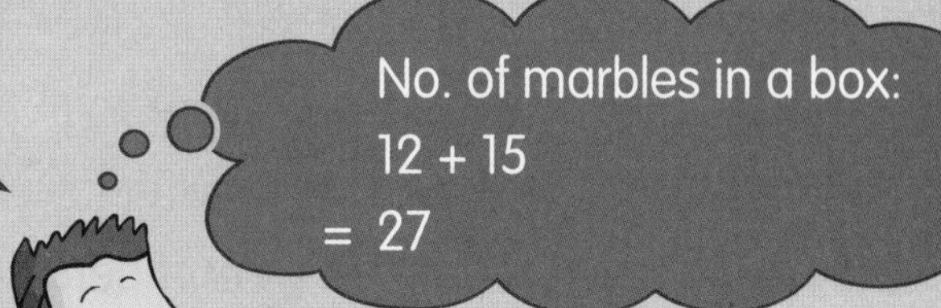

No. of marbles in a box:
12 + 15
= 27

4 x 27 = **108**

There are 108 marbles in 4 boxes.

Solve the problems.

33. Joe has 8 yellow stickers and 34 green stickers. The number of stickers that Peter has is 4 times of Joe's. How many stickers does Peter have?

4 x 42 = 168

34. A bottle of perfume costs $82, but you can save $15 if you buy it this week. How much do 8 bottles cost if Mrs. White buys them while they are on sale?

8 x 67 = 536

82+15=97

35. Janet uses 3 yellow ribbons and 6 red ribbons to make a bow. How many ribbons does she need to make 54 bows?

54 x 9 = 486

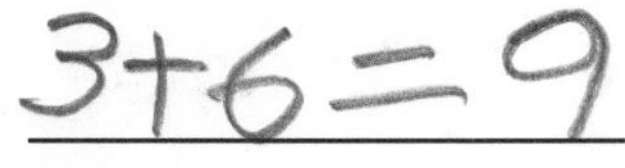

36. *A box has 16 cans of cat food. If my mom bought 3 boxes last week and 4 boxes this week, how many cans of cat food did she buy in all?*

4 x 16 = 64

16+3=64

8

Division (1)

- Divide to 81 ÷ 9.
- Understand division terms – dividend, divisor, quotient, and remainder.
- Divide 2-digit numbers by 1-digit numbers with no remainder in the tens place.

You can make 5 strings of 6 beads with 2 beads left.

Do the division.

① 5) 20

② 5) 42   ____ R ____

③ 7) 64   ____ R ____

④ 63 ÷ 9 = ________

⑤ 39 ÷ 6 = ________

⑥ 36 ÷ 4 = ________

⑦ 38 ÷ 7 = ________

⑧ 32 ÷ 8 = ________

⑨ 41 ÷ 5 = ________

⑩ 55 ÷ 9 = ________

⑪ 68 ÷ 8 = ________

⑫ 47 ÷ 6 = ________

⑬ 53 ÷ 8 = ________

Fill in the missing numbers.

⑭
```
     ☐ R ☐
9 ) 3 ☐
    3 6
    ---
      3
```

⑮
```
      5 R ☐
8 ) ☐ 4
    ☐ ☐
    ---
      4
```

⑯
```
      7 R 3
6 ) ☐ 5
    ☐ ☐
    ---
      3
```

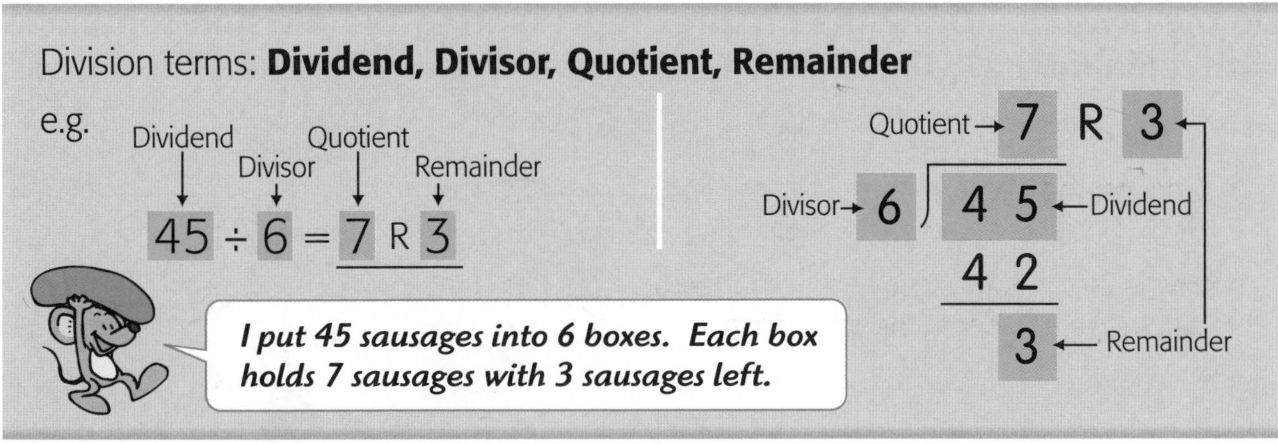

Division terms: **Dividend, Divisor, Quotient, Remainder**
e.g.
Dividend
Divisor
Quotient
Remainder
45 ÷ 6 = 7 R 3
I put 45 sausages into 6 boxes. Each box holds 7 sausages with 3 sausages left.
Quotient → 7 R 3
Divisor → 6) 45 ← Dividend
42
3 ← Remainder

Do the division. Then colour the numbers.

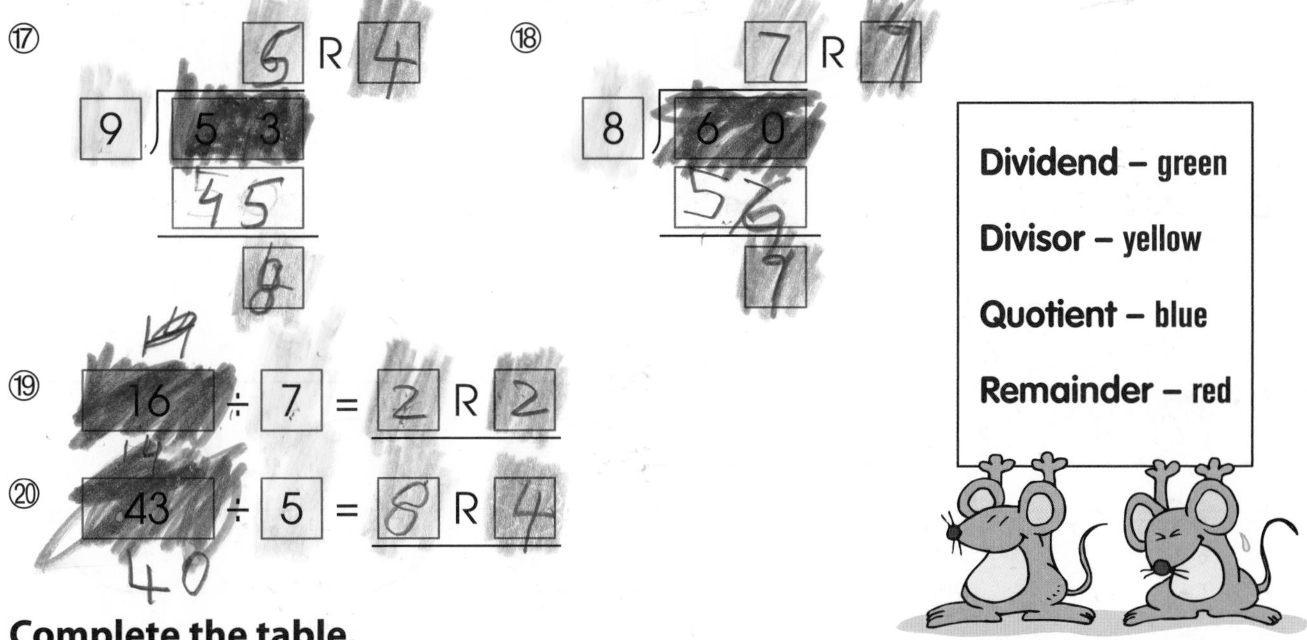

Complete the table.

㉑

Division Sentence	Dividend	Divisor	Quotient	Remainder
a. 39 ÷ 6 = ___ R ___			6	3
b.	28	5	5	
c. 43 ÷ 7 =				
d.	50	8		2
e. 67 ÷ 9 =				

Do the division. Draw the pictures representing the division sentences with remainder 2 in the circles. Find out which animal stickers the pig has.

(22)

(23)

(24)

(25)

(26)

(27)

(28) $50 \div 8 =$ ______

(29) $62 \div 7 =$ ______

(30) $47 \div 5 =$ ______

(31) $31 \div 4 =$ ______

(32) $28 \div 9 =$ ______

(33) $42 \div 8 =$ ______

(34) $65 \div 7 =$ ______

2-digit number ÷ 1-digit number: 2

1st Divide the tens.

2nd Divide the ones.

e.g. $62 \div 3 =$ **20R2**

Divide the tens.

$$\begin{array}{r} 2 \\ 3\overline{)\,62} \\ 6 \end{array}$$

Divide the ones.

$$\begin{array}{r} 20\text{ R}2 \\ 3\overline{)\,62} \\ 6 \\ \hline 2 \end{array}$$

Sometimes we need to add "0" in the quotient.

Do the division.

㉟ $2\overline{)\,49}$ ㊱ $4\overline{)\,86}$ ㊲ $3\overline{)\,98}$

㊳ $6\overline{)\,67}$ ㊴ $5\overline{)\,54}$ ㊵ $2\overline{)\,65}$

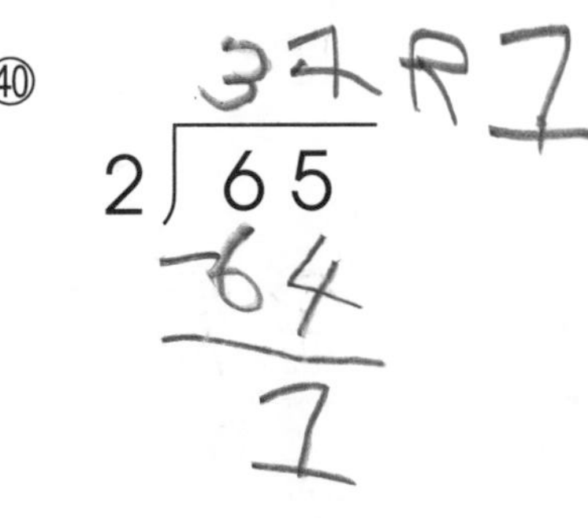

㊶ $47 \div 4 =$ ________ ㊷ $73 \div 7 =$ ________

㊸ $62 \div 6 =$ ________ ㊹ $85 \div 4 =$ ________

㊺ $59 \div 5 =$ ________ ㊻ $89 \div 8 =$ ________

㊼ ***We want to make 3 necklaces. How many beads are there on each necklace? How many beads are left?***

________ = ________

____

9

Division (2)

- Divide 2-digit numbers by 1-digit numbers.
- Solve problems involving division.

If we share the chocolates, each of us gets 13 chocolates with 1 chocolate left.

Do the long division.

① 3) 46 (__ __ R __)

② 2) 57 (__ __ R __)

③ 4) 65 (__ __ R __)

④ 5) 86

⑤ 3) 74

⑥ 6) 90

⑦ 8) 92

⑧ 4) 72

⑨ 6) 85

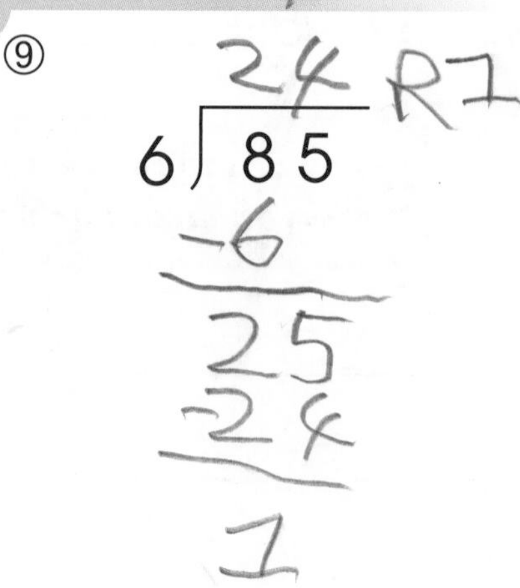

Find the answers.

⑩ 49 ÷ 3 = ______ ⑪ 52 ÷ 4 = ______

⑫ 92 ÷ 8 = ______ ⑬ 77 ÷ 6 = ______

⑭ 81 ÷ 7 = ______ ⑮ 66 ÷ 5 = ______

Find the answers. Do the long divisions in the spaces provided.

⑯ Katie divides 60 candies equally into 5 boxes. How many candies are there in each box?

______ candies

⑰ A mug costs \$3. How many mugs can be bought with \$50? How much is left?

______ mugs; \$ ______ left

⑱ Mr. Green gives 46 stickers to 3 children. How many stickers does each child get? How many stickers are left?

______ stickers; ______ sticker(s) left

⑲ Mrs. Winter divides 62 children into 4 groups. How many children are there in each group? How many children are left?

______ children; ______ children left

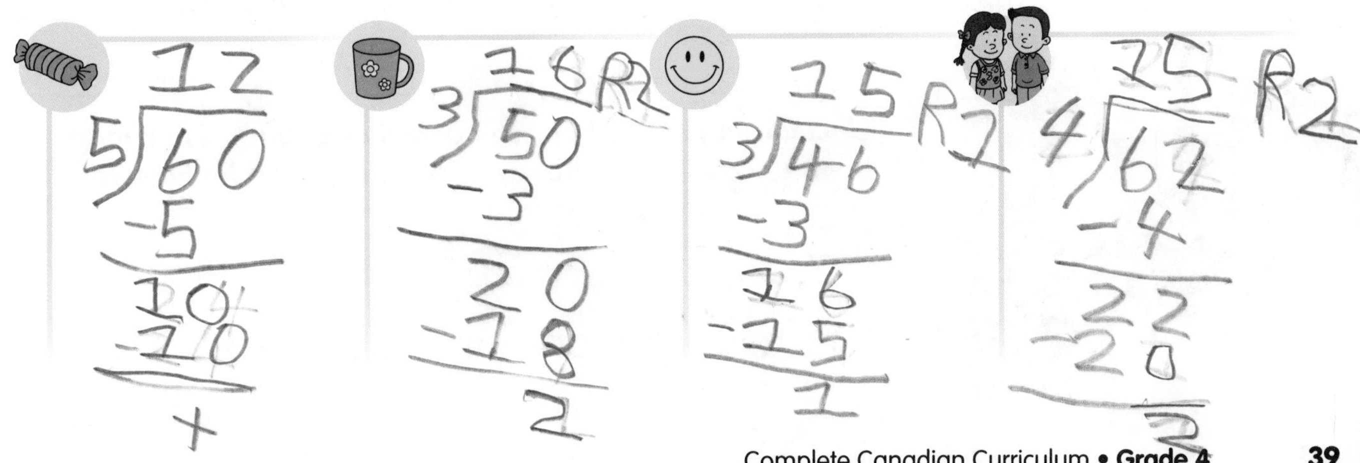

Fill in the missing numbers.

Look at the pictures. Answer the questions.

23

Jimmy puts a bag of marshmallows equally on 5 plates. How many marshmallows are there on each plate?

80 ÷ 5 = 16

16 marshmallows

24

If Mrs. Smith puts all 92 crayons into boxes, how many boxes of crayons will she get? How many crayons will be left?

92 ÷ 8 = 11R4

11 boxes; 4 crayons left

25

Uncle Sam pays $75 for the bear key chains. How many bear key chains will he get? How much will he have left?

75 ÷ 6 = 12R3

12 bear key chains; $ 3 left

Solve the problems.

㉖ Tim earned $85 in 5 weeks from delivering newspapers and George earned $72 in 4 weeks.

a. How much did each person earn in one week?

$ ______

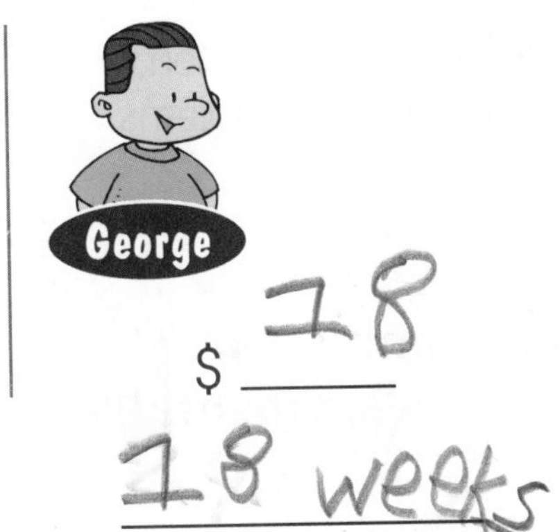

$ ______

b. Who has a better pay? ______

㉗ There are two box sizes available for Kevin to hold his 68 cupcakes.

a. How many of each box are needed to hold all the cupcakes? How many cupcakes are left?

______ boxes;

______ cupcakes left

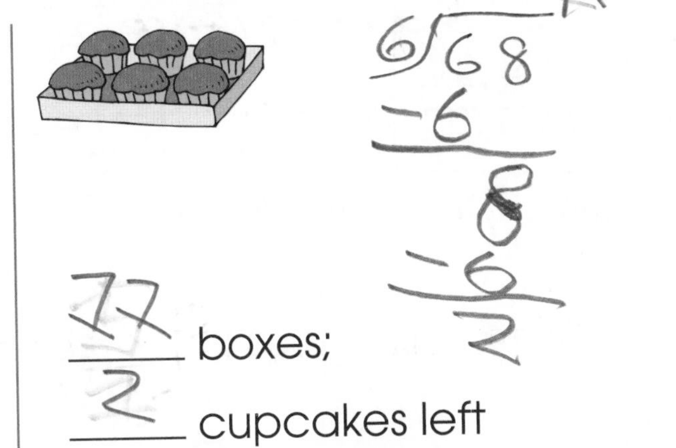

______ boxes;

______ cupcakes left

b.

If I put all the cupcakes into the bigger boxes and give the remaining ones to my friend, how many cupcakes will my friend get?

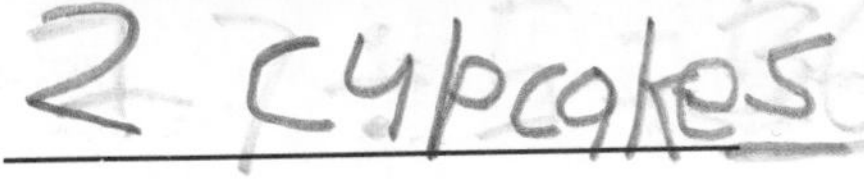

More about Multiplication and Division

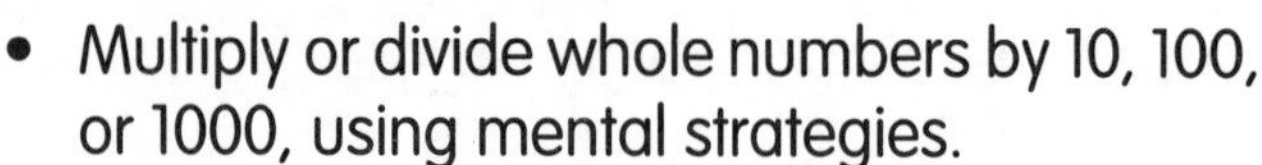

- Multiply or divide whole numbers by 10, 100, or 1000, using mental strategies.
- Use multiplication and addition to check the answers of division problems.

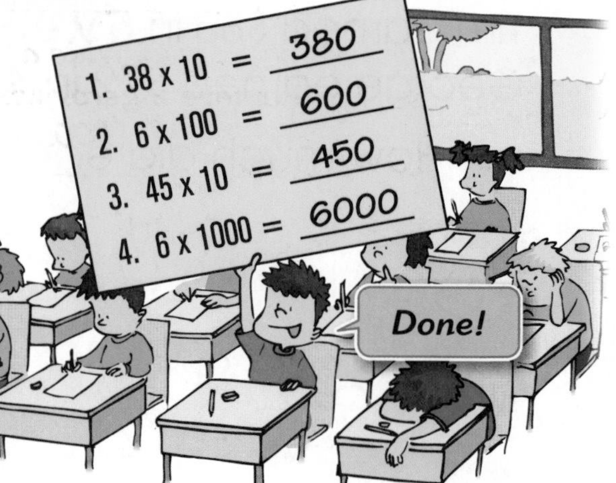

Read what Raymond says. Then find the answers mentally.

When you multiply a number by 10, add 1 zero to the number. Add 2 zeros when you multiply by 100 and 3 zeros when you multiply by 1000.

① 6 x 100 = 600

② 7 x 1000 = 7000

③ 35 x 10 = 350

④ 9 x 1000 = 9000

⑤ 27 x 100 = 270

⑥ 42 x 10 = 420

⑦ 81 x 1000 = 82000

⑧ 320 x 10 = 3200

⑨ 94 x 10 = 940

⑩ 5 x 1000 = 5000

Write 10, 100, or 1000 to complete the multiplication sentences.

⑪ 5 x 1000 = 5000

⑫ 16 x 1000 = 16 000

⑬ 32 x 10 = 320

⑭ 430 x 10 = 4300

⑮ 60 x 100 = 6000

⑯ 504 x 100 = 50 400

⑰ 100 x 10 = 1000

⑱ 75 x 1000 = 75 000

Read what Susan says. Then find the answers mentally.

When you divide a number by 10, remove 1 zero from the number. Remove 2 zeros when it is divided by 100 and 3 zeros when it is divided by 1000.

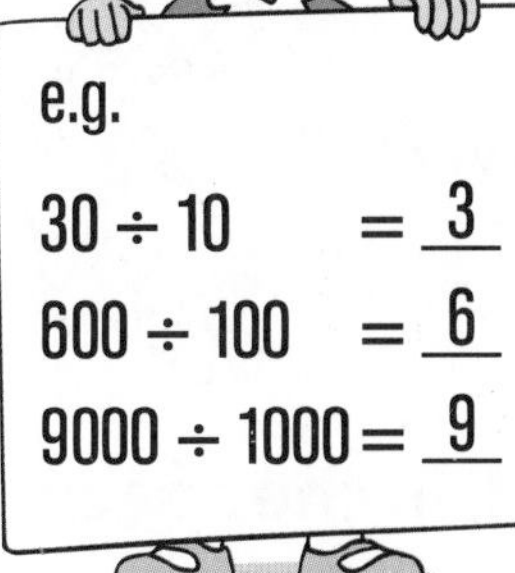

e.g.

30 ÷ 10 = 3

600 ÷ 100 = 6

9000 ÷ 1000 = 9

⑲ 40 ÷ 10 = 4

⑳ 8000 ÷ 100 = 80

㉑ 600 ÷ 10 = 60

㉒ 7000 ÷ 1000 = 70

㉓ 500 ÷ 100 = 50

㉔ 180 ÷ 10 = 18

㉕ 2050 ÷ 10 = 205

㉖ 4000 ÷ 1000 = 4

Write 10, 100, or 1000 to complete the division sentences.

㉗ 4500 ÷ 100 = 45

㉘ 3690 ÷ 10 = 369

㉙ 1200 ÷ 100 = 12

㉚ 4000 ÷ 10 = 400

㉛ 3020 ÷ 10 = 302

㉜ 5000 ÷ 1000 = 5

㉝ 4830 ÷ 10 = 483

㉞ 9000 ÷ 100 = 90

Put "x" or "÷" in the circles.

㉟ 4800 ÷ 100 = 48

㊱ 950 × 10 = 9500

㊲ 3 × 1000 = 3000

㊳ 4000 ÷ 100 = 40

㊴ 100 ÷ 100 = 1

㊵ 3600 ÷ 10 = 360

Steps to check the answer of a division problem:

1st Quotient x Divisor

2nd Answer from **1st** + Remainder

If the answer from **2nd** is the same as the dividend, the answer of the division problem is correct.

e.g. Is 64 ÷ 5 = 12R4 correct?

1st 12 x 5 = 60

2nd 60 + 4 = 64 ← same as the dividend

The answer **12R4** *is correct.*

Check the answer of each division sentence. Put a check mark in the space provided if it is correct; otherwise, put a cross and write the correct answer.

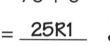

41 76 ÷ 3 = 25R1

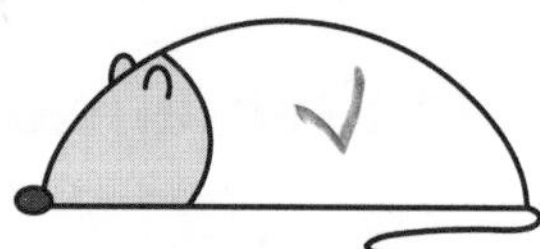

Check 1st ____ x ____ = ____

2nd ____ + ____ = ____

42 45 ÷ 2

= 22R1

Check 1st

2nd

43 89 ÷ 7

= 12R4

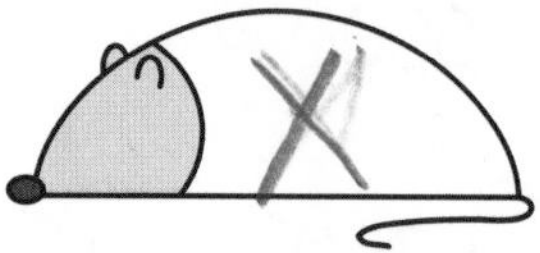

Check 1st

2nd

44 95 ÷ 6 = 15R5

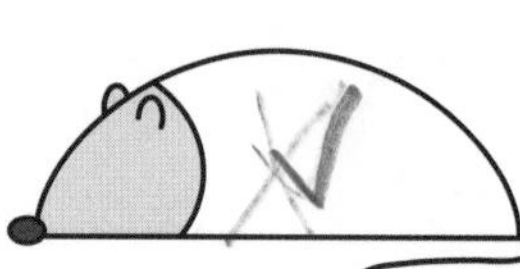

Check 1st

2nd

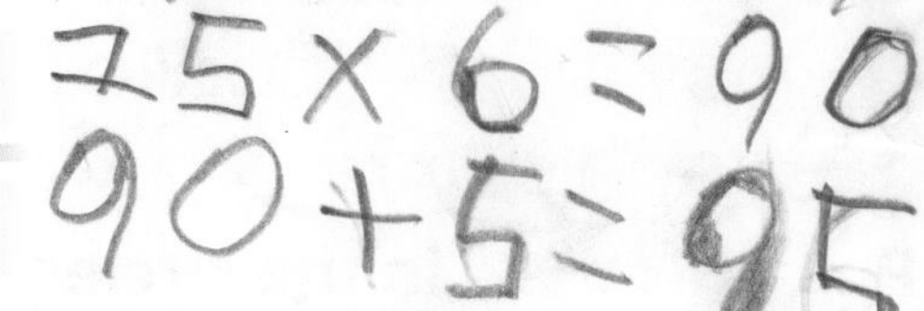

Do the division. Then check the answers.

45 69 ÷ 4 = ____

46 75 ÷ 6 = ____

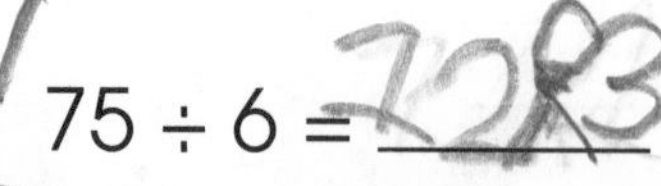

47 81 ÷ 7 = ____

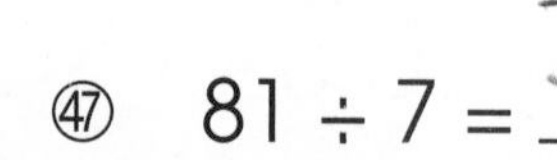

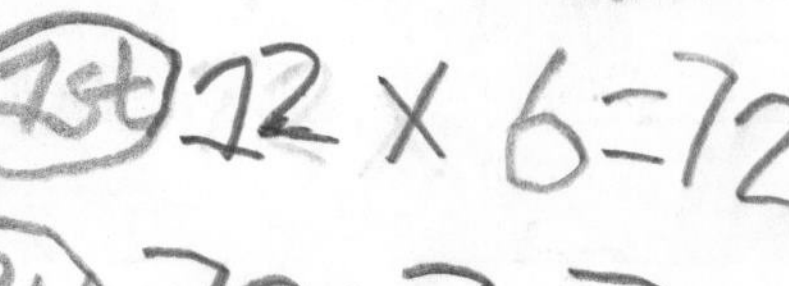

Fill in the boxes with numbers to complete the division. Then check the answers.

Solve the problems.

50. Tim has $5. Sue has 10 times Tim's amount. How much does Sue have?

51. Mr. Smith has 4600 hockey cards. If he puts all the hockey cards equally into 10 boxes, how many hockey cards will there be in each box?

52. Each ribbon is 16 cm long. What is the total length of 1000 ribbons?

53. *I have put 1300 jelly beans in my trophy. If I share my jelly beans with 9 friends, how many jelly beans will each of us get?*

11

Length and Distance

- Estimate, measure, and record length, height, and distance, using mm, cm, dm, m, or km.
- Describe the relationships between various units of length.
- Solve problems related to lengths or distances.

Don't be scared. The bridge is only 10 m long.
10 m

Fill in the blanks with the given units to complete the sentences.

mm cm m km

① The length of a highway is about 60 km.

② The length of a pencil is about 15 cm.

③ The height of the CN Tower is about 600 m.

④ A quarter is about 2 mm thick.

⑤ 

a. The leaf is about 6 cm long.

b. The worm is about 45 mm long.

⑥ a. The height of the mountain is about 3 km.

b. Aunt Mary is about 162 cm tall.

c. The distance between Aunt Mary and the mountain is about 1980 m.

d. Aunt Mary's stick is about 1 m long.

The relationships between the units:

1 km = 1000 m

1 m = 10 dm = 100 cm

1 dm = 10 cm

1 cm = 10 mm

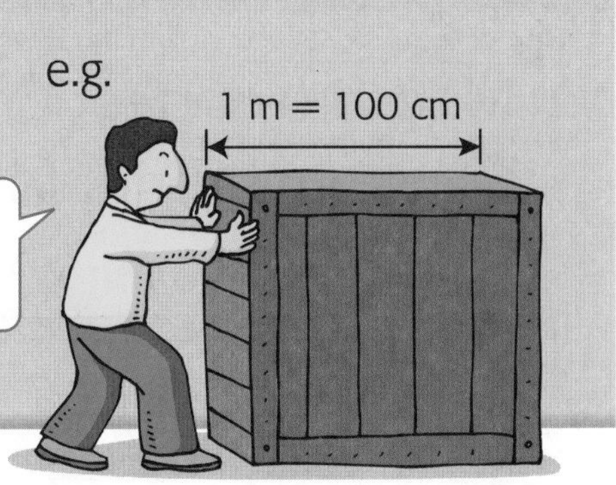

Fill in the blanks.

⑦ 6 m = 600 cm

⑧ 8 km = 8000 m

⑨ 5 cm = 50 mm

⑩ 7 m = 70 dm

⑪ 8 dm = 80 cm

⑫ 600 cm = 6 m

⑬ 3000 m = 3 km

⑭ 90 cm = 9 dm

⑮ 40 mm = 4 cm

⑯ 100 dm = 10 m

Compare the measures in each pair. Fill in the blanks.

⑰

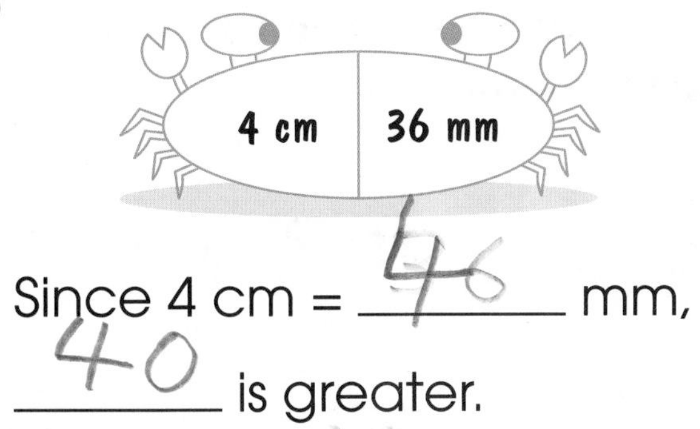

Since 4 cm = 46 mm,
40 is greater.

⑱

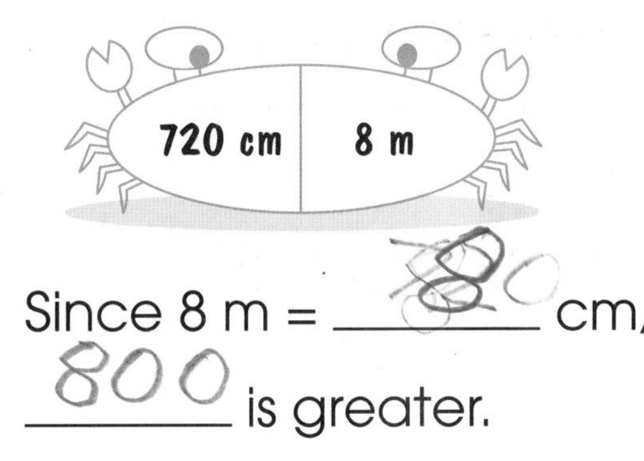

Since 8 m = 800 cm,
800 is greater.

⑲

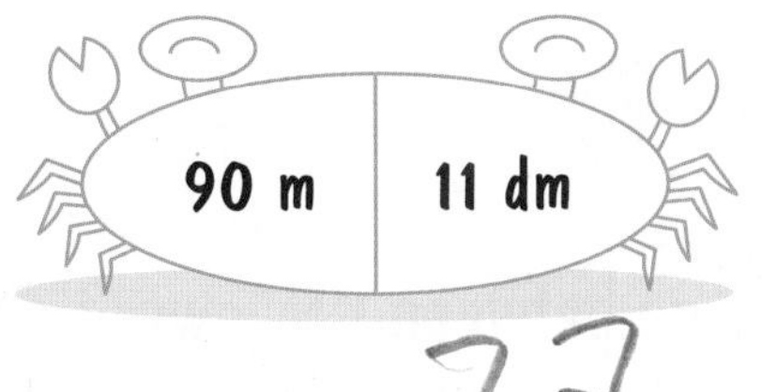

Since 90 m = 11 dm,
900 is smaller.

⑳

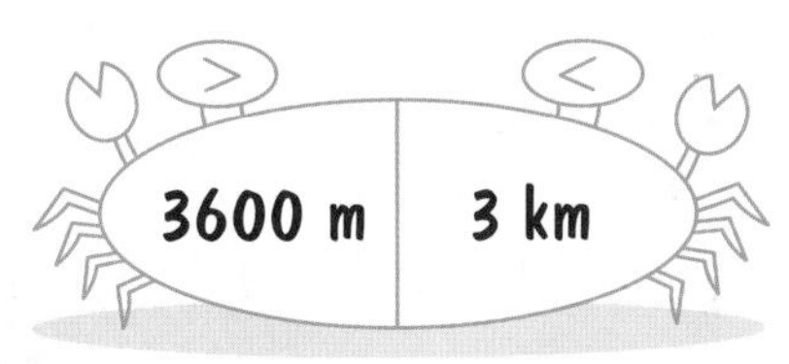

Since 3 km = 3 m,
3000 is smaller.

Do the measurement. Then draw the picture and fill in the blanks.

㉑ Measure and record the length of Ⓐ and Ⓑ. Draw a string Ⓒ 6 mm shorter than Ⓑ and record its length.

Ⓐ 92 mm

Ⓑ 126 (corrected to 116) mm

Ⓒ 120 (corrected to 110) mm

㉒ Ⓒ is 11 cm long.

㉓ Ⓒ is 18 mm longer than Ⓐ.

㉔ *If Ⓒ is cut into 2 equal pieces, how long is each piece?*

55 mm

Look at the picture. Estimate the heights or distances. Then draw lines to complete the grid to find the actual measurements.

㉕

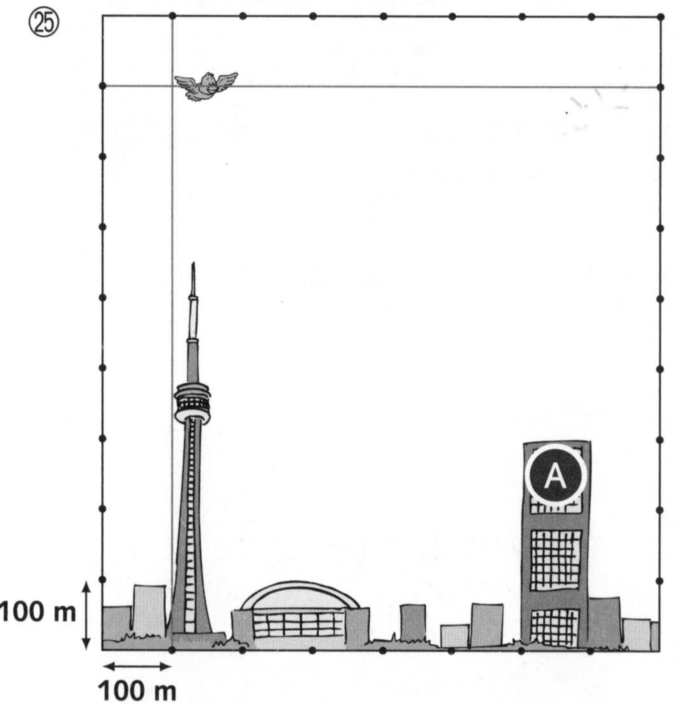

	Estimate	Actual
Height		
CN Tower:	550	m
Rogers Centre:	200	m
Building Ⓐ:	300	m
Distance between CN Tower and		
the bird:	250	m
Building Ⓐ:	450	m

Read the clue. Draw the pictures and label the distances to complete the map. Then answer the questions.

- From Deadly Swamp to Spooky Jungle: **half a kilometre**

- From Spinky Crocodiles to Spooky Jungle passing through Venus Flytrap, which is halfway between them: **3000 m**

- From Spooky Jungle to Spinky Crocodiles: **3 km 500 m**

- From Spinky Crocodiles to Treasure Chest: **1 km 800 m**

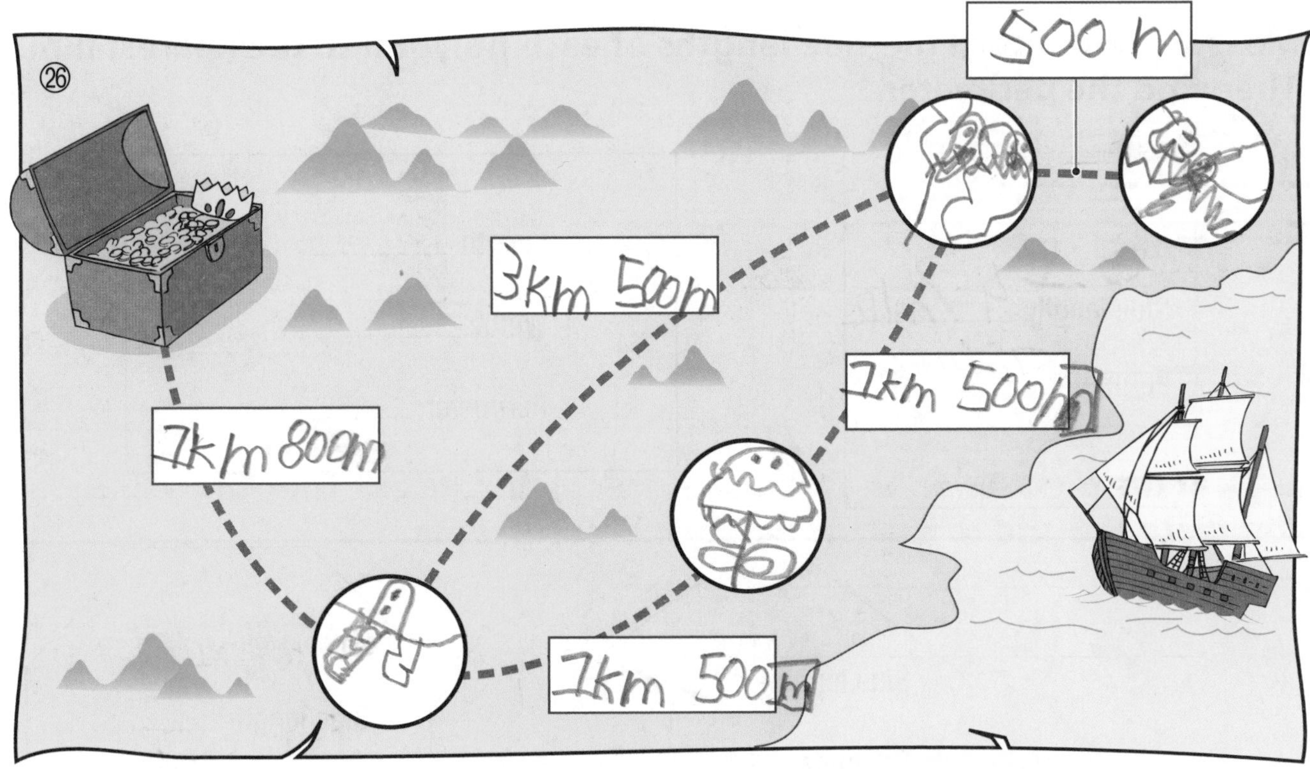

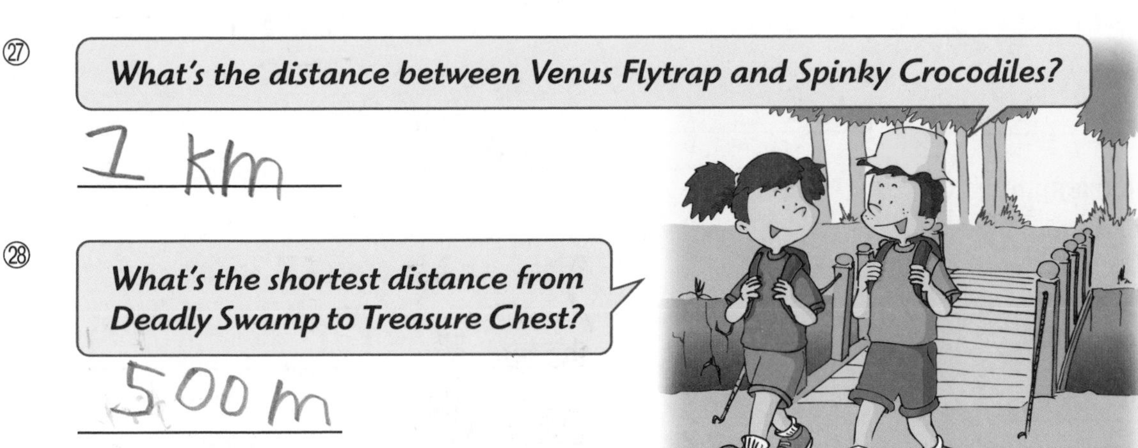

27 What's the distance between Venus Flytrap and Spinky Crocodiles?
1 km
28 What's the shortest distance from Deadly Swamp to Treasure Chest?
500 m

Perimeter: 49 + 32 + 49 + 32
= 162 (cm)

Perimeter and Area

- Estimate, measure, and record the perimeters and areas of polygons.
- Choose the most appropriate units to measure the side lengths and perimeters of various polygons.
- Find the relationship between the side lengths of a rectangle and its perimeter and area.

The perimeter of the fireplace is 162 cm.

Measure and record the side lengths of each polygon to the nearest mm. Then find the perimeter.

①

Side length: 47mm
Perimeter: 188mm

Length: 73mm
Width: 42mm
Perimeter: 230mm

Side length: 32mm
Perimeter: 160mm

Side length: 22mm
Perimeter: 176mm

Side length: 24mm
Perimeter: 144mm

Side length: 48mm
Perimeter: 144mm

Find the perimeters of the shapes.

②

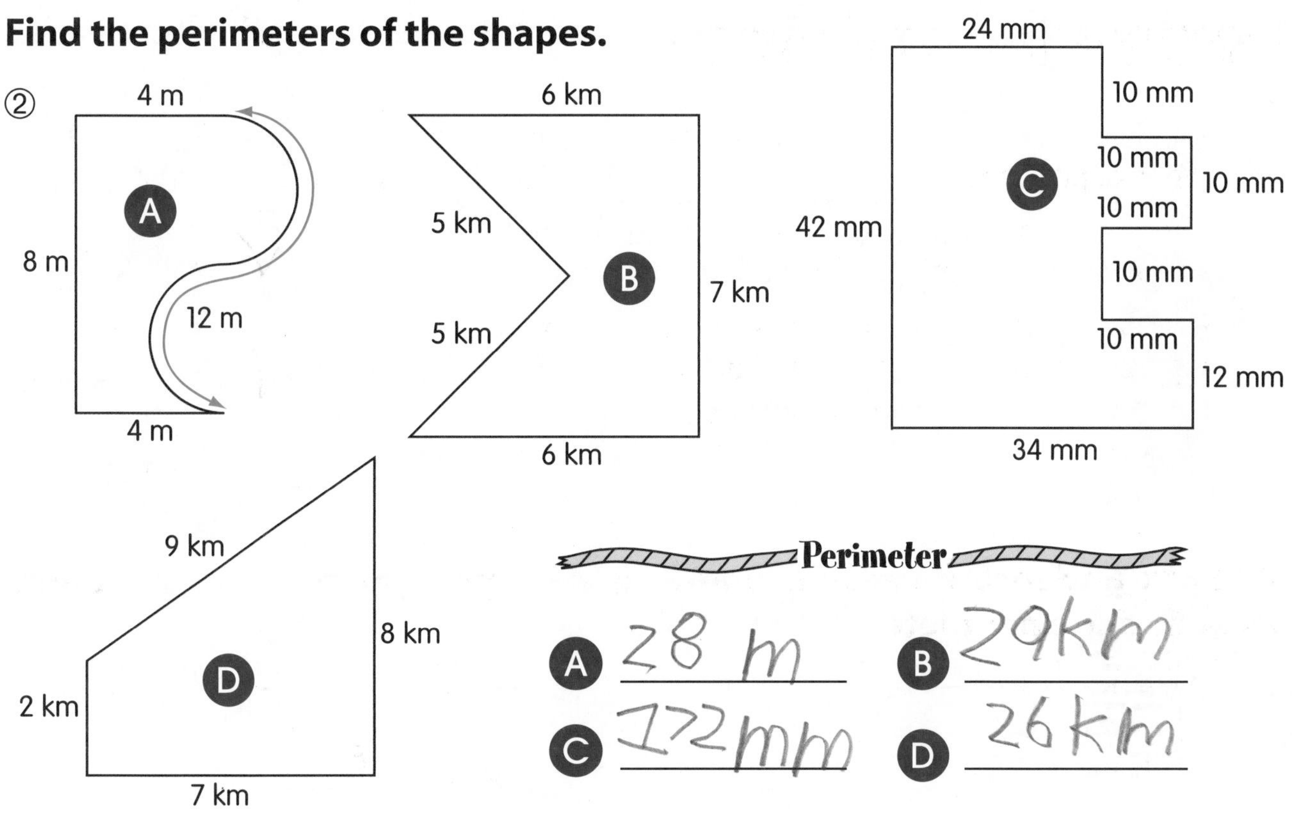

Perimeter

A 28 m

B 29km

C 172mm

D 26km

Write the most appropriate unit you would use to find the perimeter of each thing.

mm cm dm m km

③ a farm km

④ a small television dm

⑤ a door m

⑥ a button on a cellular phone mm

⑦ a frame cm

⑧ a mouse pad cm

Check the correct circle to tell what you need to consider: perimeter or area.

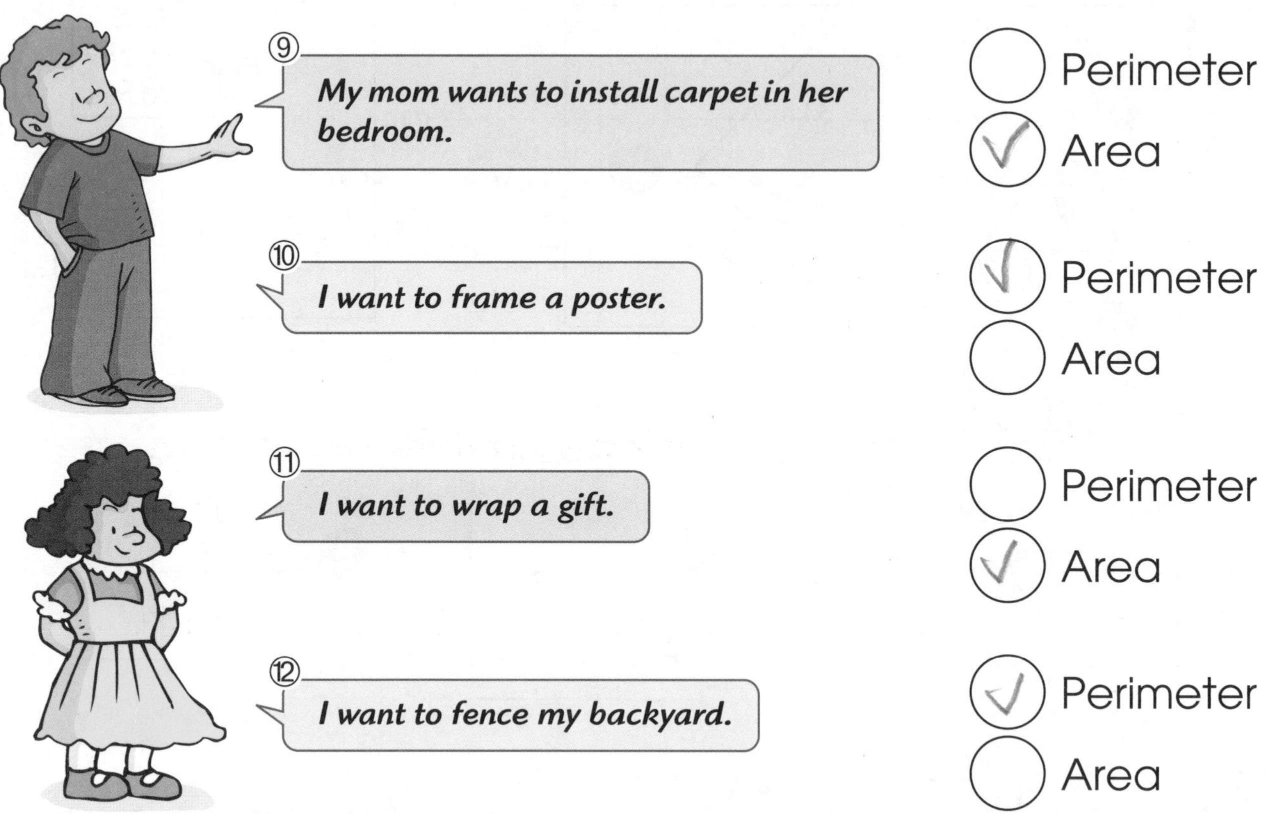
⑨ My mom wants to install carpet in her bedroom.
Perimeter
Area
⑩ I want to frame a poster.
Perimeter
Area
⑪ I want to wrap a gift.
Perimeter
Area
⑫ I want to fence my backyard.
Perimeter
Area

Draw 3 different rectangles each with a perimeter of 14 cm. Then find the area of each rectangle and write the answer on it.

⑬

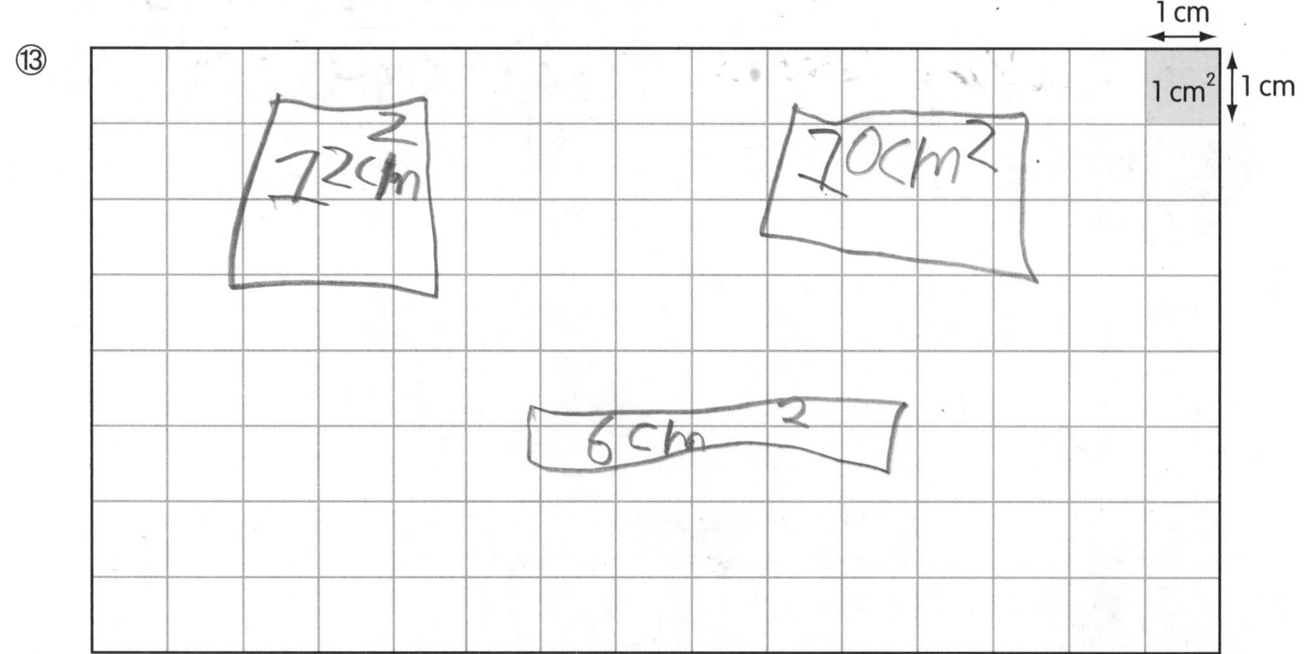
1 cm
1 cm²
1 cm
12 cm²
10 cm²
6 cm²

Find the lengths, widths, perimeters, and areas of the rectangles. Then answer the questions.

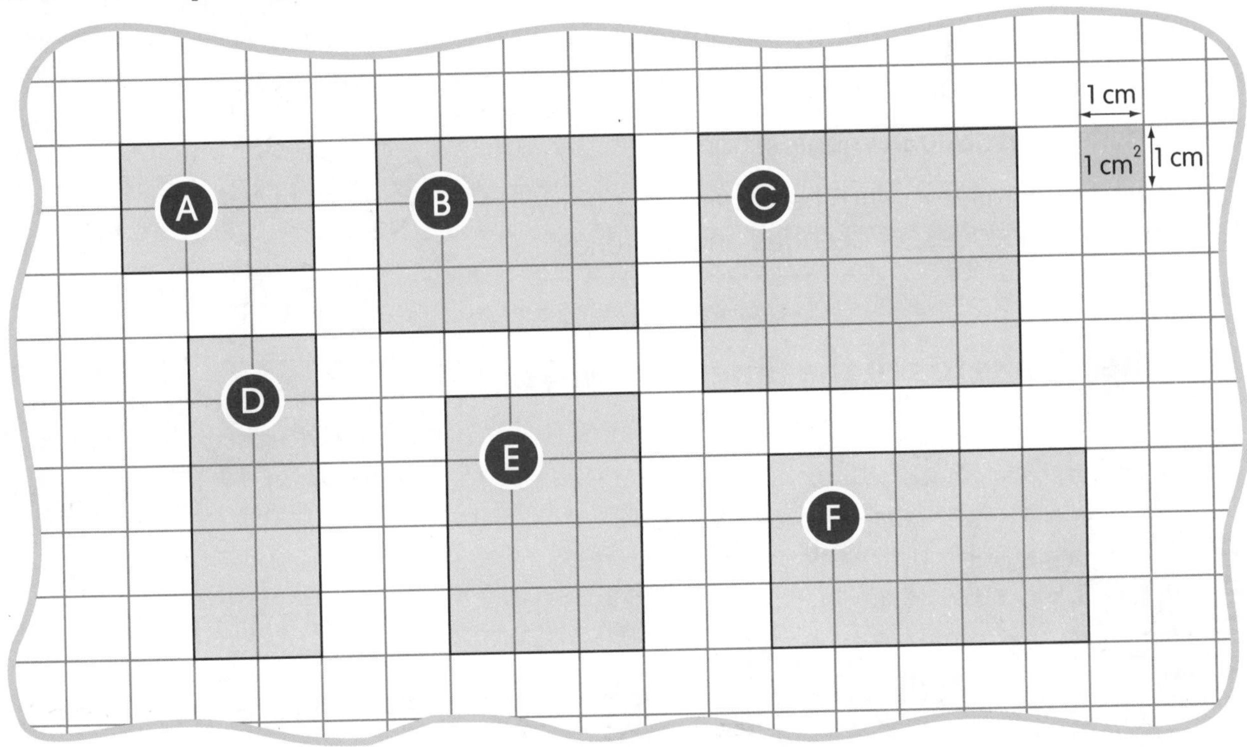

⑭

	A	B	C	D	E	F
Length	3 cm	4cm	5cm	3cm	3cm	5cm
Width	2 cm	3cm	4cm	5cm	4cm	3cm
Perimeter	10cm	14cm	18cm	14cm	14cm	16cm
Area	6cm²	12cm²	20cm	10cm²	12cm²	15cm²

⑮ *I think the perimeter of a rectangle equals the sum of its 2 lengths and 2 widths. Am I correct?*

Yes

⑯ *I can find the area of a rectangle by multiplying its length and width. Is that right?*

Yes

13

Time

- Read and write time in 12-hour notation.
- Determine elapsed time.
- Find the intervals to the nearest minute.
- Solve problems involving the relationship between years and decades, or decades and centuries.

Starts at 10:55

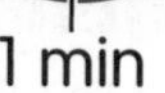

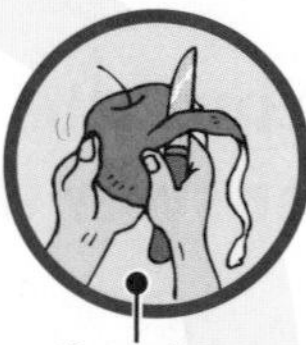

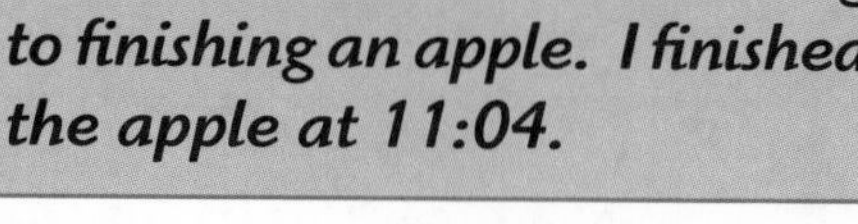

It took me 9 min from washing to finishing an apple. I finished the apple at 11:04.

Fill in the blanks to tell the times in 2 ways.

① A B C D E F

A 05: 17 ; 17 min past 5

B 09 :58 ; 2 min to 10

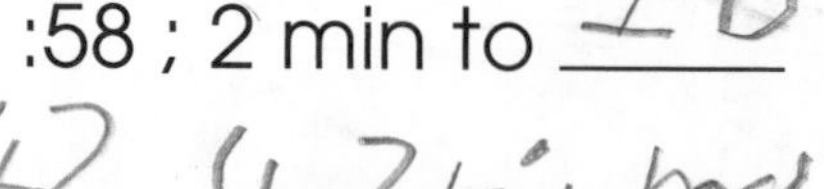

C 07:42 ; 42 min past 7

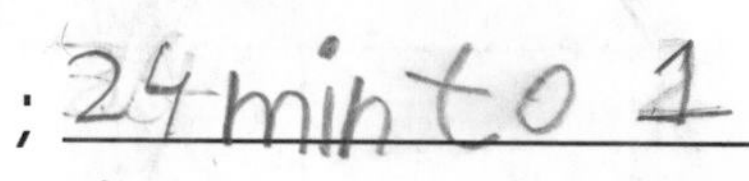

D 1:24 ; 24 min to 1

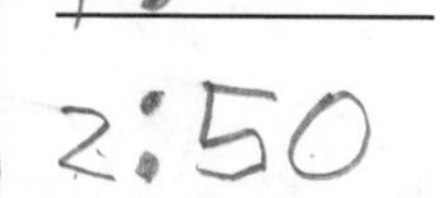

E 4:53 ; 53 min past 4

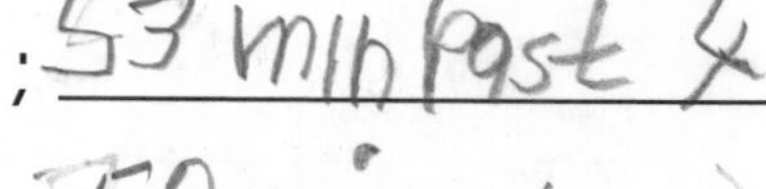

F 2:50 ; 50 min to 2

Draw the clock hands to show the times.

② 20 min to 10

③ 21 min past 8

④ 26 min to 5

Look at the pictures and the children's schedules. Answer the questions.

⑤

Brush teeth – 5 min
Eat breakfast – 10 min
Wash and get dressed – 10 min
Get backpack ready – 5 min
Get to school – 15 min

a. How long does it take Jason from waking up to arriving at school? ________

b. Will Jason be at school by 8:30 in the morning? ________

c. If Jason wants to spend the same amount of time on his morning routine but arrive at school at 8:10, what time should he wake up? ________

⑥

Make cookies – 30 min
Clean up the kitchen – 20 min
Set table – 5 min
Have afternoon tea – 15 min

a. How long does it take Maria from making cookies to finishing afternoon tea? ________

b. Will Maria finish her afternoon tea at 3:00 in the afternoon? ________

c. If Maria does not need to clean up the kitchen, what time will she have her afternoon tea? ________

We can use subtraction to find time intervals. Sometimes we need to change 1 hour to 60 minutes to find the time intervals.

The time interval is 1 h 37 min.

e.g. From 6:38 to 8:15

```
  7   75
  8̸ : 1̸5  ← 15 < 38, change
- 6 : 38     1 h to 60 min.
---------    60 + 15 = 75
  1 : 37
```

Find the time intervals. Show your work.

⑦ From 5:48 to 9:25

```
  8   85
  9̸ : 2̸5
- 5 : 48
---------
  3 : 43
```

Time interval: 3:43

⑧ From 1:52 to 4:33

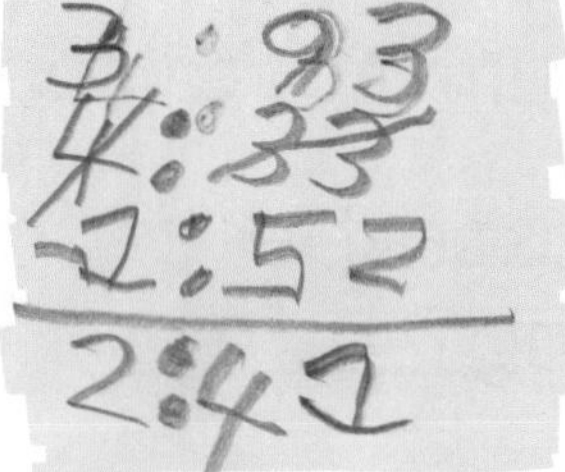

Time interval:

⑨ From 10:35 to 12:13

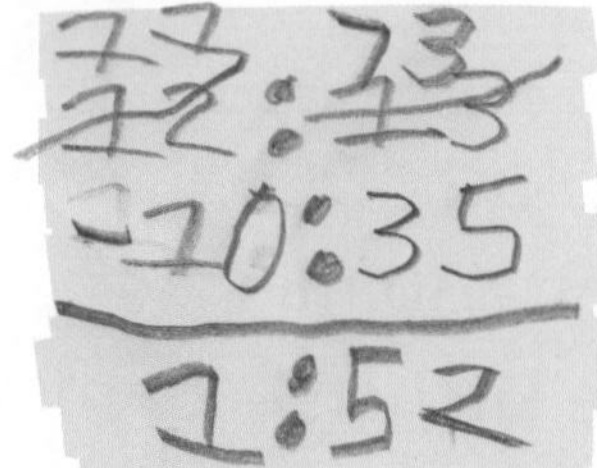

Time interval: 1:52

⑩ From 3:42 to 6:18

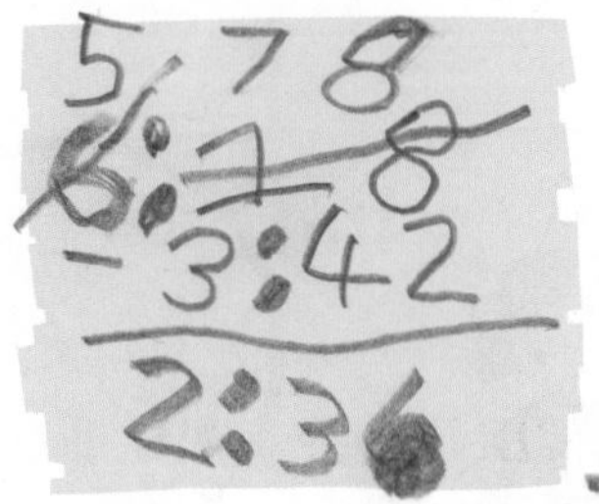

Time interval: 2:36

Solve the problems.

⑪ Andy starts building his robot at 3:52 in the afternoon and finishes at 6:27. How long does it take him to build his robot?

⑫ Ted starts his project at 4:18 and it takes him 1 hour and 25 minutes to finish it. What time does Ted finish his project?

5:43

Relationships between units of time:

1 decade = 10 years

1 century = 10 decades
= 100 years

My family has had this farm for 10 decades, or 1 century. I have been working here for 30 years, or 3 decades.

Fill in the blanks.

⑬ 30 years
= ___3___ decades

⑭ 4 centuries
= ___40___ decades

⑮ 60 decades
= ___6___ centuries

⑯ 5 decades
= ___50___ years

⑰ 800 years
= ___8___ centuries

⑱ 3 centuries
= ___30___ years

⑲ 9 centuries
= ___90___ decades

⑳ 60 years
= ___6___ decades

Read what the children say. Solve the problems.

㉑ *It is 2015. My grandfather's house was built 2 centuries ago. What year was that?*

㉒
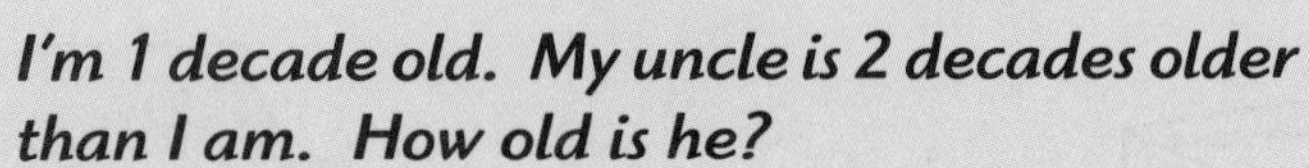

I'm 1 decade old. My uncle is 2 decades older than I am. How old is he?

___2 decades___

㉓ *If I plant an apple tree in my backyard in 2017, how old will it be in 2617?*

___2___ centuries old or ___7___ decades old

Mass, Capacity, and Volume

- Record and compare objects, using standard units of mass (e.g. g or kg) or capacity (e.g. mL or L).
- Understand the relationships between g and kg or mL and L.
- Measure and record the volumes of objects.

Choose the appropriate unit for the mass of each object. Write "g" or "kg".

① 

② 

③ 

Fill in the blanks.

④ 2 kg = ________ g

⑤ 3000 g = ________ kg

⑥ 5 kg = ________ g

⑦ 9000 g = ________ kg

⑧ 1 kg 200 g = ________ g

⑨ 1 kg 60 g = ________ g

⑩ 5 kg 4 g = ________ g

⑪ 4 kg 800 g = ________ g

Put the things in order from the heaviest to the lightest. Write the letters.

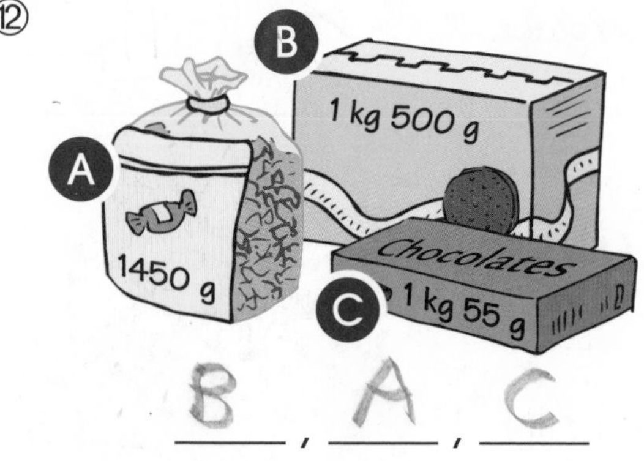

______ , ______ , ______

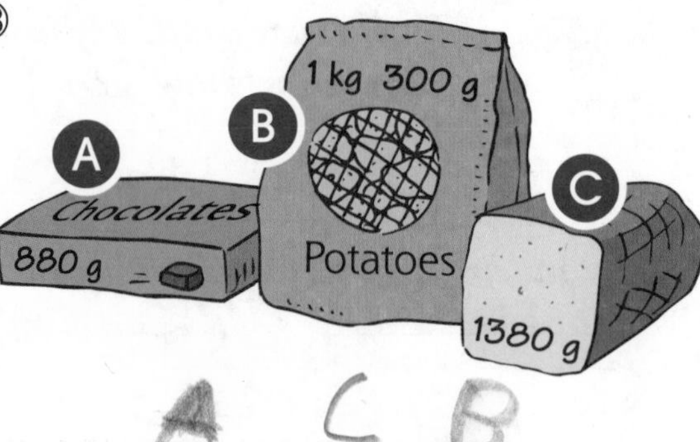

______ , ______ , ______

Litre – measures larger capacities
e.g. a bathtub

Millilitre – measures smaller capacities
e.g. a juice box

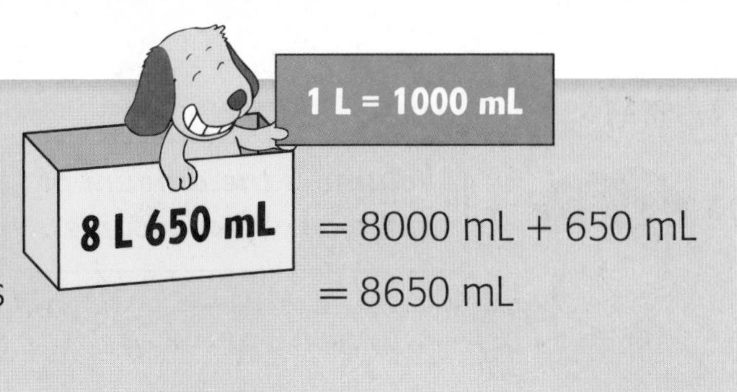

= 8000 mL + 650 mL
= 8650 mL

Choose the appropriate unit for the capacity of each container. Write "mL" or "L".

⑭ a mug mL

⑮ a big toy box L

⑯ a small water bottle mL

⑰ a pail L

Write the capacity of each container in mL. Then put each group of containers in order from the one with the greatest capacity to the one with the least.

⑱

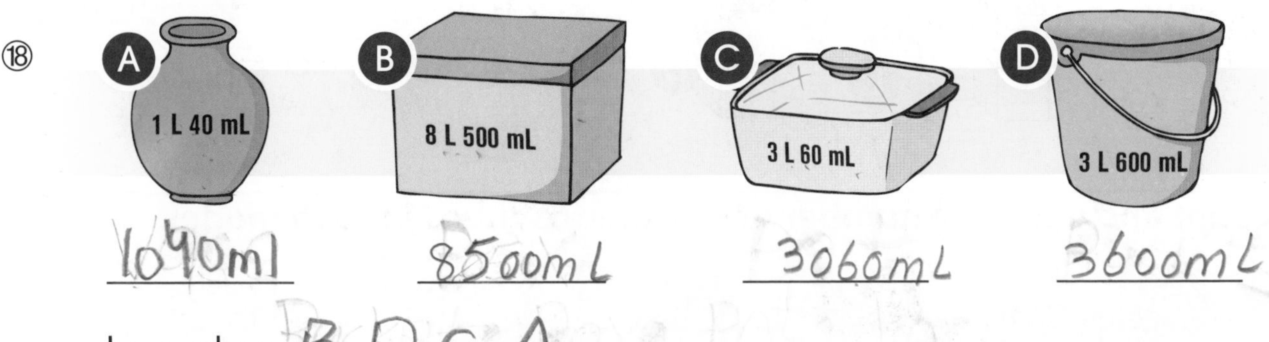

1040ml 8500mL 3060mL 3600mL

In order: B, D, C, A

⑲

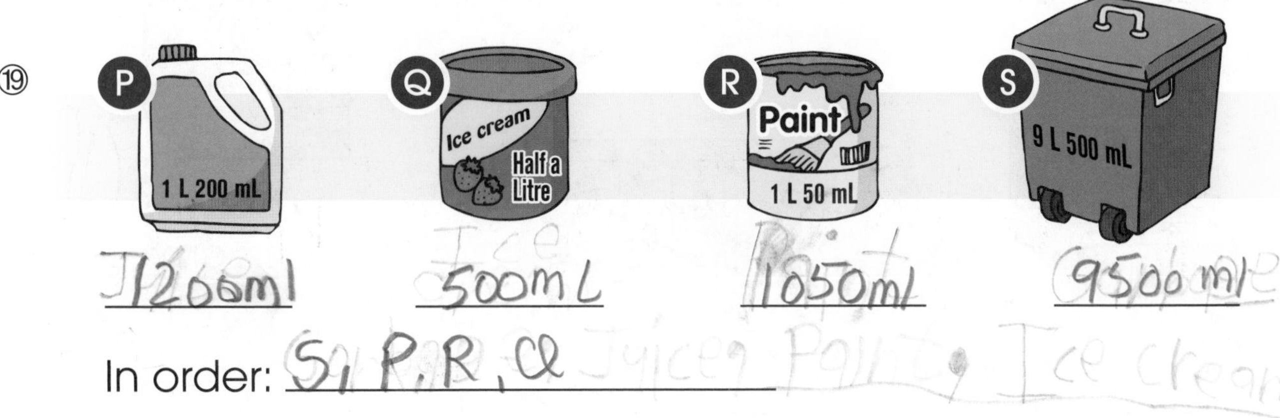

1200ml 500mL 1050ml 9500ml

In order: S, P, R, Q

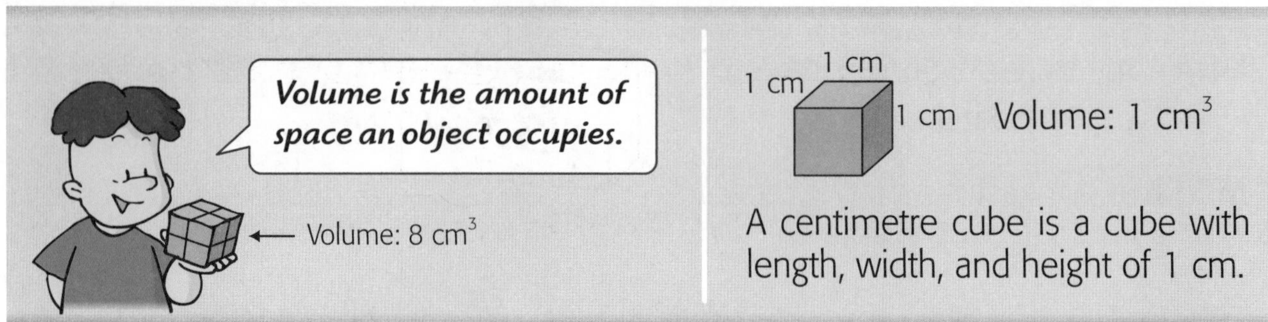

Volume is the amount of space an object occupies.
Volume: 8 cm³
1 cm
1 cm
1 cm
Volume: 1 cm³
A centimetre cube is a cube with length, width, and height of 1 cm.

Complete the table to tell which models are built with the given number of centimetre cubes. Write the letters.

⑳

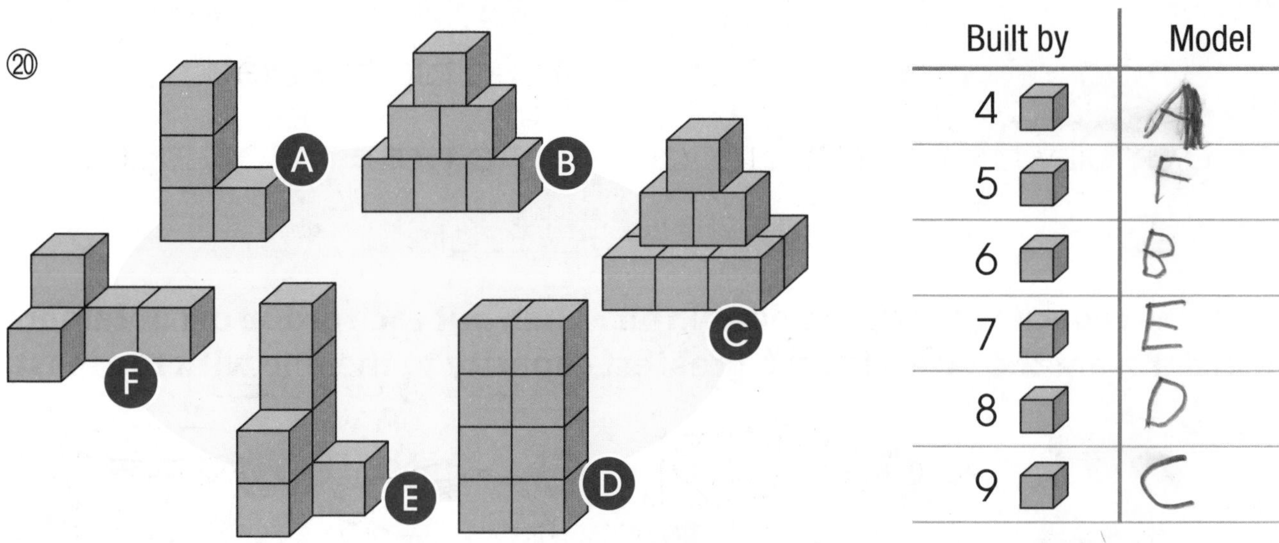

Built by	Model
4	A
5	F
6	B
7	E
8	D
9	C

Count and write the number of centimetre cubes in each model.

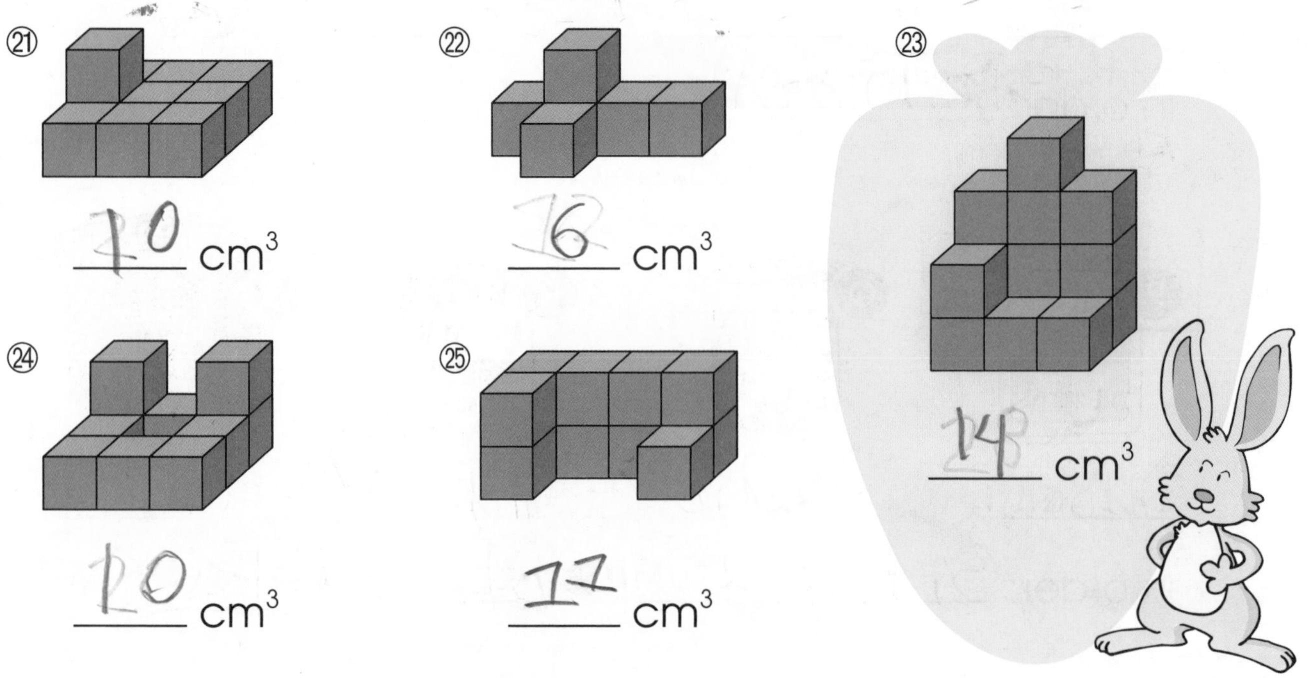

㉑ 10 cm^3

㉒ 16 cm^3

㉓ 14 cm^3

㉔ 10 cm^3

㉕ 17 cm^3

15

Fractions

- Use standard fractional notation to tell the coloured parts of a whole.
- Understand the meanings of the denominator, numerator, and equivalent fractions.
- Compare and order fractions.

Look at each figure. Trace the dotted lines. Then fill in the boxes with numbers to show the coloured parts in each figure.

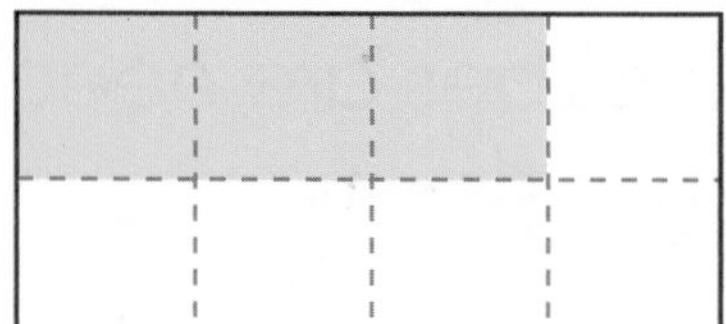

$\frac{3}{8}$ ← no. of parts coloured / ← no. of equal parts

② 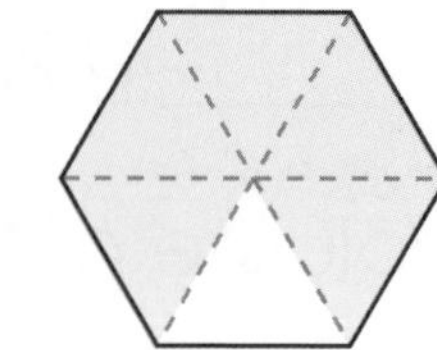

$\frac{5}{6}$ ← no. of parts coloured / ← no. of equal parts

Colour 2 parts and write a fraction to show the coloured parts in each figure.

③ 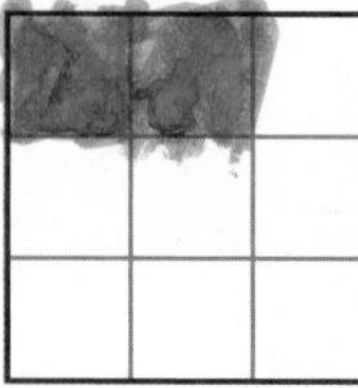

$\frac{2}{9}$ is coloured.

④ 

$\frac{2}{5}$ is coloured.

⑤ 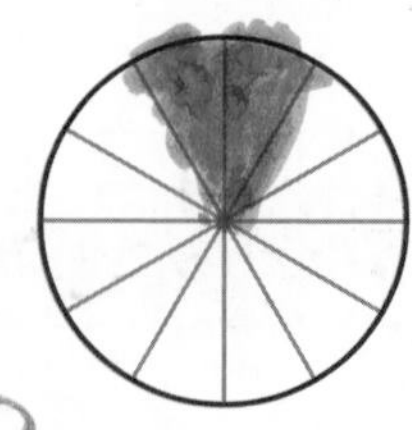

$\frac{2}{12}$ is coloured.

⑥ 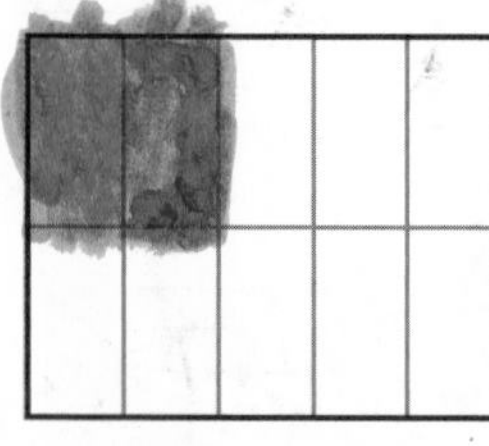

$\frac{2}{10}$ is coloured.

⑦ 

$\frac{2}{4}$ is coloured.

⑧ 

Numerator: the number above the line in a fraction

Denominator: the number below the line in a fraction

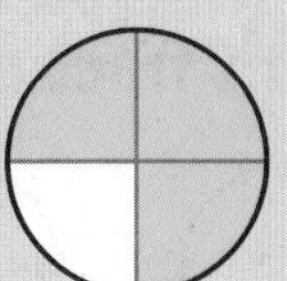

e.g. $\frac{\mathbf{3}}{\mathbf{4}}$ ← numerator (no. of parts coloured) ← denominator (no. of equal parts in a whole)

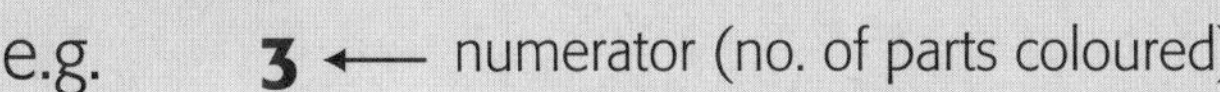

$\frac{3}{4}$ is coloured.

Circle the fractions that have a numerator greater than 4.

⑨ $\frac{3}{7}$ $\frac{5}{6}$ $\frac{1}{5}$ $\frac{7}{10}$ $\frac{3}{4}$ $\frac{2}{6}$ $\frac{2}{3}$ $\frac{9}{10}$ $\frac{7}{12}$

Colour the fractions that have a denominator smaller than 6.

⑩

$\frac{3}{5}$ $\frac{2}{3}$

$\frac{3}{9}$ $\frac{1}{4}$ $\frac{5}{8}$

Draw lines to cut each figure and colour the correct number of parts to show the fraction given.

⑪ $\frac{4}{9}$

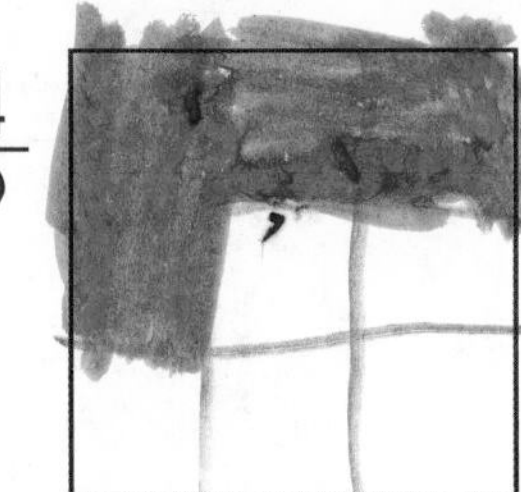

⑫ $\frac{7}{8}$

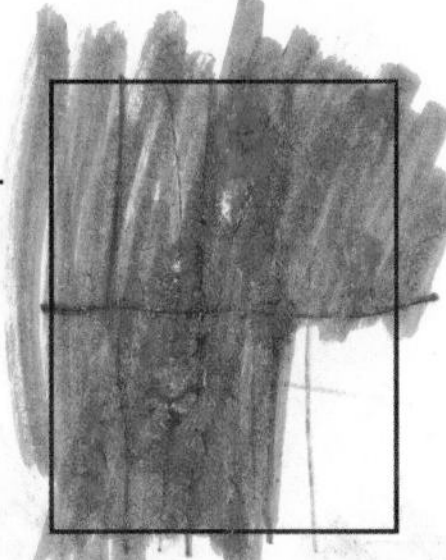

⑬ $\frac{1}{2}$

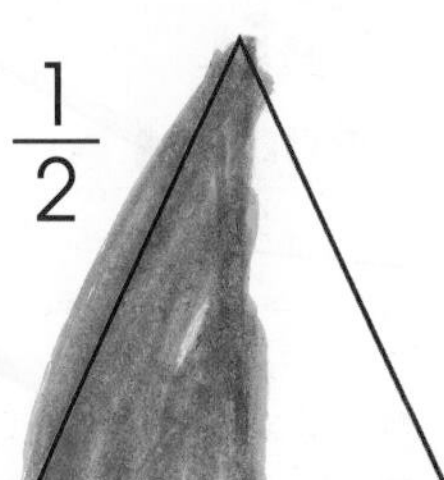

⑭ $\frac{4}{5}$

⑮ $\frac{10}{12}$

⑯ $\frac{1}{3}$

Equivalent fractions: fractions that represent the same part of a whole

e.g.

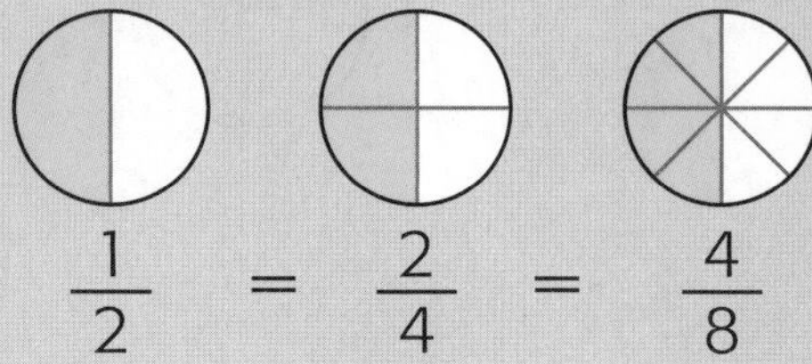

$\frac{1}{2} = \frac{2}{4} = \frac{4}{8}$

$\frac{1}{2}$, $\frac{2}{4}$, and $\frac{4}{8}$ are equivalent fractions.

Write a fraction to show the coloured parts in each figure. Then fill in the blanks with fractions to complete the sentences.

⑰

A 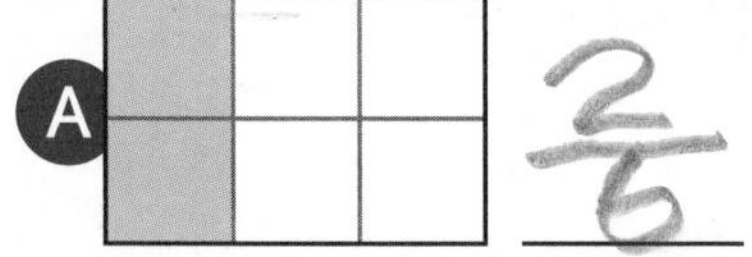

B 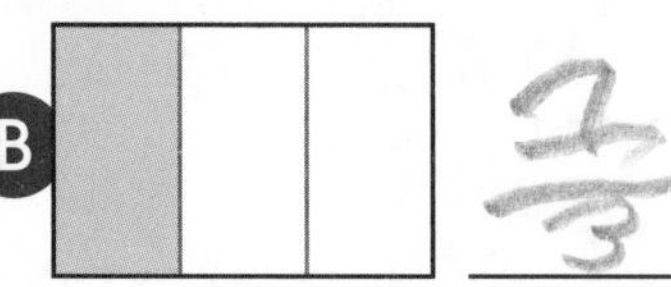

C 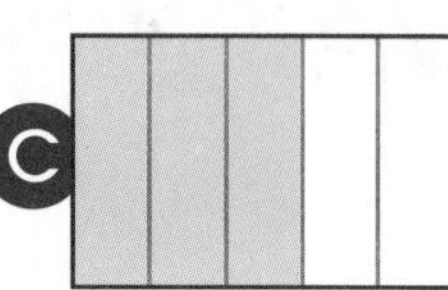

_____, _____ and _____ are equivalent fractions.

⑱

A, B 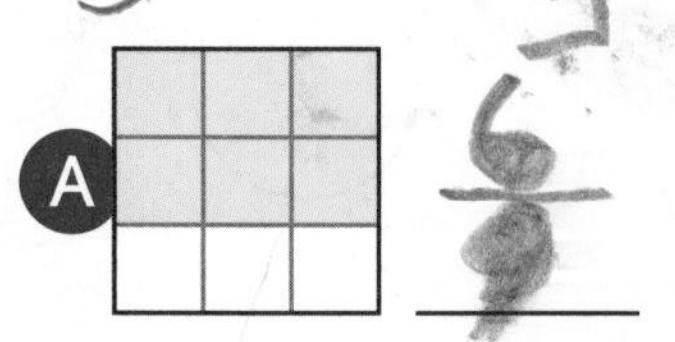

C 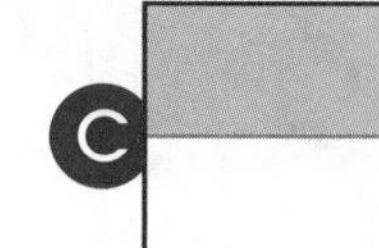

_____, _____ and _____ are equivalent fractions.

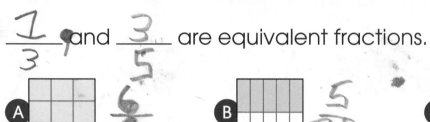

Draw figures to show that the fractions in each pair are equivalent.

⑲ $\frac{2}{5}$ $\frac{4}{10}$

⑳ $\frac{2}{3}$ $\frac{6}{9}$

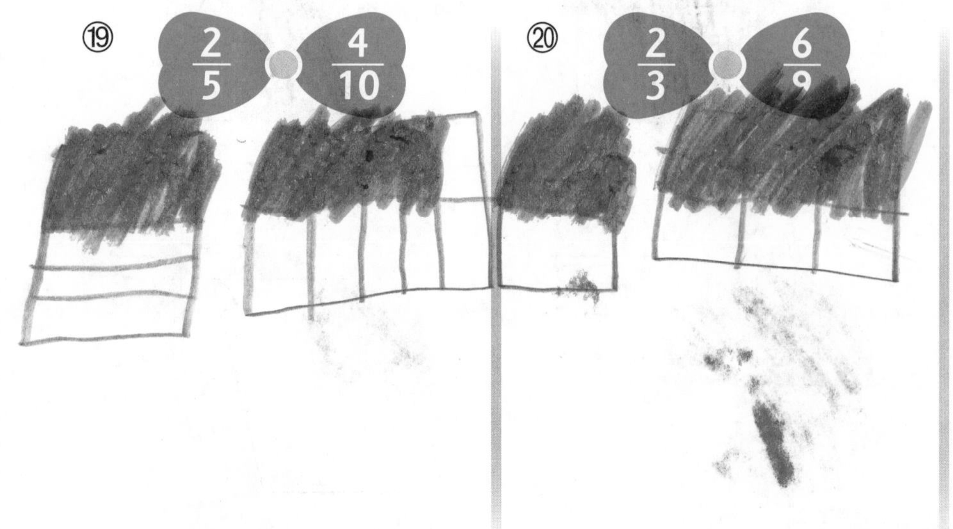

㉑ $\frac{1}{4}$ $\frac{2}{8}$

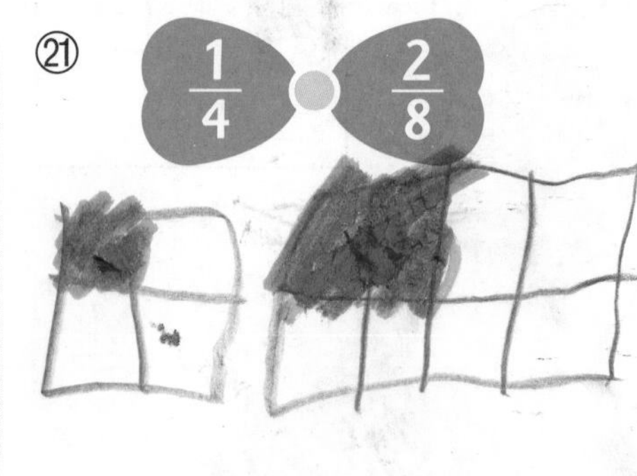

Write a fraction to show the coloured parts in each figure. Then put ">" or "<" in the circle.

(22)
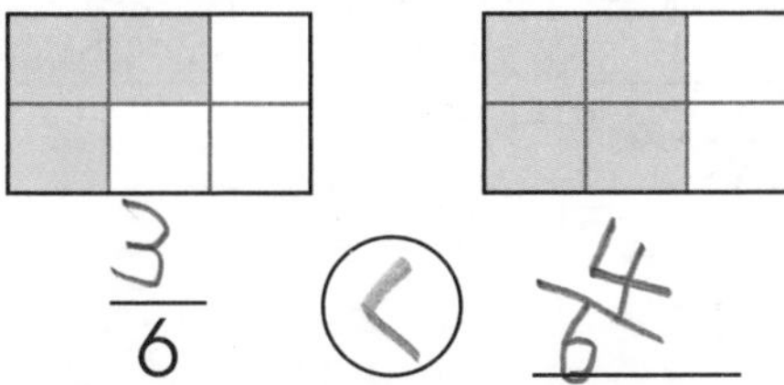

(23)
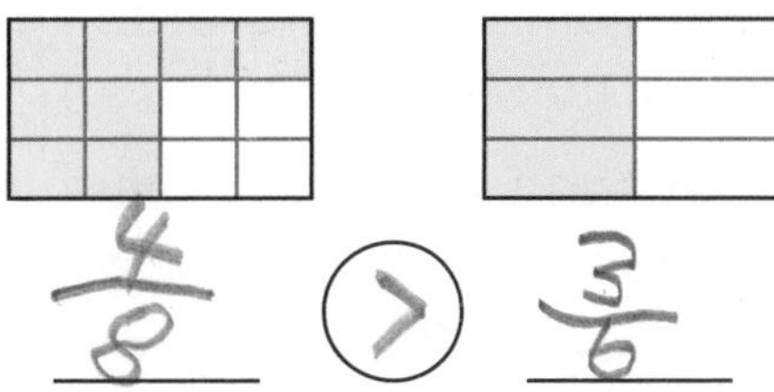

(24)
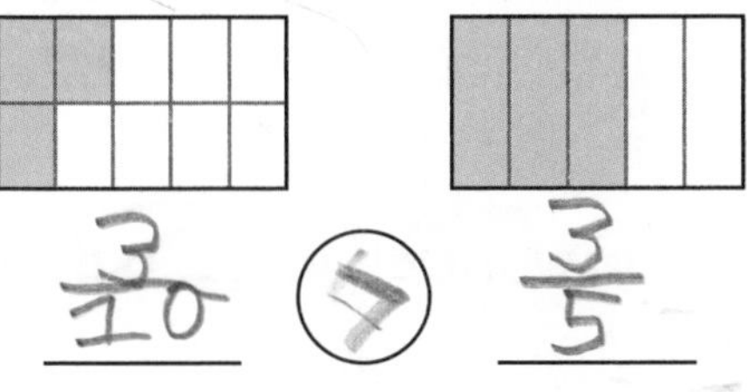

(25)
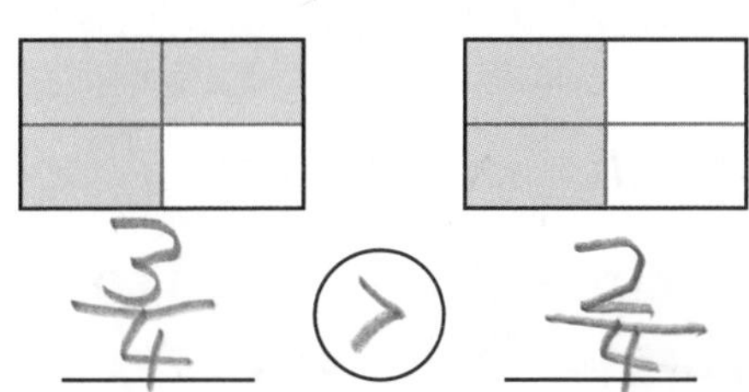

Circle the greater fraction.

(26) $\frac{7}{8}$ $\frac{6}{8}$

(27) $\frac{9}{10}$ $\frac{5}{10}$

(28) $\frac{1}{7}$ $\frac{1}{3}$

(29) $\frac{4}{9}$ $\frac{4}{5}$

(30) $\frac{2}{6}$ $\frac{6}{7}$

(31) $\frac{8}{9}$ $\frac{2}{4}$

Put the fractions in order. Then answer the question.

(32) $\frac{1}{3}$ $\frac{9}{10}$ $\frac{3}{5}$

(33) $\frac{3}{4}$ $\frac{1}{5}$ $\frac{3}{8}$

(34) $\frac{5}{9}$ $\frac{3}{10}$ $\frac{1}{4}$

(35)

I have $\frac{2}{5}$ of a pizza, Sam has $\frac{2}{10}$, Joe has $\frac{7}{8}$, and Tim has $\frac{1}{4}$. Who has the most pizza?

______ has the most pizza.

16

Decimals

- Write, compare, and order decimal numbers to tenths.
- Understand the place value in decimal numbers and the relationship between fractions and decimals to tenths.
- Use number lines to locate decimal numbers.

Put a decimal point in the correct place to show how much of each diagram is coloured. Then write the decimal in words.

①

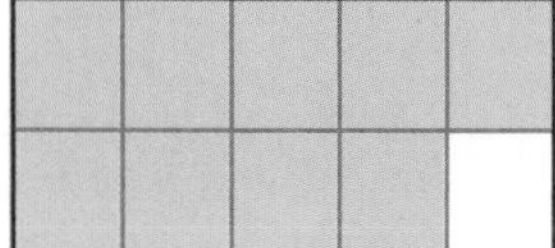

In numeral: **0 9**

In words: ______ tenths

②

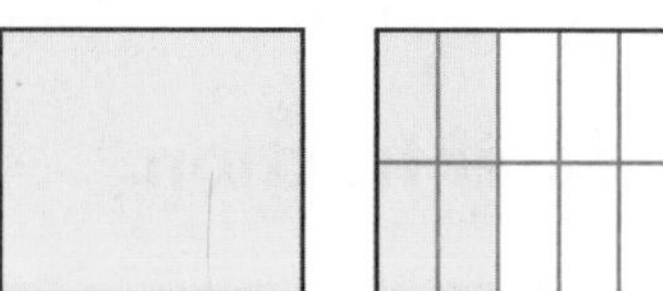

In numeral: **1 4**

In words: ______ and ______ tenths

③

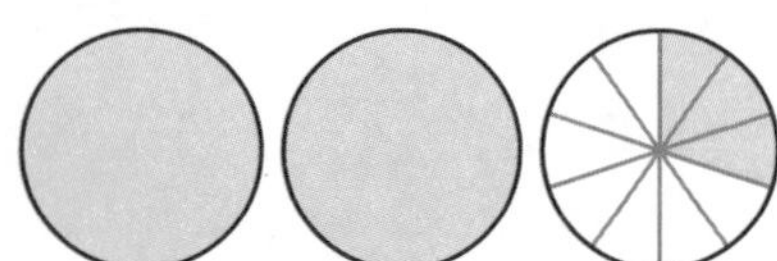

In numeral: **2 3**

In words: ______________

④

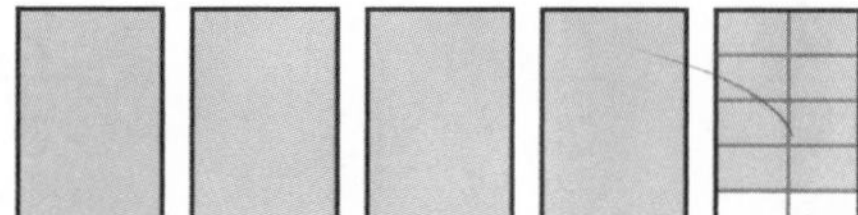

In numeral: **4 8**

In words: ______________

Colour the diagrams to match each decimal given. Then write the decimal in words.

⑤ **2.7**

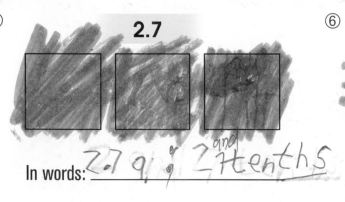

In words: ______________

⑥ **3.5**

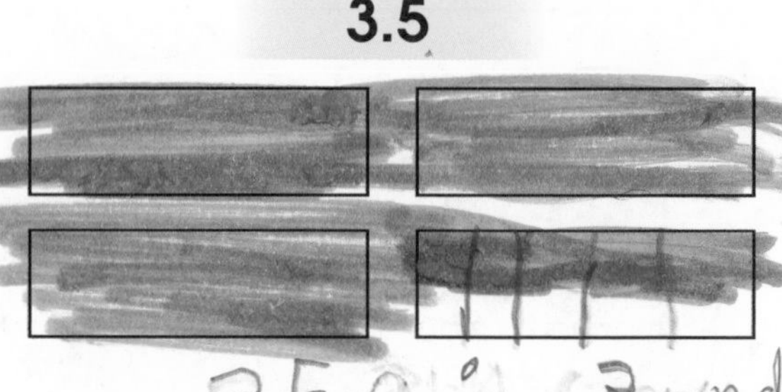

In words: ______________

Write the meaning of each digit in bold.

⑦ 5.**6** ______　　⑧ 1**7**.5 ______　　⑨ **3**2.4 ______

⑩ 10.**8** ______　　⑪ 5.**2** ______　　⑫ **9**0.3 ______

⑬ 2**5**.1 ______　　⑭ 6.**4** ______　　⑮ 3**4**.6 ______

Write as decimals. Then colour the greater one in each pair.

⑯ 6 and 2 tenths 

5 and 9 tenths 

⑰ 11 and 6 tenths 

20 and 1 tenth 

⑱ 4 and 5 tenths 

⑲ 13 and 1 tenth 

5 and 4 tenths 

1 and 3 tenths  

Write a decimal and a fraction to show how much of each diagram is coloured.

⑳ 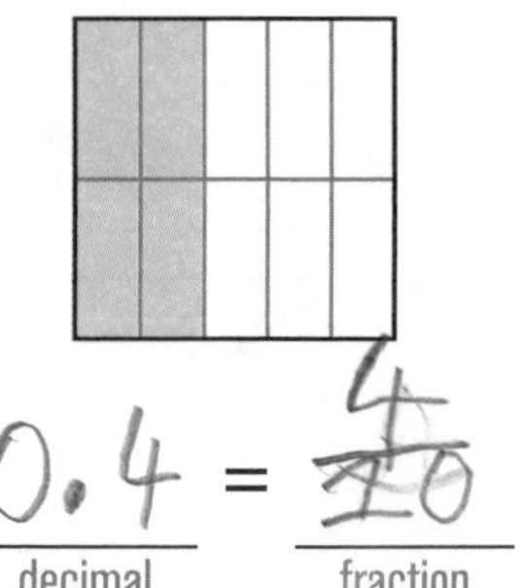

______ = ______
decimal　　fraction

㉑ 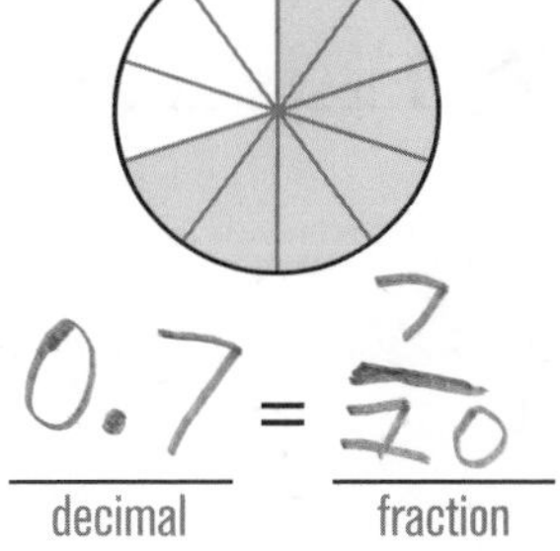

______ = ______
decimal　　fraction

㉒ 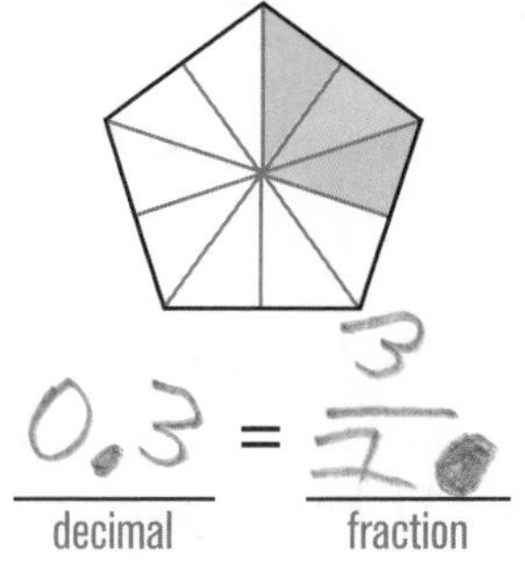

______ = ______
decimal　　fraction

Use arrows to place the numbers on the number lines. Then put the numbers in order.

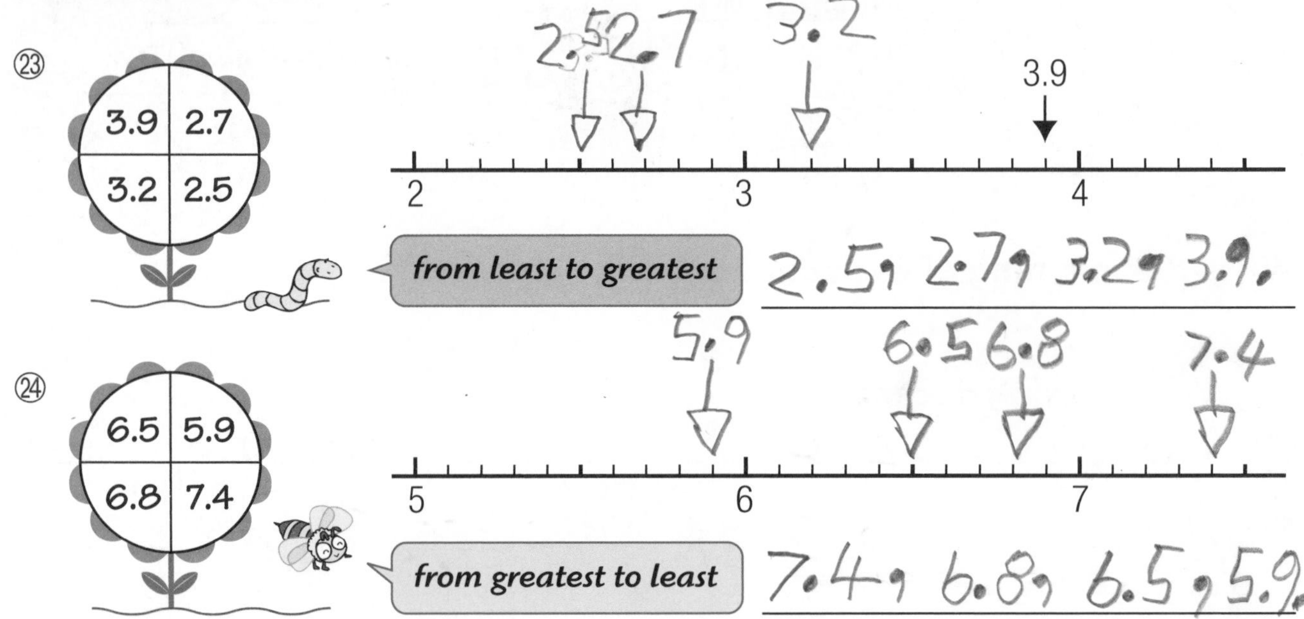

Read what the girl says. Help her draw number lines and show the locations of decimals. Then fill in the blanks.

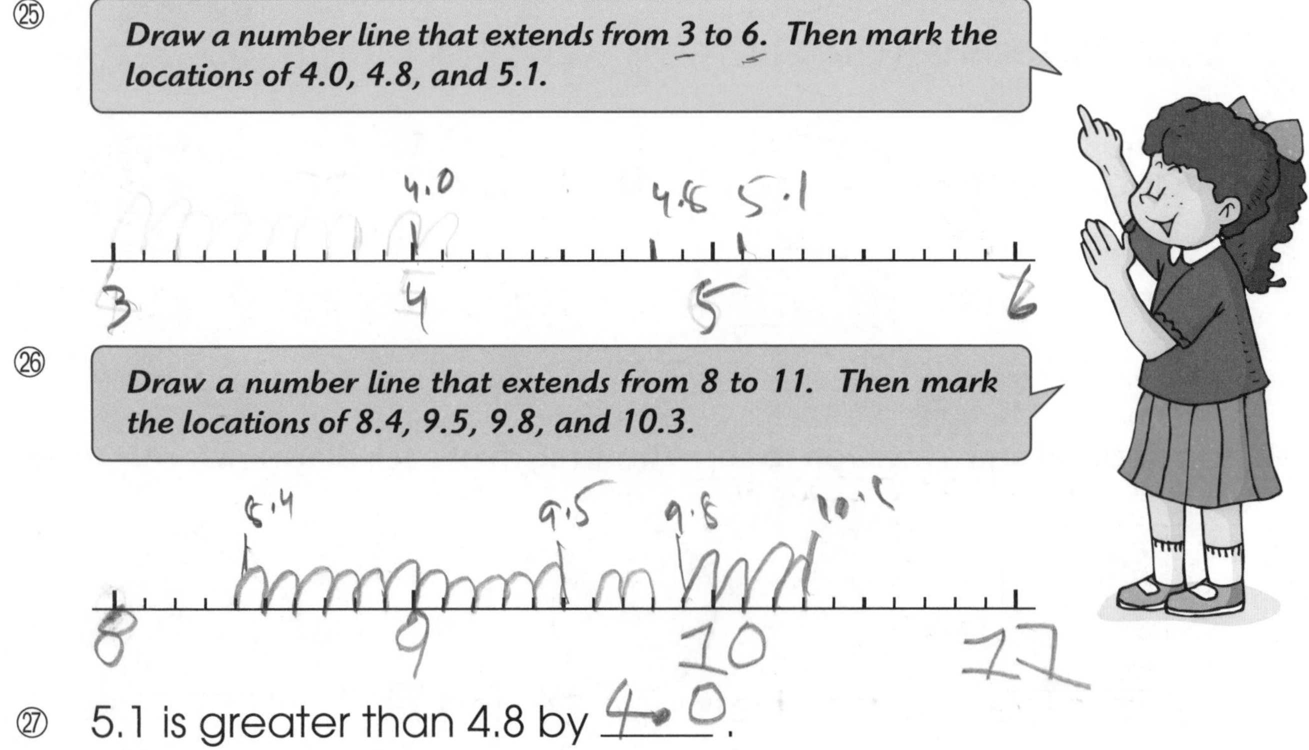

25
Draw a number line that extends from 3 to 6. Then mark the locations of 4.0, 4.8, and 5.1.
26
Draw a number line that extends from 8 to 11. Then mark the locations of 8.4, 9.5, 9.8, and 10.3.

27 5.1 is greater than 4.8 by ________.

28 9.8 is less than 10.3 by ________.

Write the decimals.

㉙ 2 tenths greater than 9.5 ________

㉚ 3 tenths less than 8.4 ________

㉛ 5 tenths greater than 7.6 ________

㉜ 2 tenths less than 5.1 ________

Fill in the missing decimals.

㉝ 6.2 6.4 6.6 ______ ______ 7.2 7.4 ______ 7.8

㉞ 9.4 9.3 9.2 ______ 9.0 ______ ______ 8.7 8.6

㉟ 4.5 5.0 5.5 ______ ______ 7.0 ______ 8.0 8.5

㊱ 8.9 9.9 ______ ______ ______ 13.9 14.9 15.9

Write the distances between Ann and the gift boxes in the spaces provided. Then answer the questions.

㊲

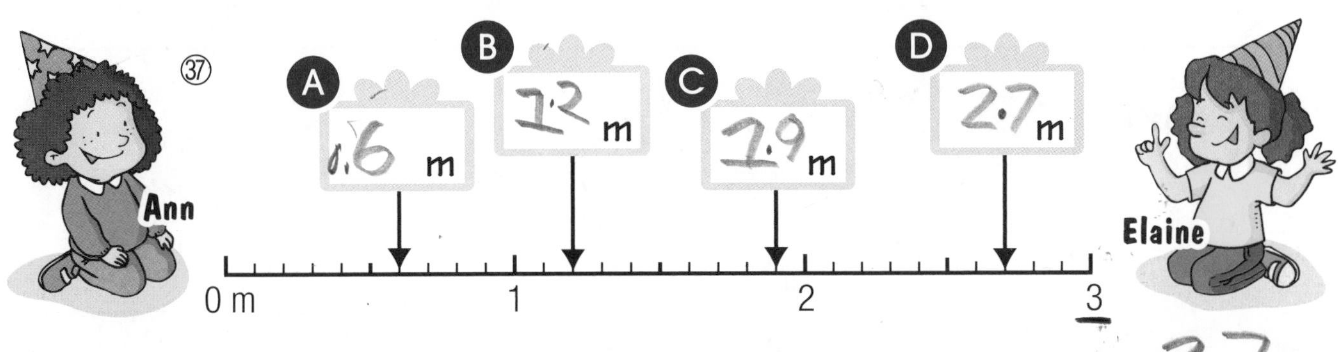

㊳ Which gift box is closest to Elaine? ________

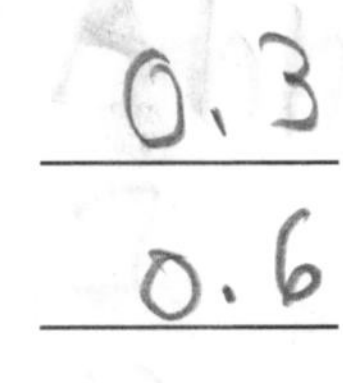

㊴ What is the distance between Elaine and the closest gift box? ________

㊵ What is the distance between Ⓐ and Ⓑ? ________

㊶ What is the distance between Ⓒ and Ⓓ? ________

17 Addition and Subtraction of Decimals

- Add or subtract decimal numbers to tenths.
- Solve problems involving addition or subtraction of decimal numbers.

Put a decimal point in the answer to complete each vertical addition.

① $\begin{array}{r} 4.5 \\ +\ 3.6 \\ \hline 8.1 \end{array}$

② $\begin{array}{r} 8.2 \\ +\ 3.6 \\ \hline 11.8 \end{array}$

③ $\begin{array}{r} 9.4 \\ +\ 4.6 \\ \hline 14.0 \end{array}$

Do the addition.

④ $\begin{array}{r} 8.5 \\ +\ 4.9 \\ \hline 13.4 \end{array}$

⑤ $\begin{array}{r} 7.5 \\ +\ 9.2 \\ \hline 16.7 \end{array}$

⑥ $\begin{array}{r} 4.6 \\ +\ 4.6 \\ \hline 9.2 \end{array}$

⑦ $\begin{array}{r} 12.7 \\ +\ 9.4 \\ \hline 22.1 \end{array}$

⑧ $\begin{array}{r} 14.4 \\ +\ 8.8 \\ \hline 23.2 \end{array}$

⑨ $\begin{array}{r} 5.3 \\ +\ 18.8 \\ \hline 23.1 \end{array}$

⑩ 16.8 + 6.2 = 23.1

⑪ 19.5 + 21.5 = 41.0

⑫ 3.9 + 12.7 = 16.6

⑬ 9.4 + 7.8 = 16.2

⑭ 5.6 + 5.8 = 11.3

⑮ 9.2 + 17.8 = 26.1

The children are playing games. Help them find their total scores. Then answer the questions.

Record

	1st Round	2nd Round		1st Round	2nd Round
Tim	9.6	5.8	Lucy	7.6	6.6
Ray	8.1	11.9	Sue	10.7	3.3
Mark	12.5	6.3	Lily	8.2	4.4

⑰ Who has the highest score? Ray

⑱ Who has the lowest score? Lily

⑲ What is the total score of the boys' team? 53.2

14.4+20.0+18.8 = 53.2

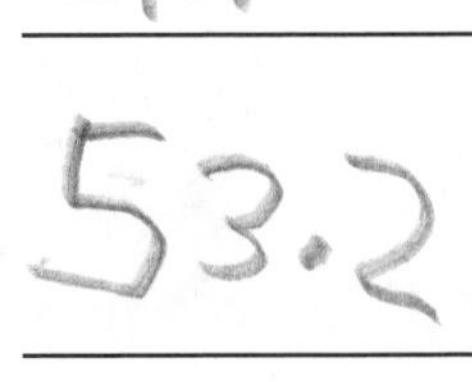

⑳ What is the total score of the girls' team? 30.8

14.2+14.0+12.6 = 30.8

㉑ Which team has a higher score? Boys team

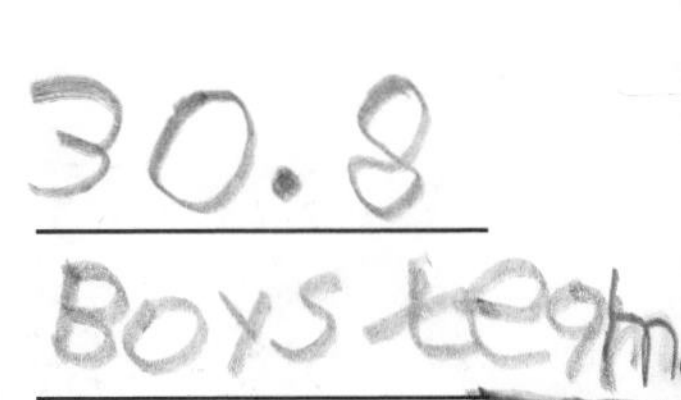

Subtracting decimals:

1st Align the decimal points.

2nd Subtract the same way we subtract whole numbers.

3rd Put the decimal point in the answer.

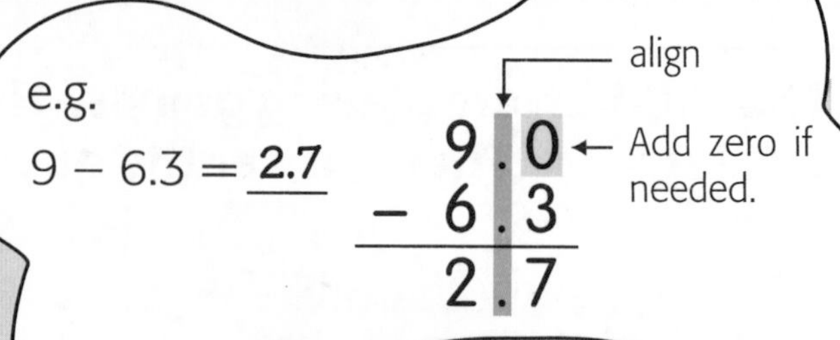

Do the subtraction.

㉒ 14.7 – 5.8 = ______

㉓ 10.2 – 4.6 = ______

㉔ 8.5 – 2.7 = ______

㉕ 8 – 3.4 = ______

㉖ 14 – 6.9 = ______

㉗ 20 – 13.2 = ______

㉘ 7.7 – 5.9 = ______

㉙ 8.5 – 4.8 = ______

㉚ 13.6 – 6.7 = ______

㉛ 15 – 9.8 = ______

Fill in the missing numbers.

㉜
$$\begin{array}{r} 1\,\square\,.\,\square \\ -\quad 6\,.\,8 \\ \hline 9\,.\,1 \end{array}$$

㉝
$$\begin{array}{r} 2\,\square\,.\,3 \\ -\quad 8\,.\,\square \\ \hline 1\,1\,.\,6 \end{array}$$

㉞
$$\begin{array}{r} \square\,5\,.\,\square \\ -\;1\,\square\,.\,6 \\ \hline 2\,3\,.\,8 \end{array}$$

Find the answers.

㉟ 9.5 + 2.7 = ______

㊱ 18.7 – 6.9 = ______

㊲ 13.4 – 8.9 = ______

㊳ 20 – 18.4 = ______

㊴ 7.6 + 8.6 = ______

㊵ 2.5 + 19.8 = ______

Solve the problems.

㊶

Aunt Linda has a box of juice. If she drinks 0.8 L of juice, how much juice will be left?

______ = ______ ______

㊷

Nicholas has two bags of candies. How many kilograms of candies does he have in all?

______ = ______ ______

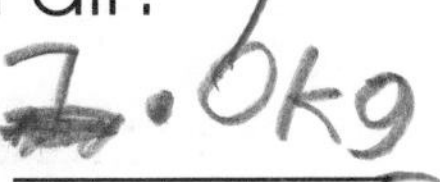

㊸

Uncle Jason is 0.4 m taller than Ann. How tall is Uncle Jason?

______ = ______ ______

㊹

Mr. Shaw cuts the rope into two pieces. If one piece is 16.4 m long, how long is the other piece?

______ = ______ ______

㊺

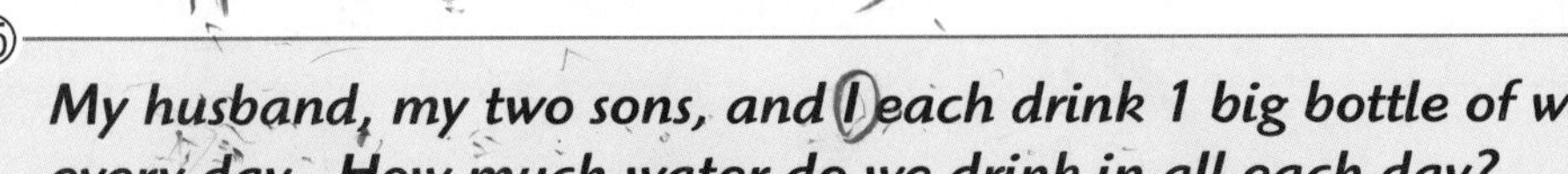

My husband, my two sons, and I each drink 1 big bottle of water every day. How much water do we drink in all each day?

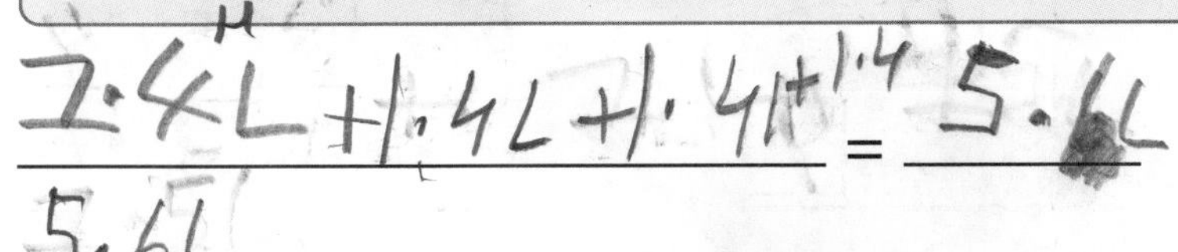

______ = ______

______

Money

- Read and write money amounts to $100.
- Add and subtract money amounts to make purchases and change up to $10.

$98.65
– $82.99
$15.66

~~$98.65~~
$82.99

I can save $15.66 if I buy it today.

Estimate and find the exact amount of money in each group.

① A

B

C

D

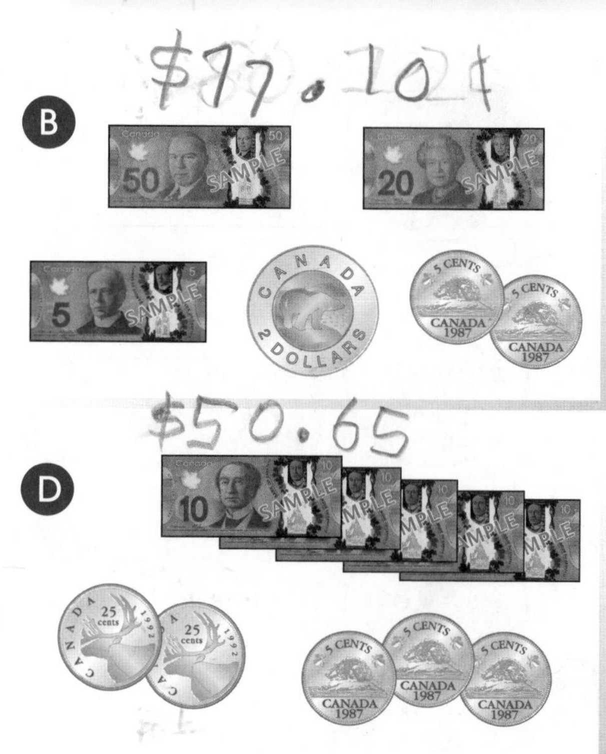

Group	Estimate	Actual
A	dollars cents	dollars cents or $
B		
C		
D		

Draw the fewest bills and coins to show the cost of each item. Then find the total costs and price differences.

②

Ⓐ **$45.63**

(20) + (20) + (5)
(50) + (10) + (2) + (1)

Ⓑ **$53.17**

(5) + (2) + (1)
(20) + (5) + (2)

Ⓒ **$97.55**

(50) + (20) + (20) + (5) + (2)
(50) + (5)

Ⓓ **$32.82**

(20) + (10) + (2)
(50) + (10) + (10) + (2)

Key

50	$50
20	$20
10	$10
5	$5
	$2
	$1
	25¢
	10¢
	5¢
	1¢

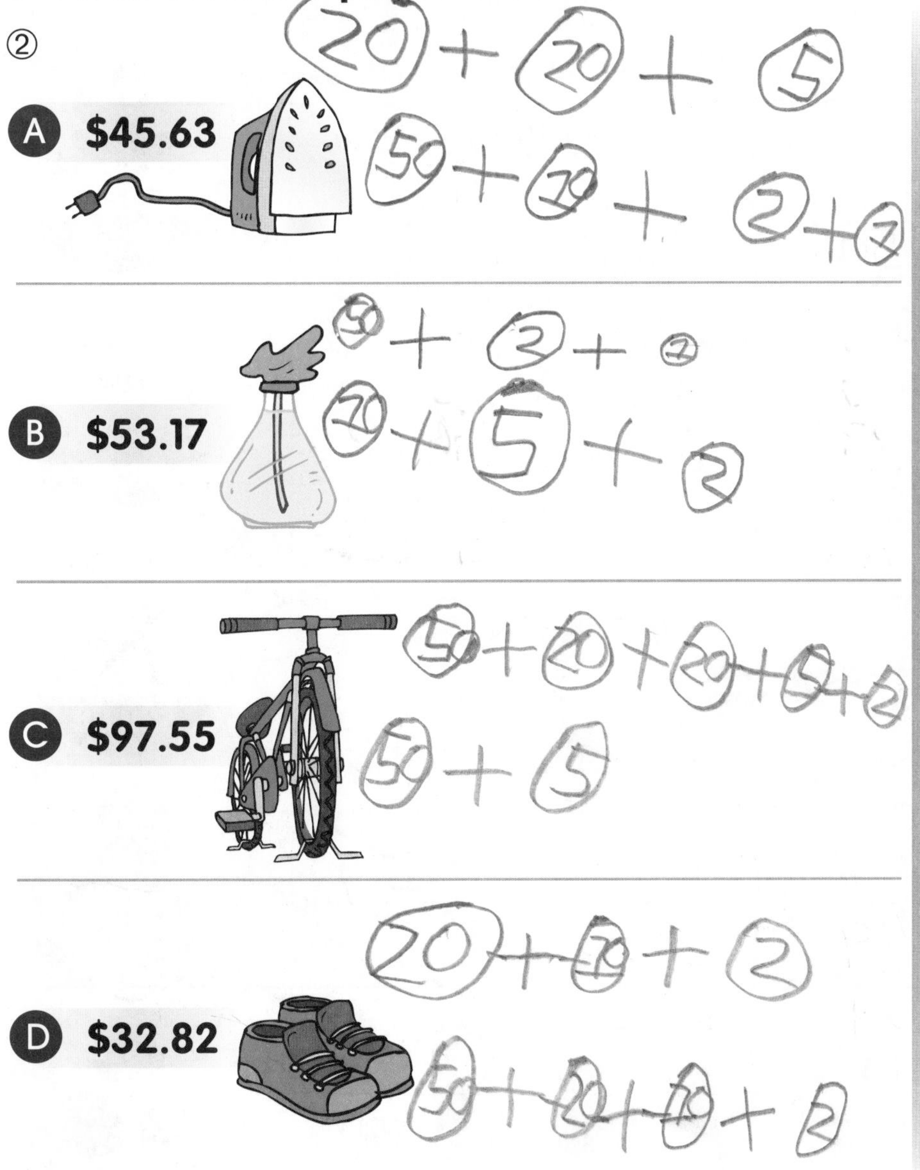

③ **Total Cost**

Ⓐ and Ⓓ

$45.63
+ $32.82
$78.45

Ⓑ and Ⓓ

$53.17
+ $32.82
$85.99

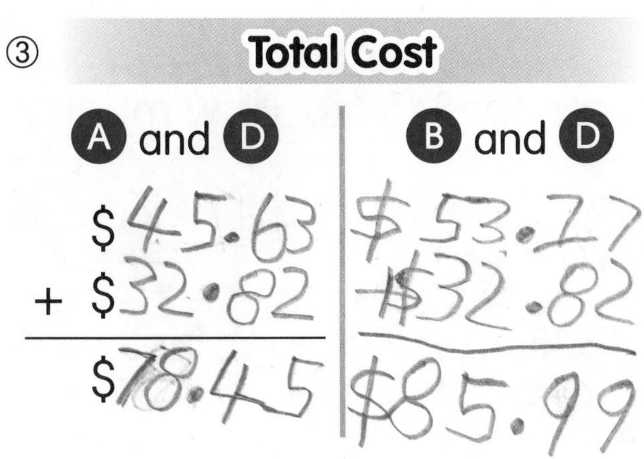

④ **Price Difference**

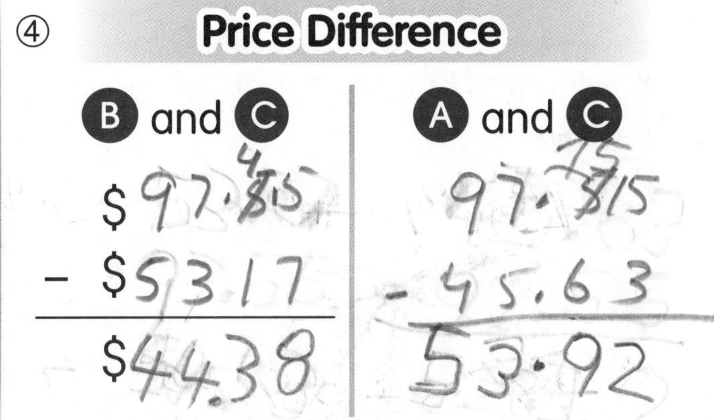

Ⓑ and Ⓒ

$97.⁴$\overset{4}{8}$5
- $53.17
$44.38

Ⓐ and Ⓒ

97.⁷⁵$\overset{15}{8}$15
- 45.63
53.92

Look at the cost of each item. Fill in the missing information on each receipt. Then answer the questions.

⑤
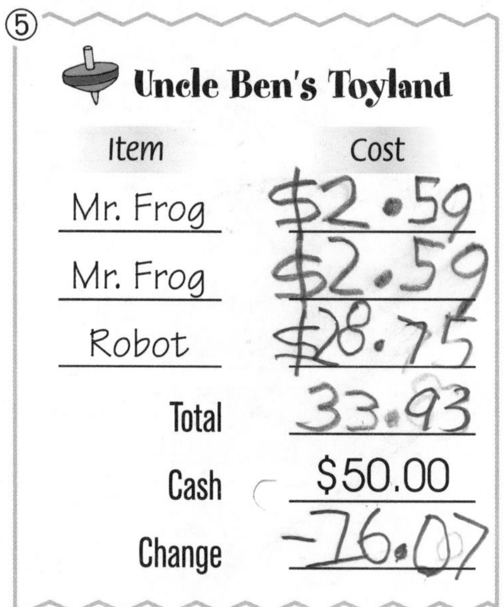

Uncle Ben's Toyland
Item
Cost
Mr. Frog
Mr. Frog
Robot
Total
Cash
$50.00
Change

⑥
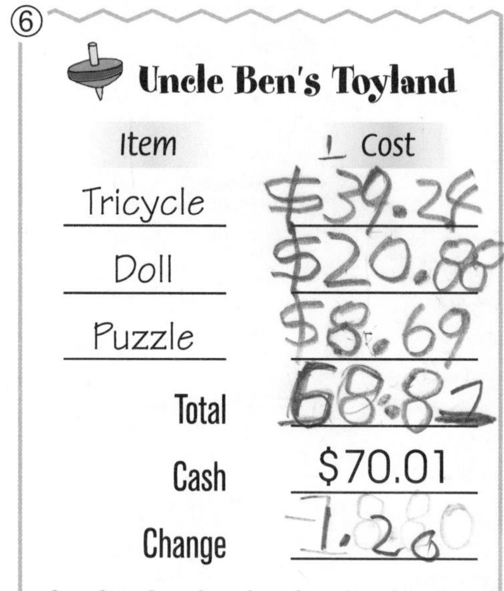

⑦
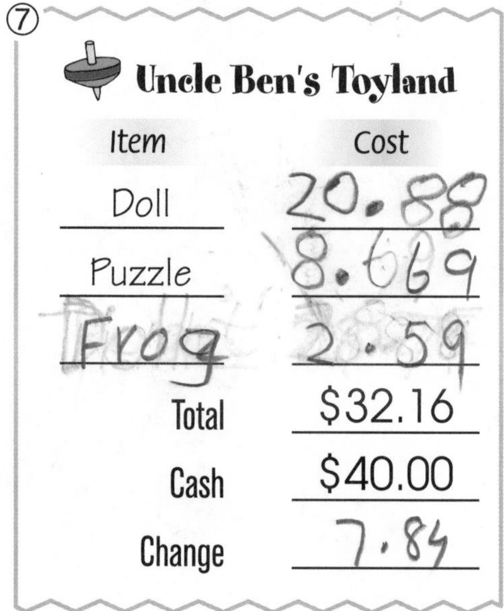

Uncle Ben's Toyland
Item
Cost
Doll
Puzzle
Total
$32.16
Cash
$40.00
Change

⑧
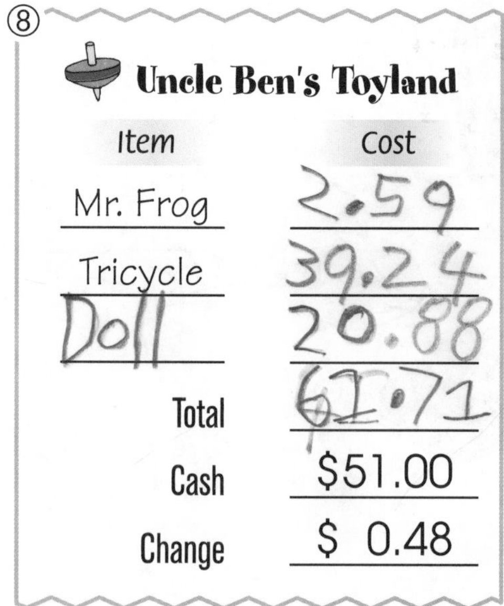

Uncle Ben's Toyland
Item
Cost
Mr. Frog
Tricycle
Total
Cash
$51.00
Change
$ 0.48

⑨ Jimmy buys a robot and a toy car for $45.64. How much is the toy car?

______ = ______

⑩ If the sale price of the tricycle is $28.66, how much is saved?

______ = ______

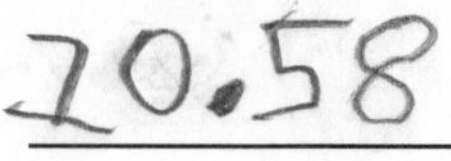

Solve the problems.

⑪ a. How much do two cakes cost?

b. If Mrs. Smith pays $40 for a cake, what is her change?

$32.65

⑫ a. Jack has $28. If he wants to buy a calculator, how much more does he need?

b. If a storybook costs $7.65 more than a calculator, how much does the storybook cost?

$40.89

⑬ a. *I've bargained with the salesman for a better price. If I pay only $42.98 now, how much do I save?*

b. *If I want to buy two bags at this bargain price, how much do I need to pay?*

19

2-D Shapes (1)

- Draw the lines of symmetry of 2-D shapes.
- Identify and compare different types of quadrilaterals.

Sam, don't you know that they are all quadrilaterals?

Trace the dotted lines to show the lines of symmetry of each shape. Then write the numbers.

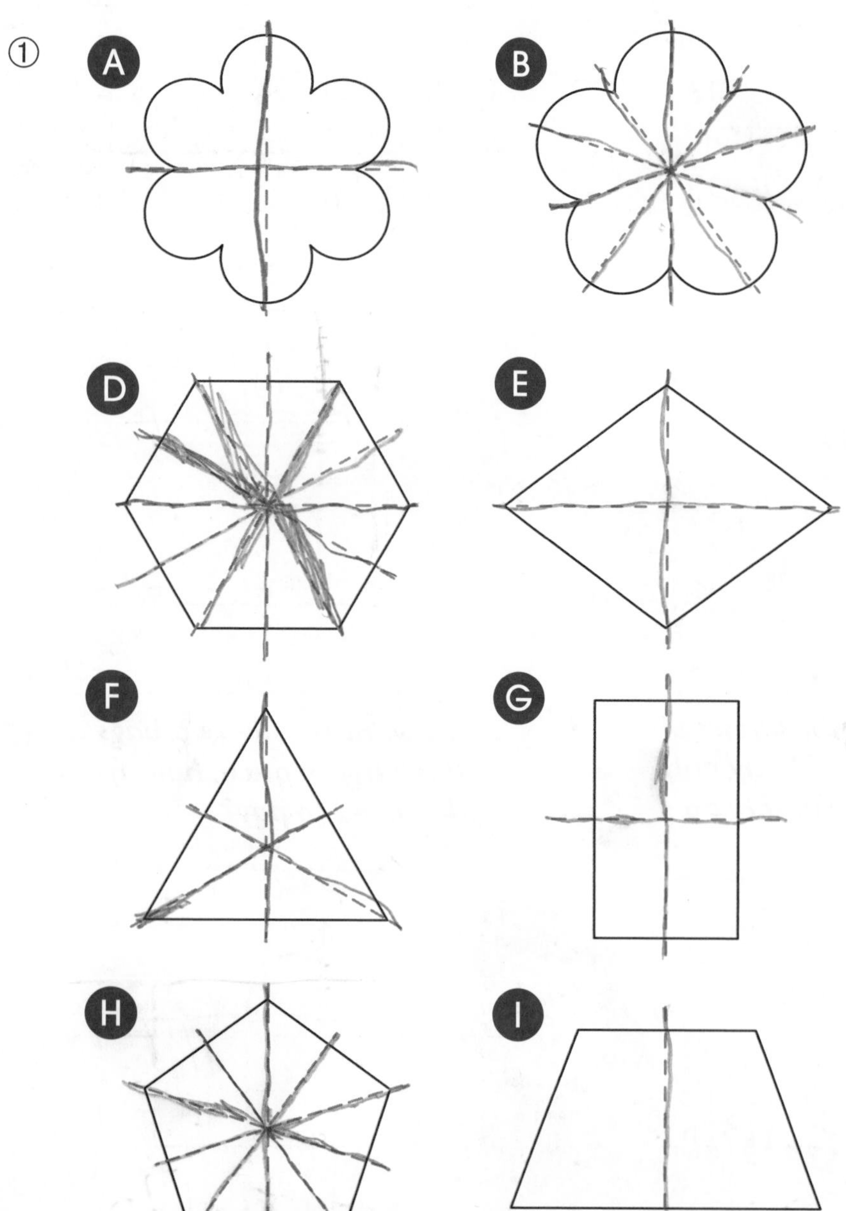

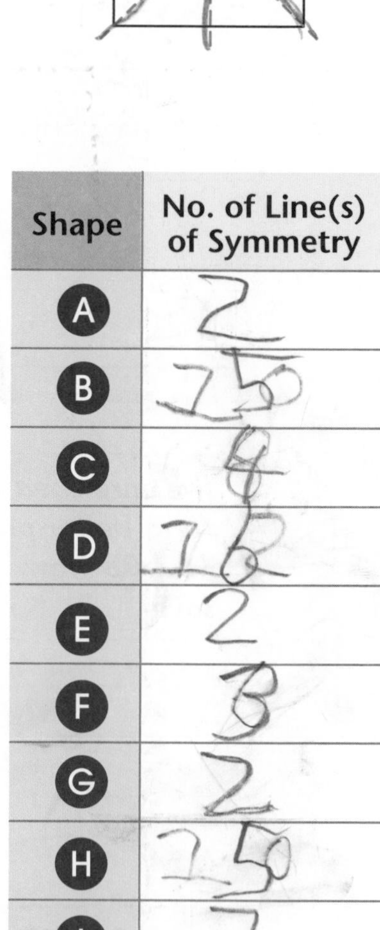

Shape	No. of Line(s) of Symmetry
A	2
B	15
C	4
D	16
E	2
F	3
G	2
H	15
I	1

Put a check mark in the circle if the sentence is correct; otherwise, put a cross.

② 
A rectangle has 2 lines of symmetry. 

③ A regular pentagon has 5 lines of symmetry. 

④ A parallelogram has 1 line of symmetry. 

⑤ *The bigger a square is, the more lines of symmetry it has.* 

The dotted line is the line of symmetry of each shape. Draw the missing side to complete the shape. Then name the two small shapes that you can see in the big shape.

⑥ 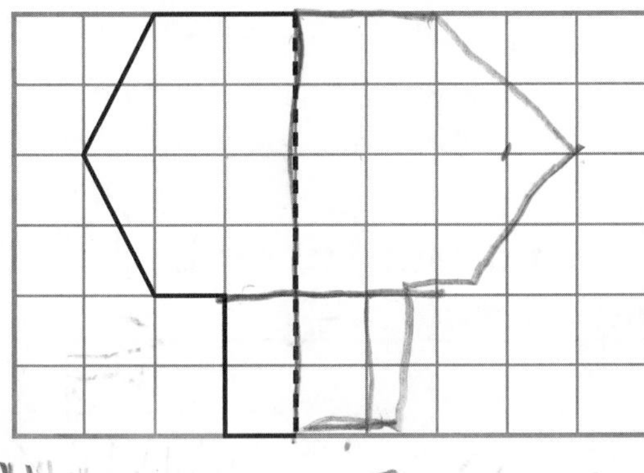

____ ; 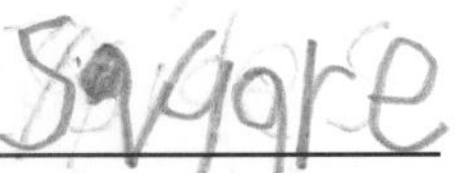

⑦ 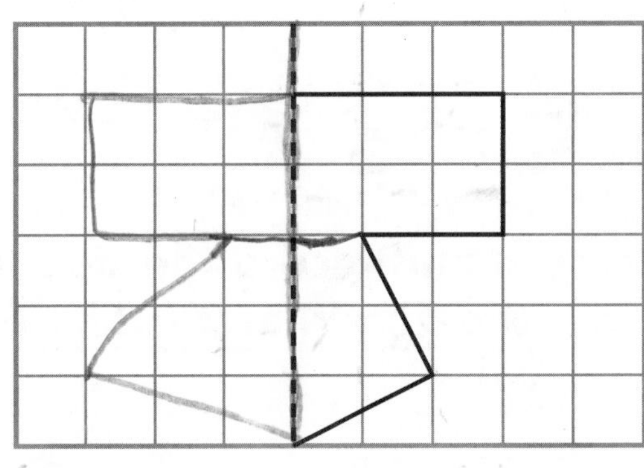

____ ; 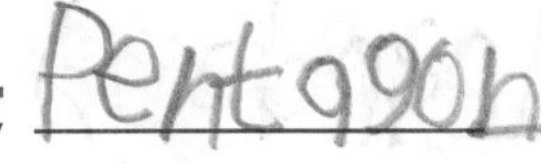

⑧ 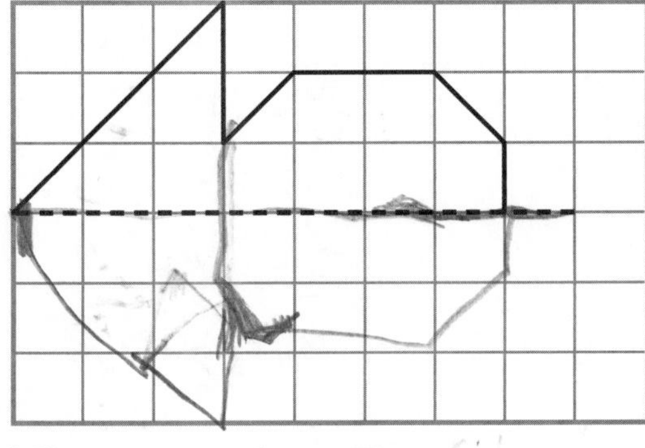

____ ; ____

⑨ 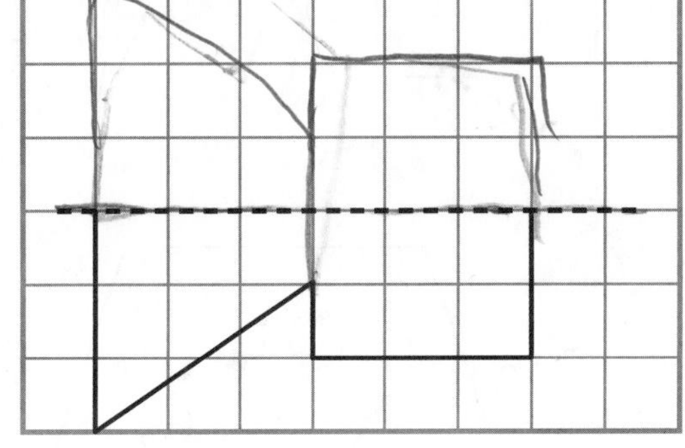

____ ; ____

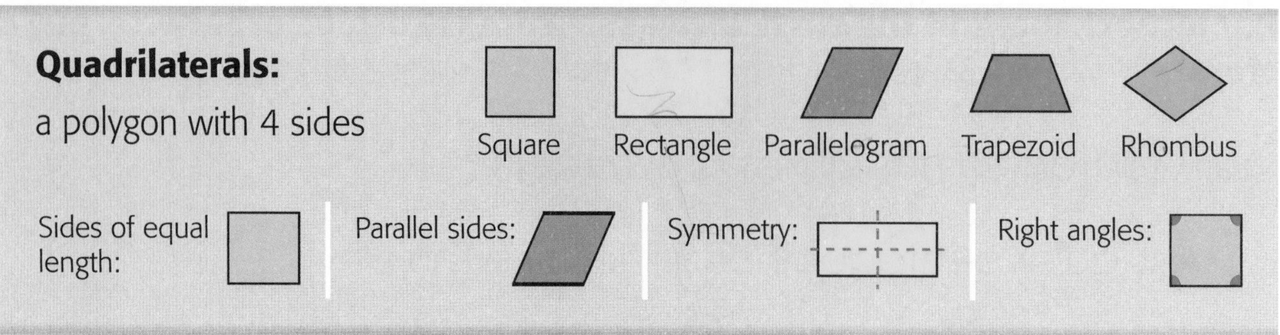

Quadrilaterals:

a polygon with 4 sides

Square Rectangle Parallelogram Trapezoid Rhombus

Sides of equal length: Parallel sides: Symmetry: Right angles:

Draw the missing side of each quadrilateral. Then name it.

⑩

Name

A ___square___

B ___Trapezoid___

C ___Parallelogram___

D ___Rectangle___

E ___Rhombus___

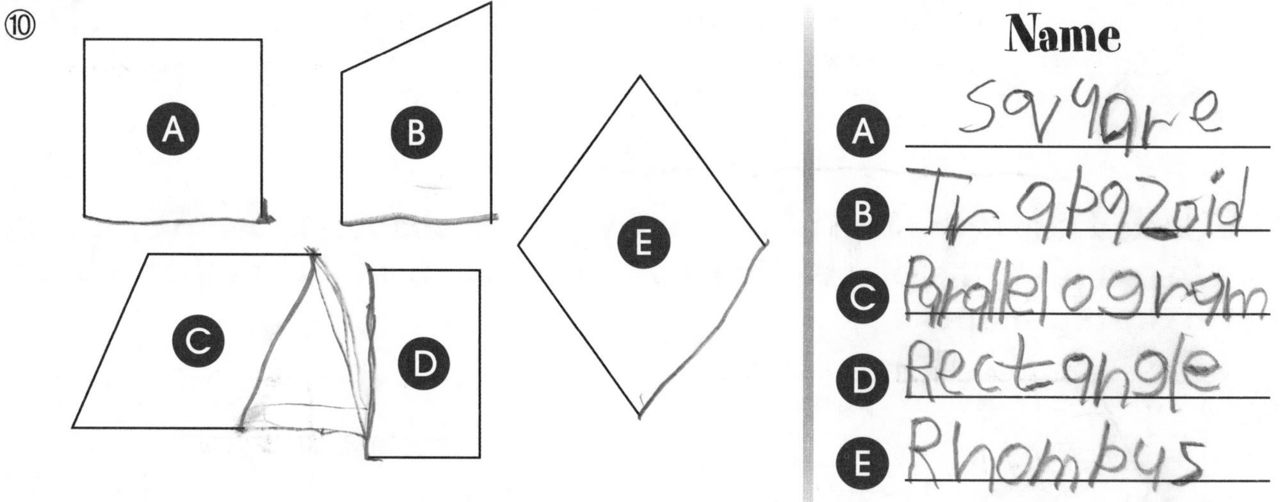

Measure and record the side lengths of each quadrilateral in cm. Then colour the quadrilateral if its sides have equal length.

⑪

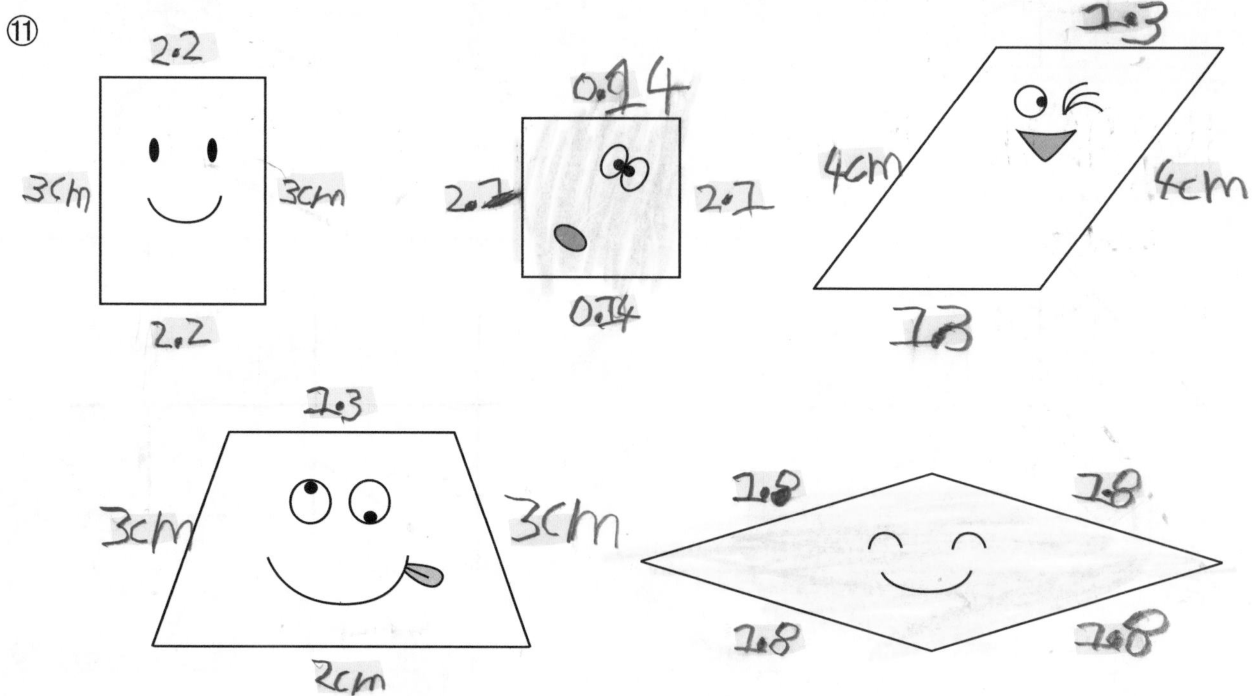

Colour each pair of parallel sides of each quadrilateral in different colours. Then answer the questions.

⑫

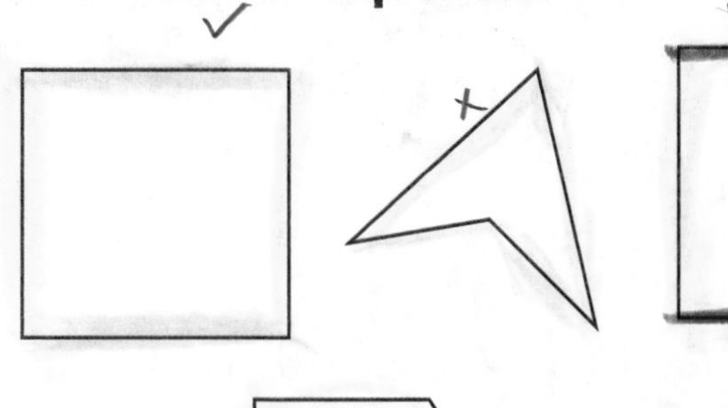

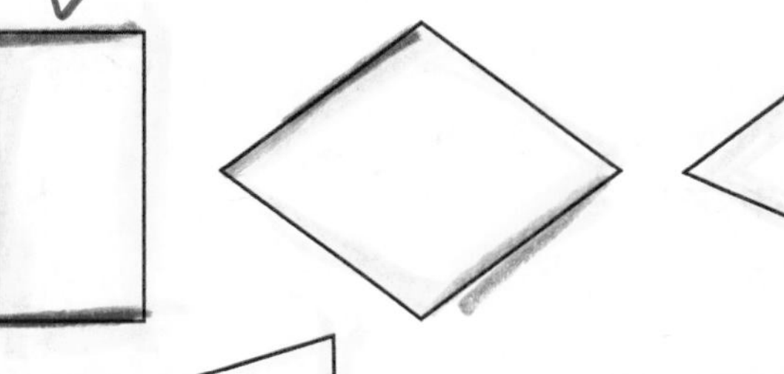

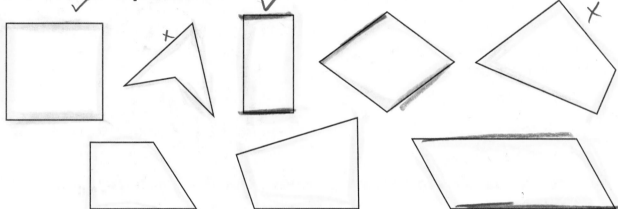

⑬ *Which quadrilateral has only 1 pair of parallel sides?*

Trapezoid

⑭ *Name two quadrilaterals that have 2 pairs of parallel sides.*

rectangle, rhombus, square Parallelogram

Draw a quadrilateral to match the descriptions.

⑮
- 2 lines of symmetry
- 4 right angles

⑯
- 4 sides with the same length
- no right angle

⑰
- 1 pair of parallel sides
- 2 right angles

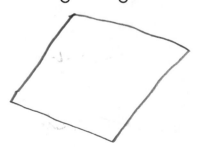

⑱

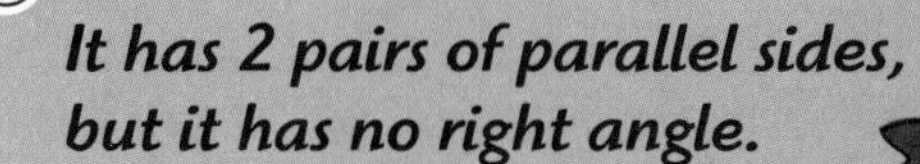
It has 2 pairs of parallel sides, but it has no right angle.

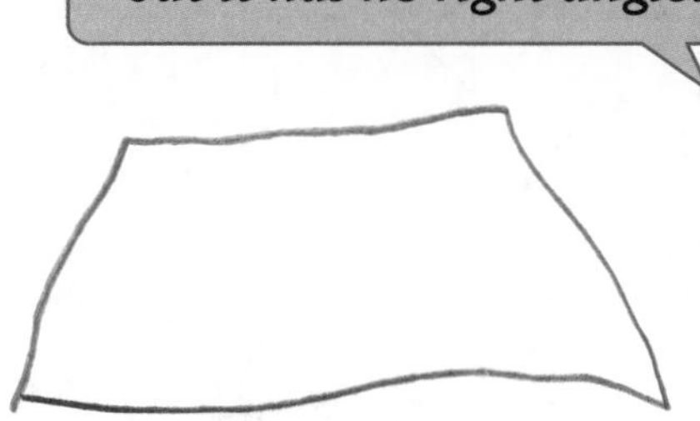

20

2-D Shapes (2)

- Identify and describe angles.
- Relate the names of the angles to their measures in degrees.
- Draw symmetrical designs.

I've chewed off a piece with a right angle.

See how the paper is folded and opened. Use the given words to describe the angles that are formed.

straight angle right angle half of a right angle

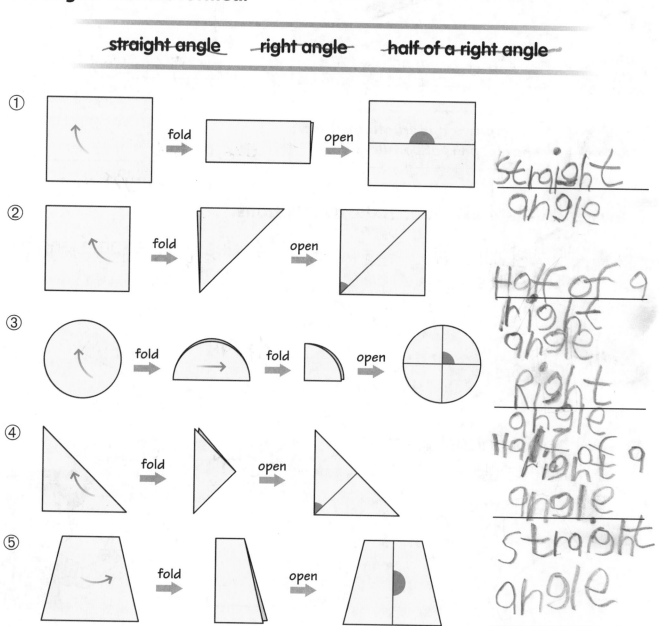

① fold → open → straight angle

② fold → open → Half of a right angle

③ fold → fold → open → Right angle

④ fold → open → Half of a right angle

⑤ fold → open → straight angle

Degree (°): a unit for measuring angles

A right angle is 90°.

= 90°

Two right angles make a straight angle.

+ = (180°)

Half of a right angle = 45°

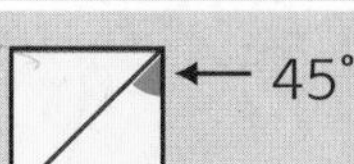

Find the measure in degrees for each marked angle.

⑥

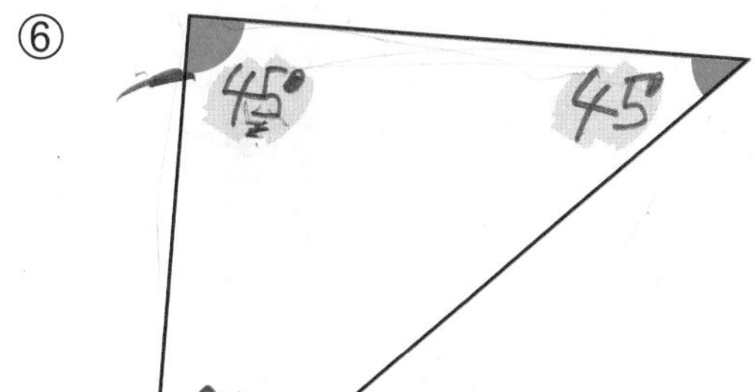

⑦

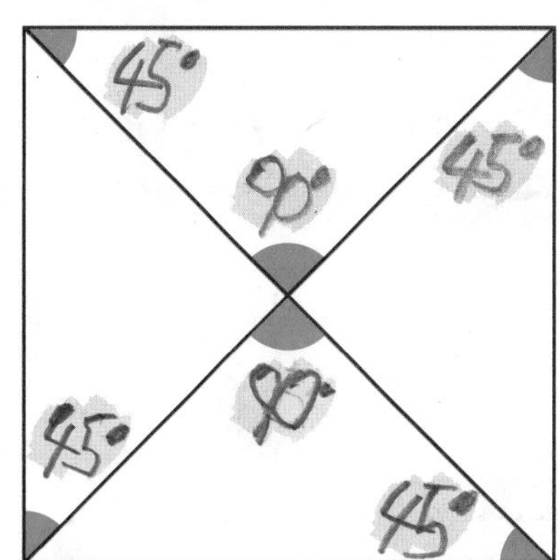

See how the paper is cut. Find the measure in degrees for each angle formed by the cut vertices.

⑧

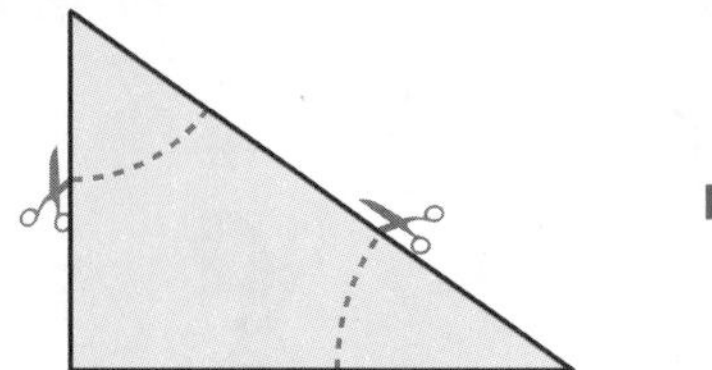

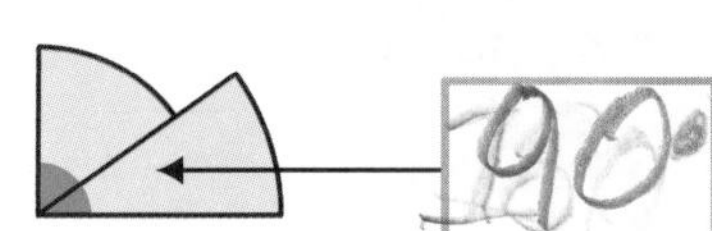

⑨

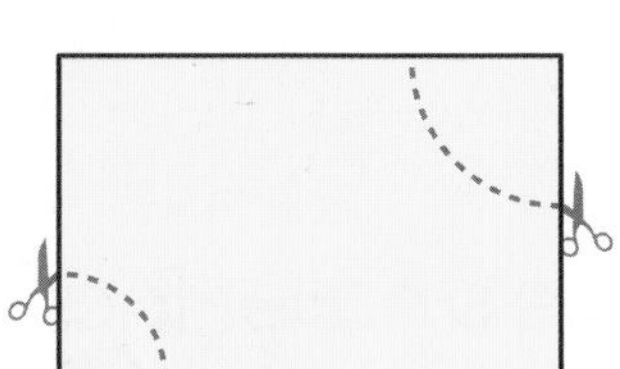

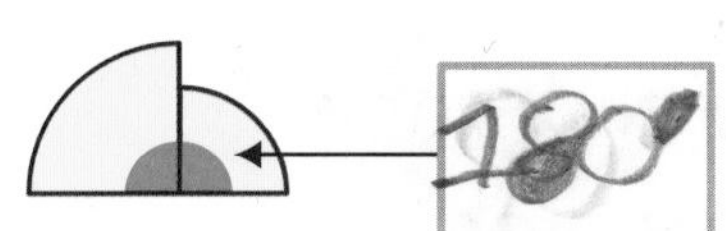

⑩

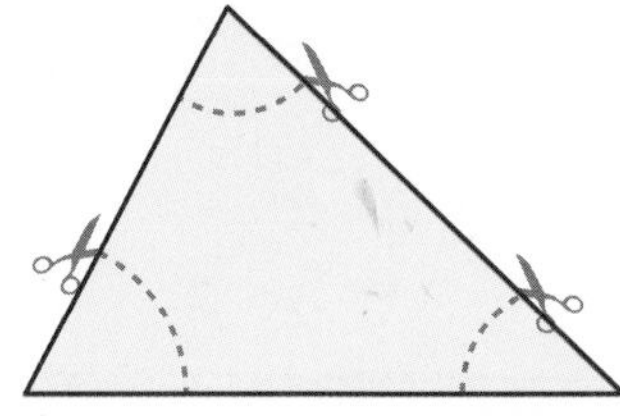

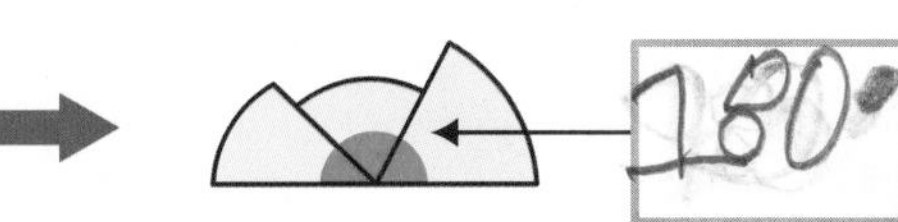

Check the correct pictures to match what the children are describing.

⑪

The angle the door makes with the wall is smaller than a right angle but greater than half of a right angle.

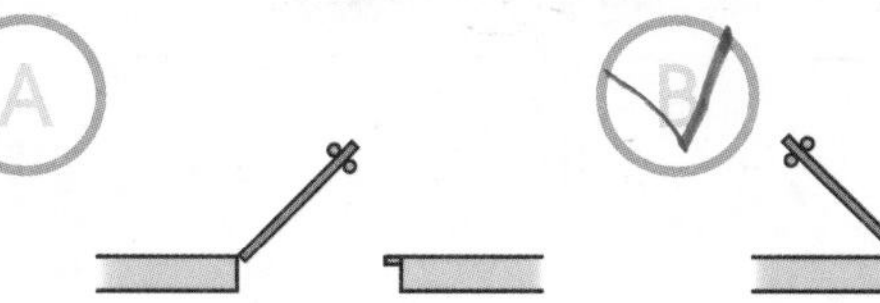

A B C

⑫

The angle that I can make with my legs is smaller than a straight angle but greater than a right angle.

A B C

⑬

I can make an angle of 180° with my pencils.

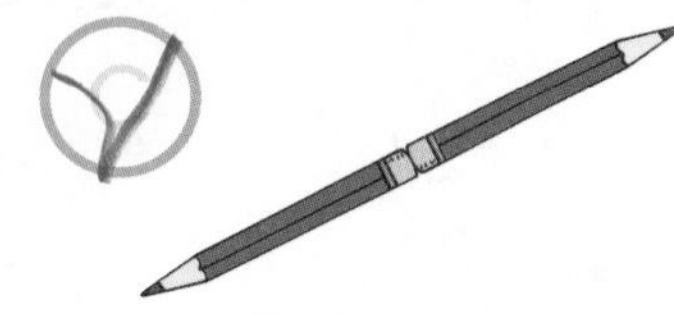

A B C

⑭

I can make an angle that is smaller than 180° but greater than 90° with my scissors.

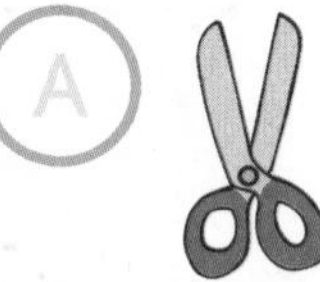

A B C

Draw a line to construct each angle.

⑮ an angle that is greater than 90° but smaller than 180°

⑯ an angle smaller than 90° but greater than 45°

180°

Describe the angles formed by the clock hands.

⑰ It Shows The Time
It Is 4:00

⑱ It Shows The Time
It Is 4:35

Draw the missing parts of each symmetrical picture.

⑲

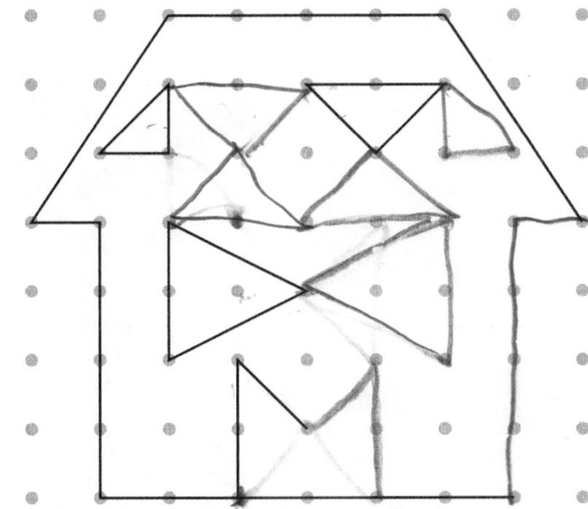

⑳

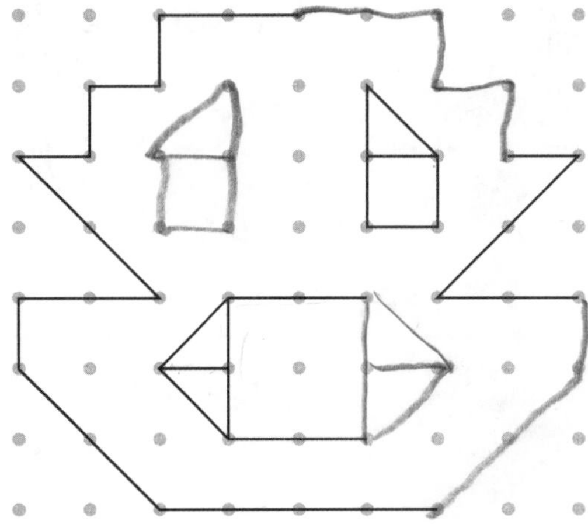

㉑

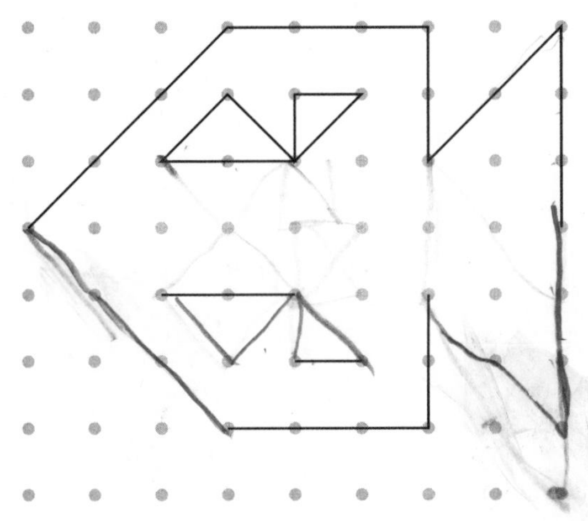

㉒

3-D Figures (1)

- Identify and describe different prisms and pyramids.
- Construct and sketch the skeletons of 3-D figures.

Name each 3-D figure. Then count and write the number of triangular faces that each figure has.

①

A B C D E F G H

	Name	No. of Triangular Faces
A	Rectangular Prism	0
B	Rectangle base Pyramid	4
C	Hexagonal prism	0
D	Pentagonal base Pyramid	4
E	Triangular Prism	2
F	Triangular base Pyramid	4
G	Pentagonal Prism	0
H	Hexagonal base Pyramid	6

The children are describing their 3-D figures. Fill in the blanks with the correct words or numbers to complete the descriptions.

② *It is a* squyare base pyramid. *It has* 4 *triangular face(s) and* 1 *rectangular face(s). It has* 5 *vertices and* 8 *edges.*

③ *It is a* rectangular prism. *It has* 0 *faces,* 6 *vertices, and* 8 *edges. All the faces are in the shape of a* polygon.

See how the children above described their 3-D figures again. Use the same way to describe these 3-D figures.

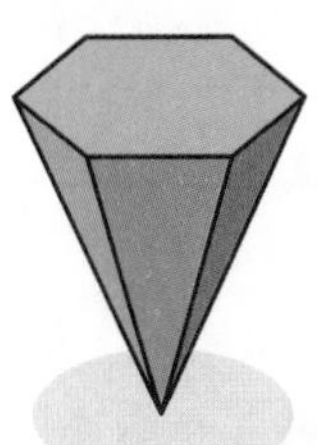

It is a hexagonal base pyramid. It has 6 triangular faces) and It has 8 vertices and 12 edges.

⑤

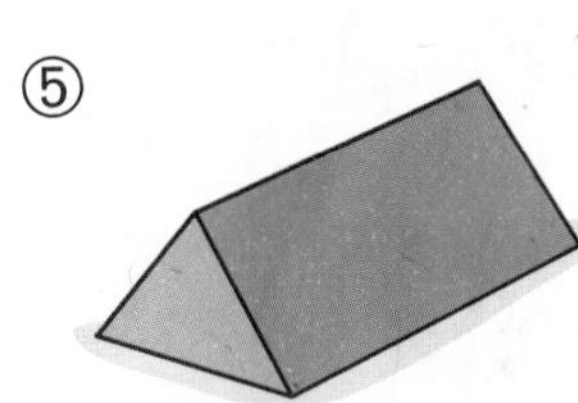

It is a triangular prism. It has 5 faces, and It has 6 vertices and 9 edge.

⑥

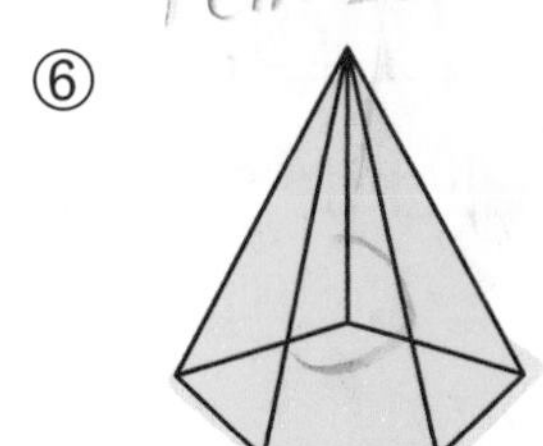

Pentagonal base 1

It is a pentagonal base pyramid. It has 5 faces and It has 6 vertices and 10 edge.

Draw the missing edges to complete the skeleton of each 3-D figure. Then name the figure and fill in the blanks.

⑦ **A**

Name: Rectangular base pyramid

Things needed to build it:

- 8 sticks
- 5 marshmallows

B

Name: Hexagonal prism

Things needed to build it:

- 18 sticks
- 12 marshmallows

C

Name: Triangular prism

Things needed to build it:

- 9 sticks
- 6 marshmallows

D

Name: Pentagonal base pyramid

Things needed to build it:

- 10 sticks
- 6 marshmallows

E

Name: Rectangular prism

Things needed to build it:

- 12 sticks
- 8 marshmallows

Complete the tables. Then answer the questions.

⑧ **Prisms**

	No. of Vertices	No. of Edges	No. of Faces
Triangular prism	6	9	5
Rectangular prism	8	12	6
Pentagonal prism	10	15	7
Hexagonal prism	12	18	8

⑨ **Pyramids**

	No. of Vertices	No. of Edges	No. of Faces
Triangular pyramid	4	6	4
Rectangular pyramid	5	8	5
Pentagonal pyramid	6	10	6
Hexagonal pyramid	7	12	7

⑩ *I built a 3-D figure that has 6 vertices. What figure did I build?*

Triangular Prism And Pentagonal Base Pyramid

⑪ *I built a 3-D figure that has 12 edges. What figure did I build?*

Rectangular Prism And Hexagonal Base Pyramid

⑫ *I used 12 sticks with the same length to build a 3-D figure. What figure did I build?*

Rectangular Prism And Hexagonal Base Pyramid

3-D Figures (2)

- Identify nets of prisms and pyramids.
- Draw and describe nets of rectangular and triangular prisms.
- Construct 3-D figures using only congruent shapes.

Check the correct net for each 3-D figure.

① Rectangular pyramid

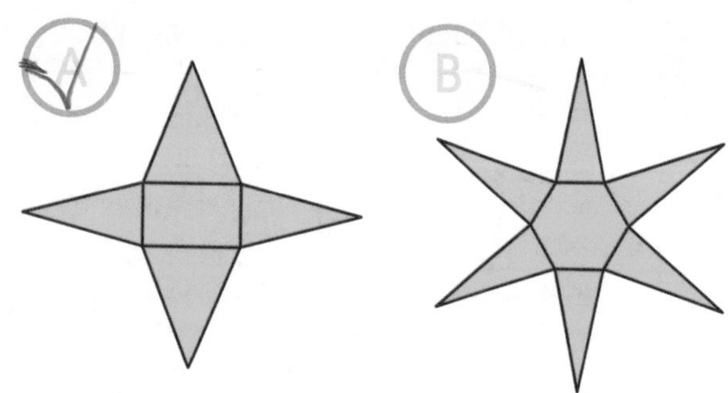

② Hexagonal prism

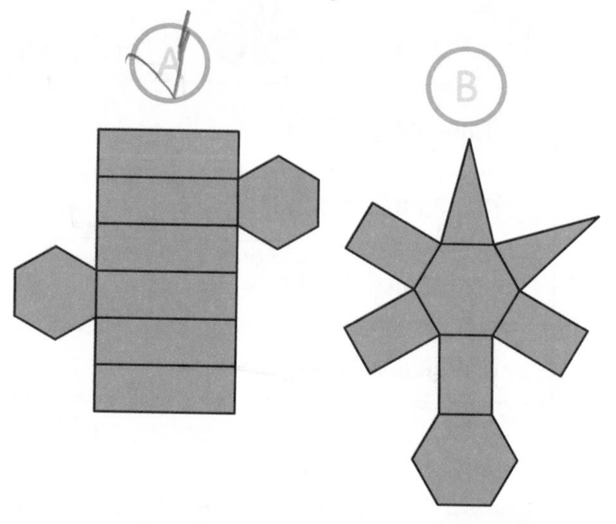

③ Triangular prism

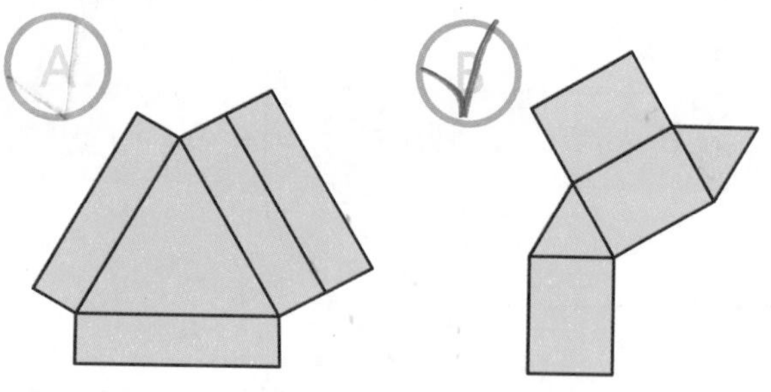

④ Pentagonal pyramid

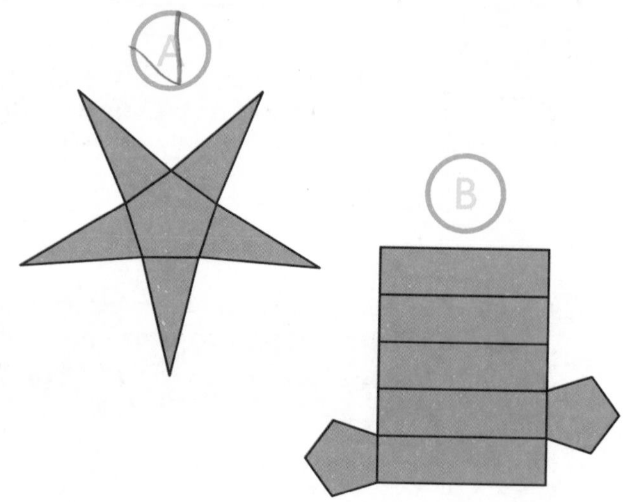

⑤ Cube

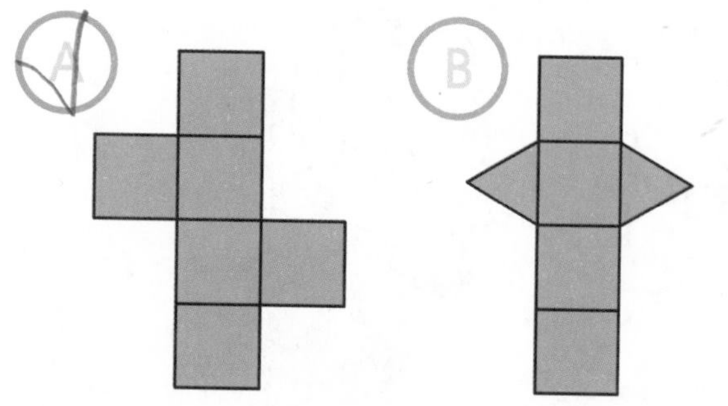

Draw the missing parts of each net.

⑥

⑦

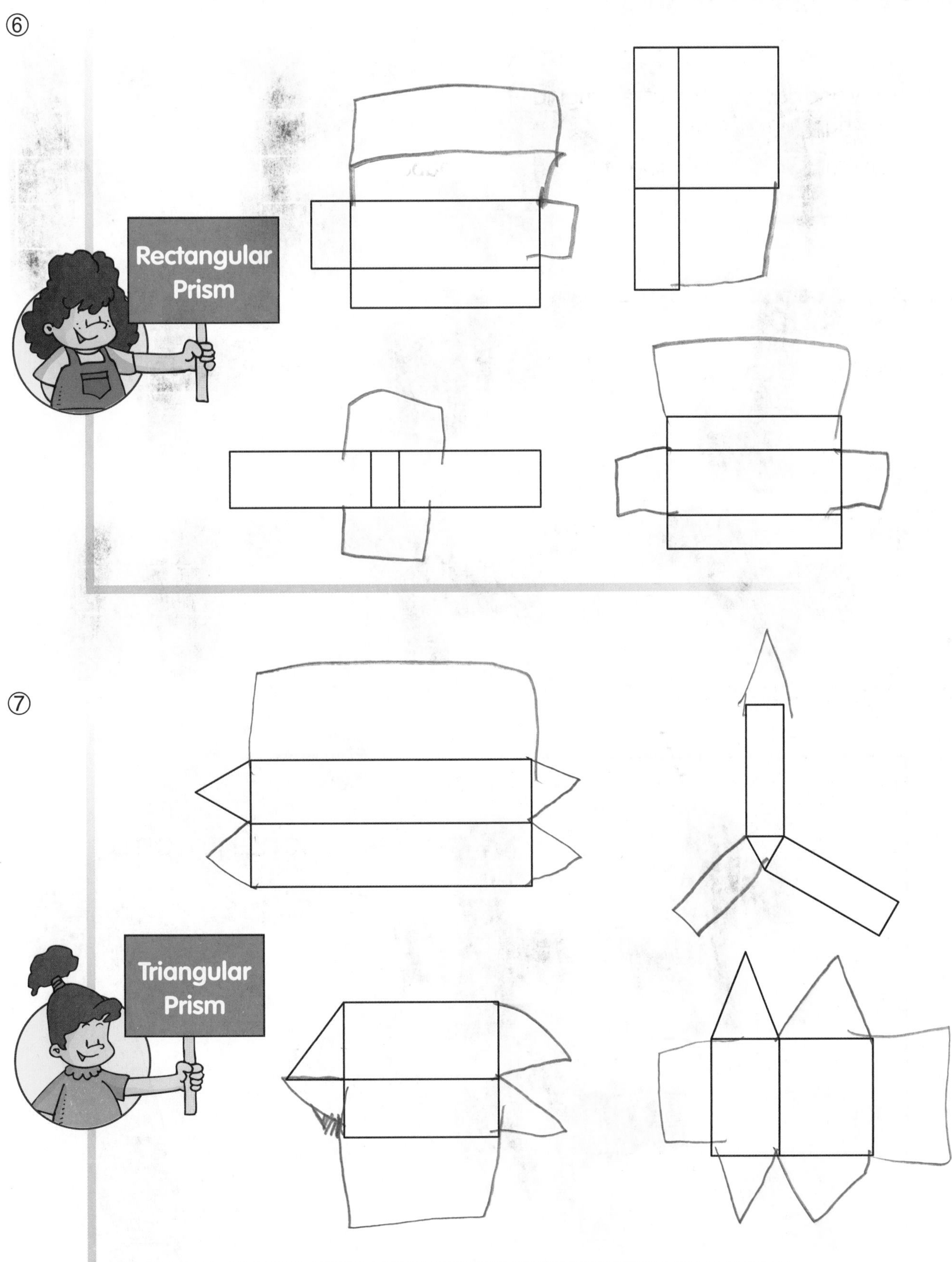

Colour the nets that can form cubes. Then draw 3 more nets that are different from the coloured ones.

⑧

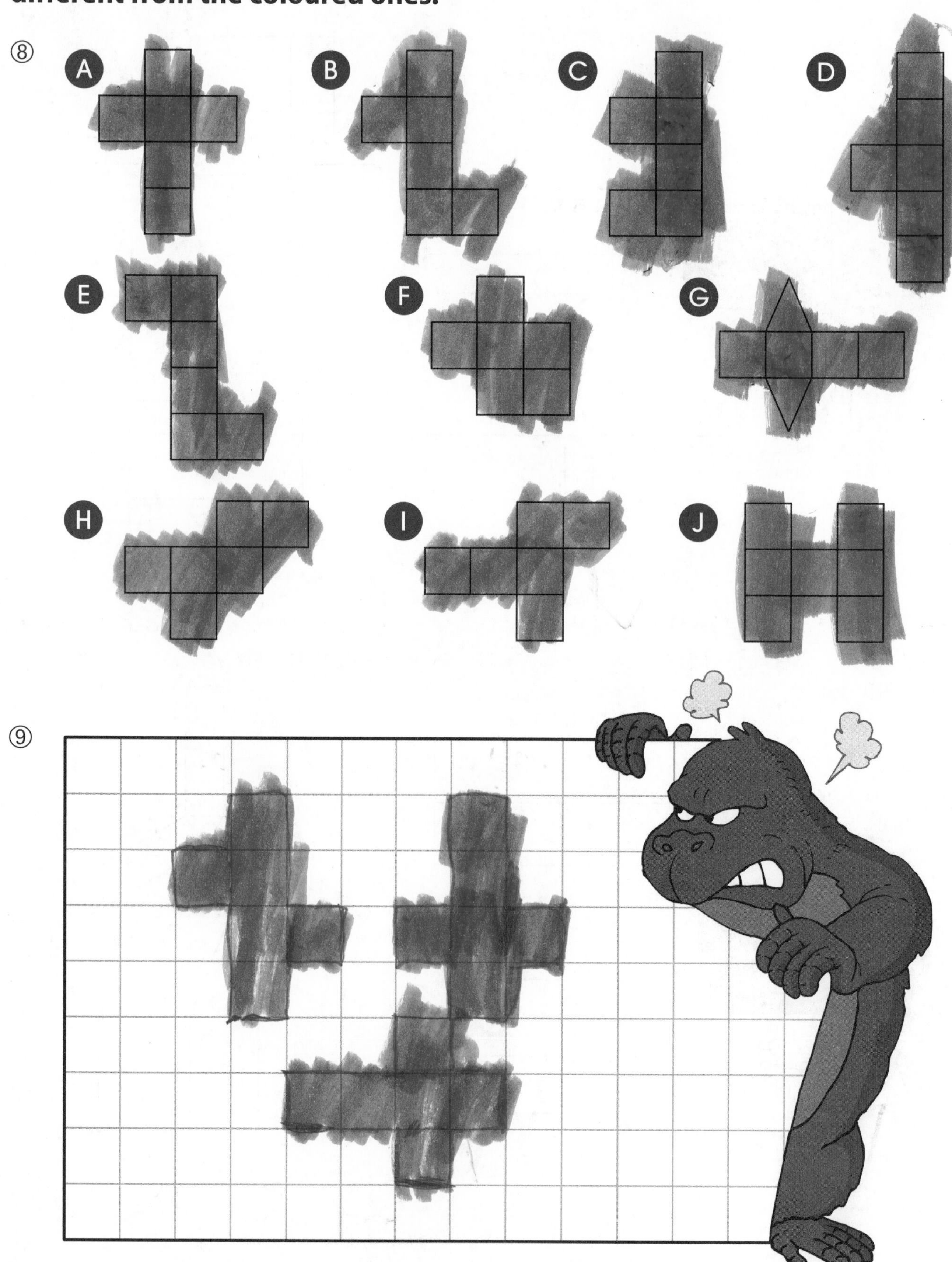

⑨

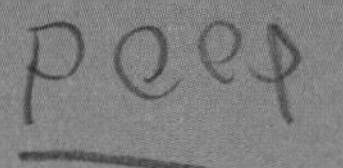

Tetrahedron:

a 3-D figure with 4 faces; each face is an equilateral triangle

Do you like my tetrahedron?

Check the net that can form a tetrahedron.

⑩ A

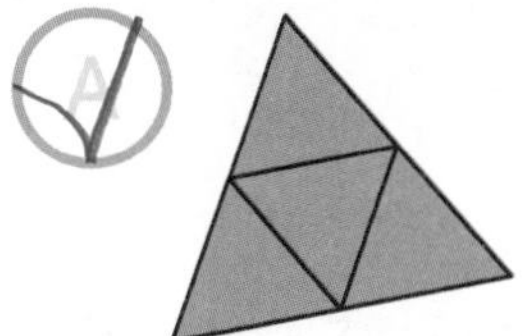

B

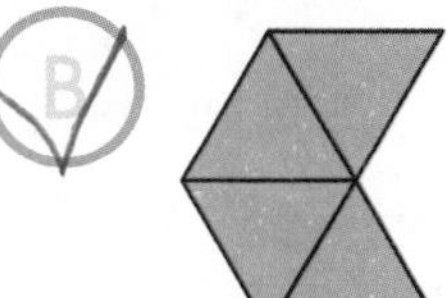

C

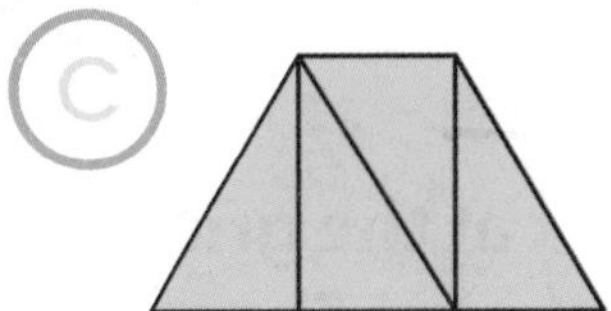

D

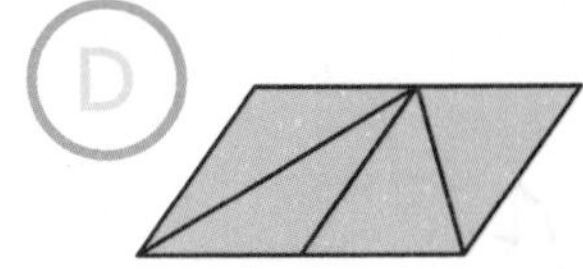

E

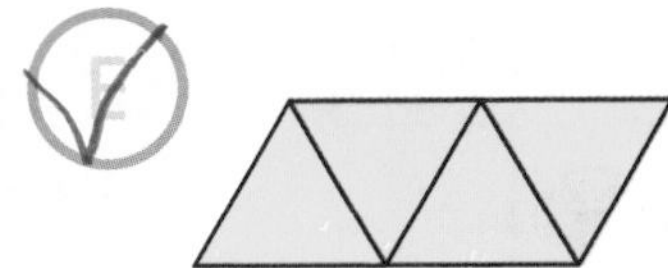

F

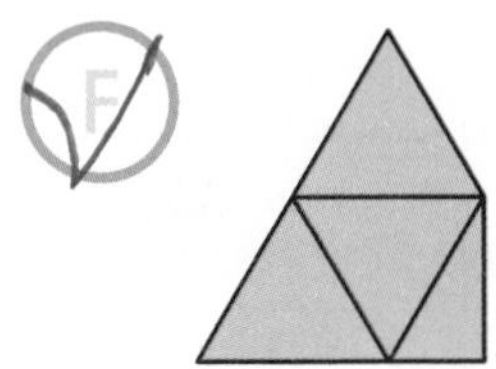

Trace the triangle in the circle with tracing paper. Then cut it out and use it to draw the missing face(s) of each net for a tetrahedron.

⑪

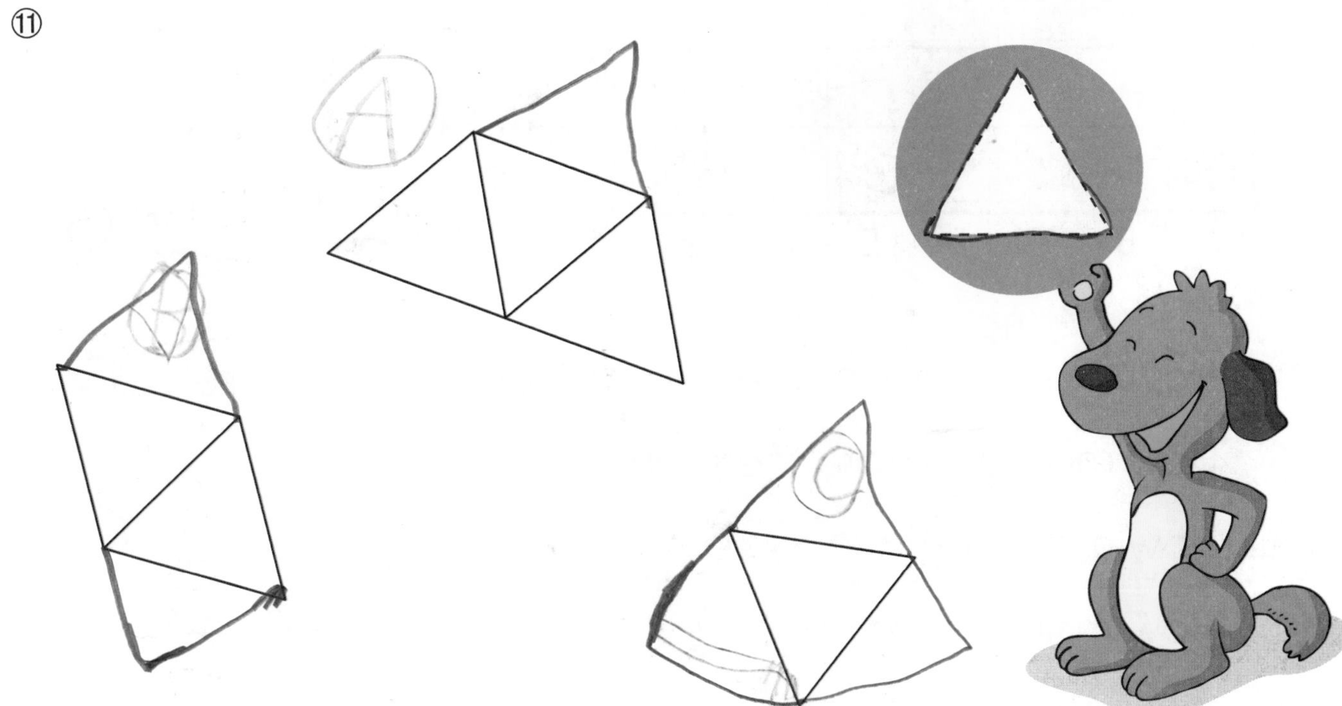

Grids

- Identify and describe the location of an object using a grid system.
- Describe movement from one location to another.

We have to go 2 squares up and 3 squares left to get to our new home.

Look at the grid. Write the locations of the toys. Then answer the questions.

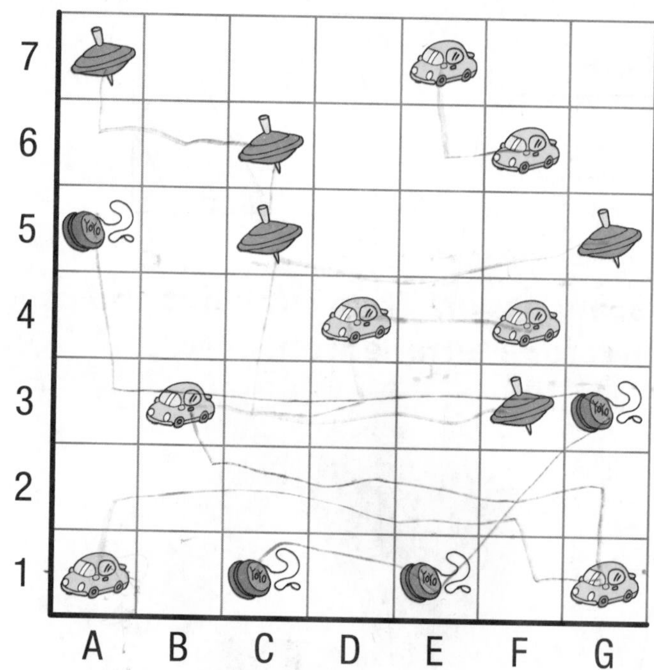

① Locations of the Toys

Car

Top

Yo-yo

② How many columns are there on the grid? ________

③ How many rows are there on the grid? ________

④ How many toys are there in column F? ________

⑤ How many toys are there in row 4? ________

⑥ Which row has the most toys? ________

Look at the grid. Answer the questions.

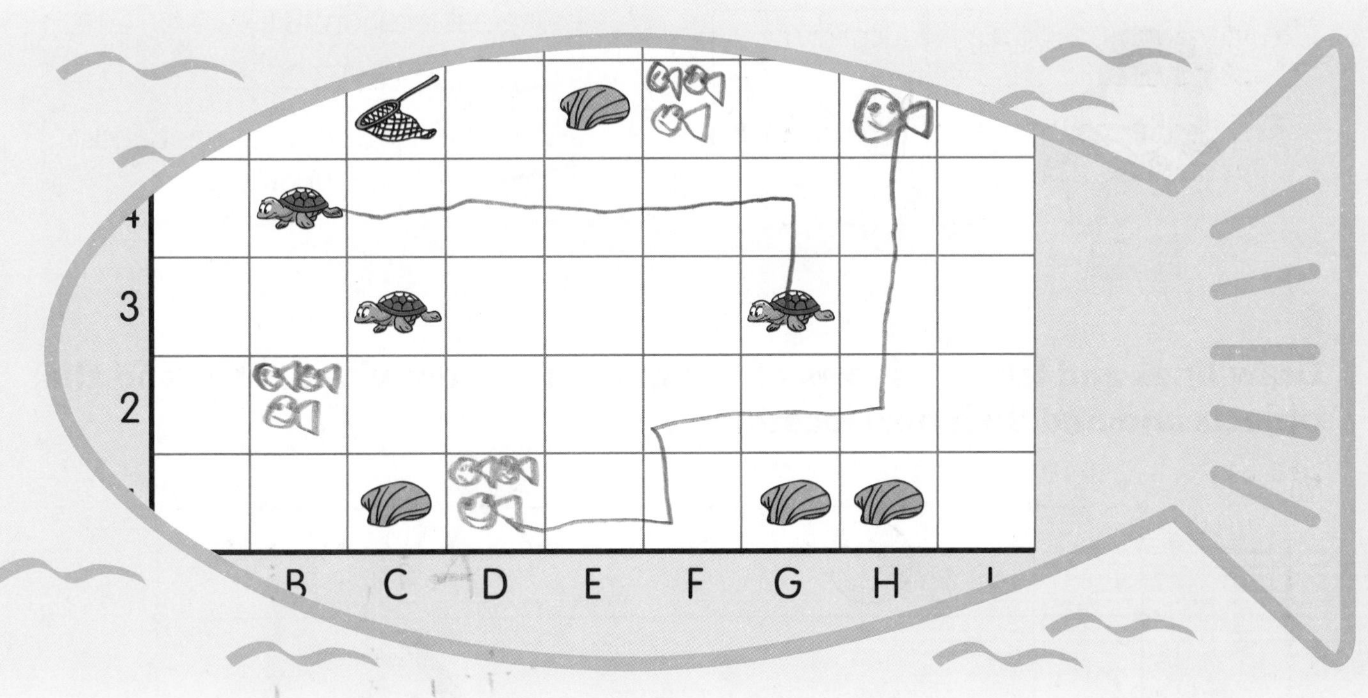

⑦ a. Locations of the shells: C1, E5, G1, H1.

b. Locations of the turtles: B4, C3, G3.

⑧ Draw 1 big fish at H5 and 3 small fish at B2, D1, and F5.

⑨ If the shell at E5 sinks to the bottom, what is its new location? Describe the path that it takes.

The New Location is a net in C5.

⑩ If the big fish wants to eat the closest small fish, which one should it eat? Describe the path that it takes.

He will eat small fish in D1.
3 squares down. 2 squares left. 1 square down. 2 squares left.

⑪ The turtle at G3 wants to find its friend at B4. What is the shortest path that it should take?

It could take 1 square up and 5 squares left.

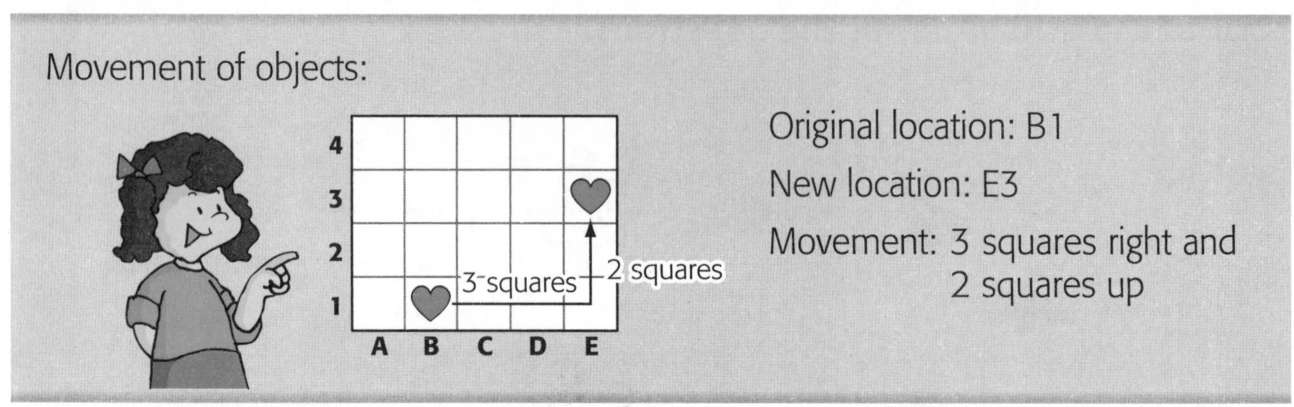

Movement of objects:

Original location: B1

New location: E3

Movement: 3 squares right and 2 squares up

Draw lines and label the axes of the grid. Then draw the paths and the objects and find their new locations.

⑫

⑬ 

Move the pencil 2 squares left and 3 squares down. What is its new location?

______

⑭ 

Move the cat 6 squares right and 3 squares up. What is its new location?

______

⑮

Move the happy face 3 squares right, 2 squares down, and then 4 squares left. What is its new location?

Complete the grid. Then draw the pictures and answer the questions.

⑯ B4 | E1 | F3 E3 | D5 | D2 D3 C2 C3

Adventure Land

2							Tim
1							
		B			E		G

⑰ What is the location of Tim?

⑱ What is the location of the monster?

⑲ How many squares are covered by the swamp?

⑳ How many squares are covered by the poisonous thorn?

㉑ *What is the safest way Tim should take to get to the monster?*

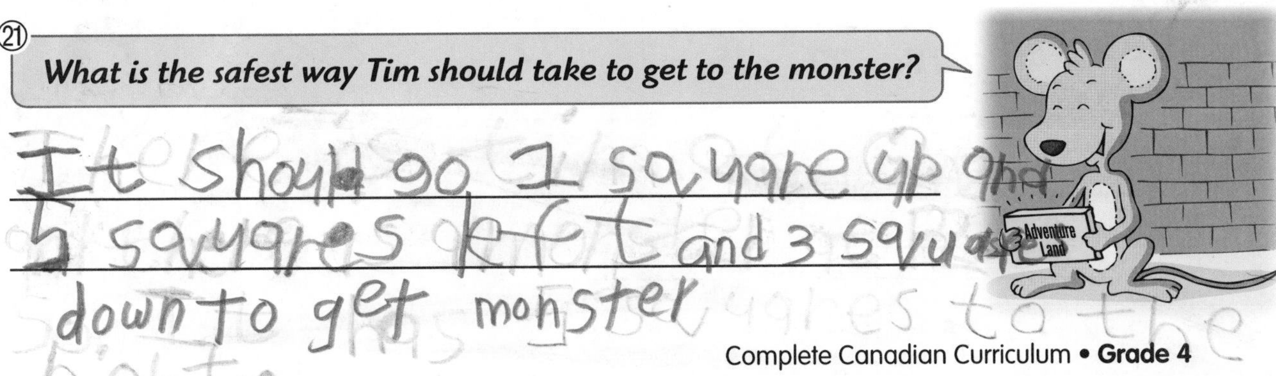

Patterning (1)

- Extend, describe, and create repeating, growing, or shrinking number patterns.
- Connect each term in a pattern with its term number.
- Create a number pattern involving addition, subtraction, or multiplication.

One, two, four, eight, growing.
Nine, seven, five, three, shrinking.
One, two, one, two, repeating.
I love number patterning.

Describe each number pattern with the given words. Then write the next two numbers.

growing   repeating   shrinking

① **5 6 8 9 11 12 14**

It is a growing pattern. The next two numbers are 15 and 17.

② **90 80 70 60 50 40**

It is a shrinking pattern. The next two numbers are 30 and 20.

③ **5 11 11 5 11 11 5 11**

It is a repeating pattern. The next two numbers are 11 and 5.

④ **81 80 78 77 75 74 72**

It is a growing *pattern. The next two numbers are* 71 *and* 69.

Follow each pattern rule to create a number pattern. Then describe the pattern.

⑤ *I start at 5. I add 1, and then add 3, and then 1, and then 3, and so on to create this number pattern.*

5 ___ ___ ___ ___ ___ a ______ pattern

⑥ Start at 10. Multiply each number by 2 to get the next number.

___ ___ ___ ___ ___ ___ a ______ pattern

⑦ Start at 95. Subtract 1, and then subtract 2, and then 1, and then 2, and so on.

___ ___ ___ ___ ___ ___ a ______ pattern

⑧ 

I start at 45. I subtract 3, and then add 1, and then subtract 3, and then add 1, and so on to create this number pattern.

___ ___ ___ ___ ___ ___ a ______ pattern

Find out the pattern rule for each number pattern. Circle the correct answer.

⑨ 8 16 15 30 29 58

- −2 x1
- −1 x2
- x2 −1

⑩ 72 70 67 65 62 60

- −3 −2
- −2 −3
- −2 +3

⑪ 24 26 27 29 30 32

- x1 +2
- +1 +2
- +2 +1

⑫ 2 6 7 21 22 66

- x3 +1
- x1 +3
- +4 +1

We can record the patterns in a table of values that shows the term numbers and the terms.

e.g. 1, 4, 7, 10, ...

Term Number	1	2	3	4
Term	1	4	7	10

The 4th term is **10**.

Record each number sequence in a table of values. Then fill in the blanks.

⑬ 9, 13, 17, 21, 25, 29, 33, ...

a.

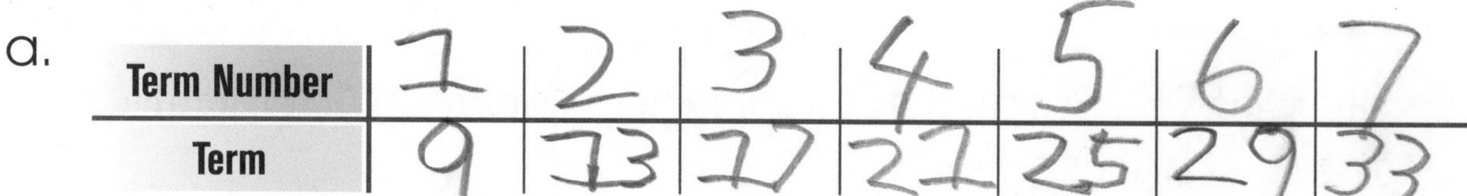

Term Number	1	2	3	4	5	6	7
Term	9	13	17	21	25	29	33

b. The 3rd term is 17 and the 6th term is 29.

⑭ 86, 85, 83, 82, 80, 79, 77, ...

a.

Term Number	1	2	3	4	5	6	7
Term	86	85	83	82	80	79	77

b. The 2nd term is 85 and the 5th term is 80.

⑮ 7, 14, 13, 26, 25, ...

a.

Term Number	Term
1	7
2	14
3	13
4	26
5	25

b. *The 7th term is* 49.

⑯ 8, 12, 10, 14, 12, ...

a.

Term Number	Term
1	8
2	12
3	10
4	14
5	12

b. *The 8th term is* 18.

Follow each pattern rule to write the first 6 terms of a number sequence.

⑰ Start at 2 and multiply each term by 3 to get the next term.

2, 5, 8, 11, 14, 17.

⑱ Start at 10 and add 2 to each term to get the next term.

10, 12, 14, 16, 18, 20.

Use a table to show the first week's savings of each girl. Then answer the questions.

⑲ **Ann**

She saves 20¢ on the first day. Then each day after that she saves 4¢ more than the day before.

Term Number	Term
1	4
2	8
3	12
4	16
5	20
6	24

⑳ **Sue**

She saves 48¢ on the first day. Then each day after that she saves 3¢ less than the day before.

Term Number	Term
1	3
2	6
3	9
4	12
5	15
6	18

㉑ *On which day do the girls save the same amount? How much does each save?*

Term number. 15.

25

Patterning (2)

- Make predictions related to repeating geometric and numeric patterns.
- Extend and create repeating patterns that result from reflections.
- Determine the inverse relationship between multiplication and division and find the missing numbers in equations.

No. of Groups 1 2 3
No. of □ 1 2 3
No. of ● 2 4 6
I know there are 5 squares and 10 circles in 5 groups.

Follow the pattern to draw the next two groups of shapes. Then complete the table and fill in the blanks.

① a.

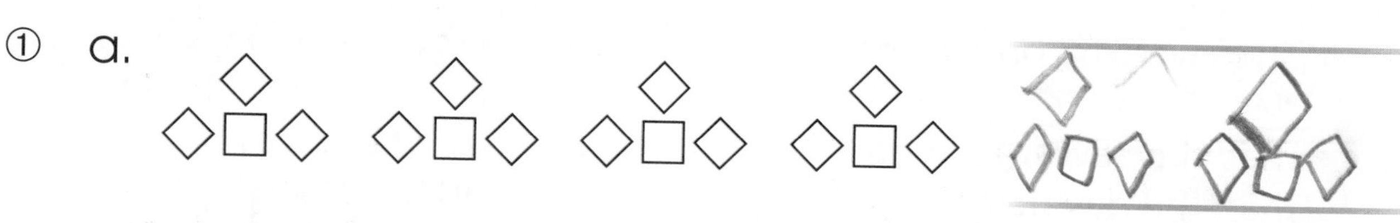

b.

No. of Groups	1	2	3	4	5	6
No. of Squares	2	4	6	8	10	12

c. *There are* 16 *squares in 8 groups.*

② a.

b.

No. of Groups	1	2	3	4	5	6
No. of Rectangles	1	2	3	4	5	6
No. of Parallelograms	2	4	6	8	10	12

c. *There are* 9 *rectangles and* 18 *parallelograms in 9 groups.*

The line in bold is the line of reflection. Complete each reflection image. Then follow the pattern that is created by using the shape itself and its reflection image to fill the spaces.

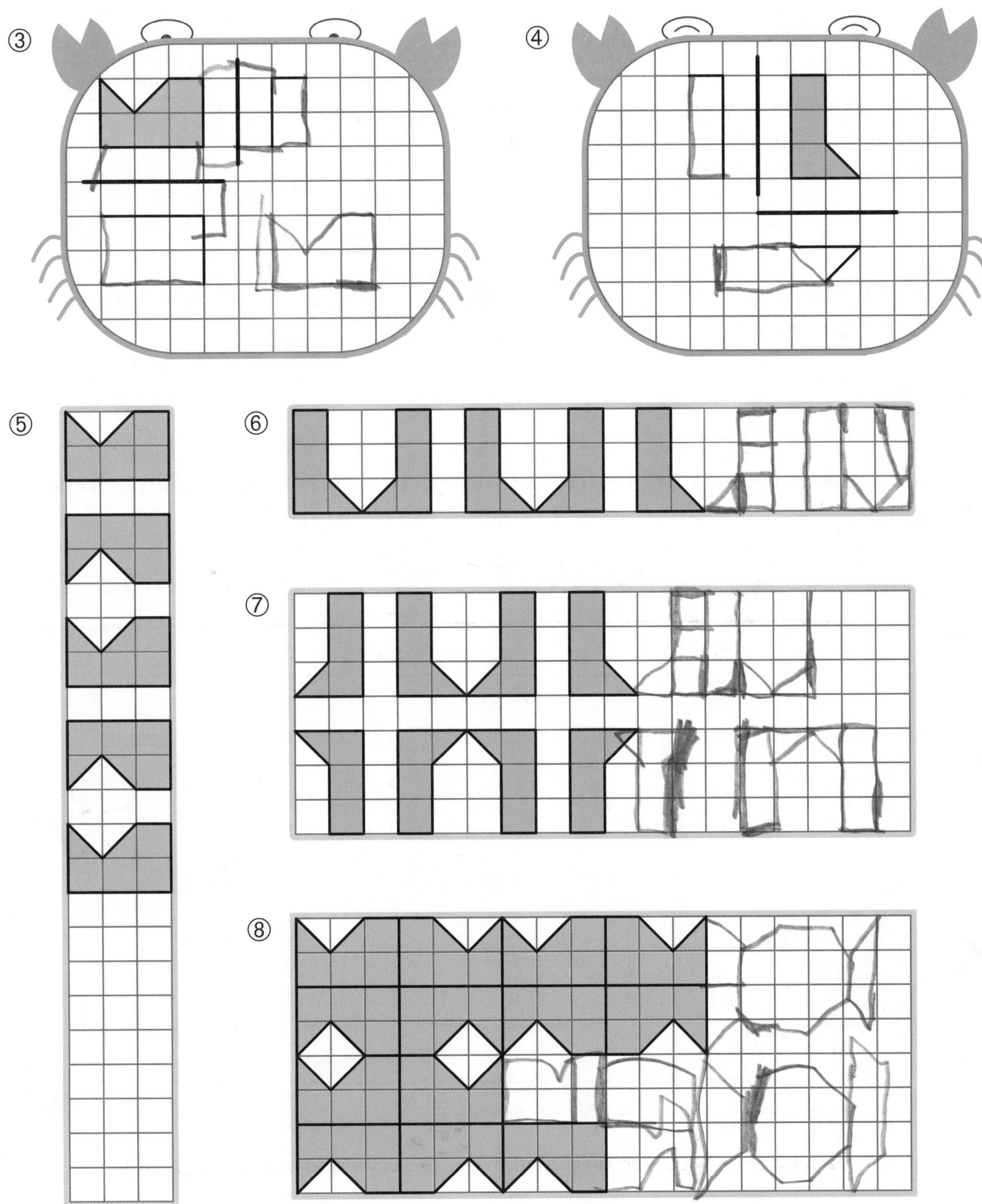

Look at each given number sentence. Find the missing number.

⑨ 4 x 5 = 20
20 ÷ 4 = 5

⑩ 27 ÷ 9 = 3
3 x 9 = 27

⑪ 14 x 2 = 28
28 ÷ 2 = 14

⑫ 64 ÷ 4 = 16
4 x 16 = 64

⑬ 91 ÷ 7 = 13
7 x 13 = 91

⑭ 24 x 3 = 72
72 ÷ 3 = 24

Find the missing number in each equation. Then write a matching division sentence.

⑮ 4 x 6 = 24
24÷6=4

⑯ 9 x 8 = 72
72÷9=8

⑰ 3 x 10 = 30
30÷10=3

⑱ 13 x 5 = 65
65÷13=5

⑲ 15 x 6 = 90
90÷15=6

⑳ 4 x 24 = 96
96÷24=4

㉑ 11 x 9 = 99
99÷11=9

㉒ 25 x 3 = 75
75÷25=3

㉓ 2 x 16 = 32
32÷16=2

Use the "guess-and-test" method to find answers.

e.g. ♥ x 19 = 95

Guess	Test
2	**2** x 19 = 38 (not 95) ✘
3	**3** x 19 = 57 (not 95) ✘
5	**5** x 19 = 95 ✔

Use the "guess-and-test" method to find the missing numbers.

㉔ 18 x ★ = 72

Guess	Test

★ = ____

㉕ ☀ x 17 = 85

Guess	Test

☀ = ____

㉖ 78 ÷ ☽ = 26

Guess	Test

☽ = ____

Find the missing numbers.

㉗ 7 x ____ = 119

㉘ 9 x ____ = 45

㉙ 50 ÷ ____ = 5

㉚ ____ x 12 = 96

㉛ ____ ÷ 7 = 6

㉜ 48 ÷ ____ = 24

㉝ 6 x ____ = 6000

㉞ ____ x 7 = 70

㉟ ____ x 100 = 500

㊱ 1000 x ____ = 4000

Do you remember when a whole number is multiplied by 10, 100, or 1000, you can just add 1 zero, 2 zeros, or 3 zeros to the number to get the answer?

26

Graphs (1)

- Read and describe data presented in stem-and-leaf plots and double bar graphs.
- Understand and identify the median and mode in a set of data.

No. of Hours of Practice Last Month

Stem	Leaves
2	0 0 3 5 9
3	0 1 1
4	(2) 3 4 4
5	1 4 7 7 7

17 children were surveyed.

The median number of hours of practice is 42 hours.

Look at the stem-and-leaf plot. Answer the questions.

Number of Bounces in One Minute

Stem	Leaves
2	0 1 1 3 4 8 9
3	1 1 2 2 2 3 3 3 3
4	0 0 1 6
5	4 5 5

① *How many children were surveyed in all?* 23

② What is the highest record? 55

③ What is the lowest record? 20

④ How many children got the highest record? 2

⑤ How many children had 32 bounces? 3

⑥ How many children had more than 45 bounces? 4

⑦ *I'm good at basketball. There were only two children with more bounces than I. Do you know how many bounces I had?*

Read the graph showing the favourite storybooks of the children. Then answer the questions.

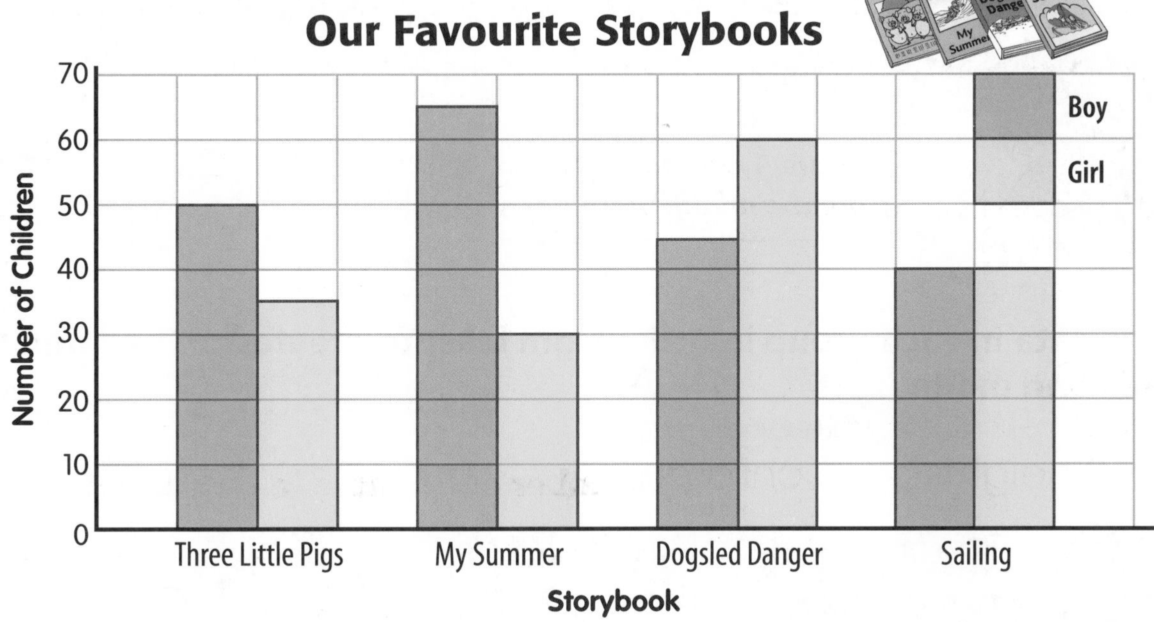

⑧ Title of the graph: Our Favourite storybooks

⑨ Label of the vertical axis: Number of Children

⑩ Label of the horizontal axis: Storybook

⑪ How many boys like "Three Little Pigs"? 50

⑫ How many girls were surveyed in all? 165

⑬ How many children were surveyed in all? 365

⑭ Which storybook is liked by the same number of boys and girls? How many boys and girls in all like this book? Sailing, 80.

126 children

⑮ *239 of the surveyed children are members of the Reading Club. How many children are not members of the Reading Club?*

126

365 − 239 = 126

Median is the middle value in a set of values arranged in order. If there is an even number of numbers, the median is the average of the two middle numbers.

e.g. 3, 10, 12, 28 Median = average of 10 and 12
= 11

There are 4 numbers. 10 and 12 are the middle numbers.

The median is **11** .

Put the data in each group in order from least to greatest. Then find the median and mode.

⑯ The heights of 15 children:

130 cm 145 cm 128 cm 130 cm 144 cm
130 cm 132 cm 142 cm 141 cm 136 cm
135 cm 135 cm 129 cm 130 cm 141 cm

In order: 128, 129, 130, 132, 135, 136, 141, 142, 144, 145

Median: 135 cm

Mode: 130 cm

⑰ The savings of 20 children:

$3 $2 $4 $5 $5 $2 $3 $4 $7 $9
$10 $4 $5 $7 $8 $10 $5 $6 $2 $9

In order: 2, 2, 2, 3, 3, 4, 4, 4, 5, 5, 5, 5, 6, 7, 7, 8, 9, 9, 10, 10

Median: $5

Mode: $5

⑱ The number of marbles that 17 children have:

45 66 29 58 27 54 66 23 40
26 54 58 70 66 25 66 66

In order: 23, 25, 26, 27, 29, 40, 45, 54, 58, 66, 66, 66, 66, 66, 70

Median: 54

Mode: 66

Stem-and-leaf plot:

e.g.

Stem	Leaves
1	9 9
2	3 6 6 7
4	8 9 9 9
5	0 4 4

Since these 13 numbers are put in the correct order, the number in the middle is the median.

The median of this set of data is **48**.

Look at each stem-and-leaf plot. Find the median.

⑲ Number of Hours Spent on Watching TV Each Week

Stem	Leaves
1	0 0 1 4 5 8
2	1 3 3 3 3 4 9
3	0 4

Median: 23 hours

⑳ Number of Hours Spent on Practising the Guitar Each Month

Stem	Leaves
1	5 5 6 6 8
2	3 3 7 7 7 7
3	0 1 1
4	2 3 5 5

Median: 27 hours

㉑ Ages of a Group of People

Stem	Leaves
0	6 7 7 8 9 9
1	4 5
2	2 2 3 6 7 8
3	0 0 1 6 9

Median: 22 years old

㉒ Weights of Bags of Potato Chips (in g)

Stem	Leaves
5	3 3 6 6 8 8
6	5 5 5
7	0 0 8 9
9	0 0 5 5 9
10	0 5 7 7 8

Median: 78 g

㉓ Lengths of Games (in min)

Stem	Leaves
9	8 8
10	0 2 5 5 6 8 8
11	6 6 9 9
12	0 0 1

The median is 108.

27

Graphs (2)

- Complete or make stem-and-leaf plots or double bar graphs to show the data.
- Draw conclusions or describe the shape of a set of data across its range of values, presented in tables or graphs.

Number of Flowers We Visited

Stem	Leaves
3	3 5 5
5	4 4 6 (6) 7 7 8
6	2 2
9	0

This set of data bunches up around the median.

Uncle Jim recorded the number of pizzas sold each day in April. Help him complete the stem-and-leaf plot to show the data. Then answer the questions.

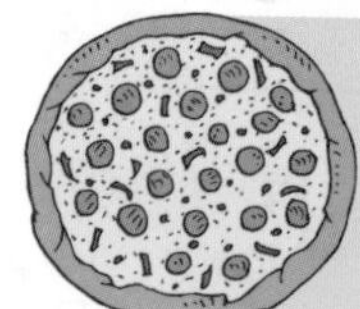

75	29	63	62	75	44	60	65	44	46	29	30	34	62	63
35	34	48	44	68	70	44	65	63	75	44	35	60	44	60

①

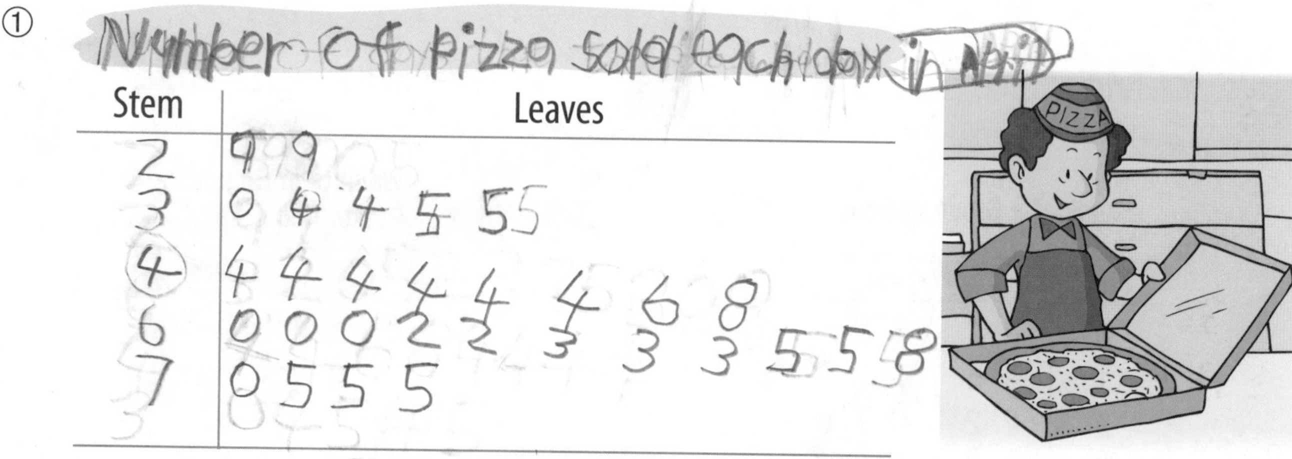

② On how many days in April were more than 68 pizzas sold? ____________

③ Check the correct sentences to describe the data.

(A) The mode number of pizzas sold is 44.

(B) This set of data spreads out evenly.

(C) The median number of pizzas sold is 54.

See how many marbles the children have. Help them answer the questions and make a double bar graph with a title and a key to show the data.

	Ann	Jill	Bob	Tony	Sue
Green Marbles	85	75	65	50	35
Red Marbles	45	75	80	85	30

④ What is the range of the data? 4 days

⑤ In multiples of what number will be the appropriate scale of the graph? 55 marbles

⑥

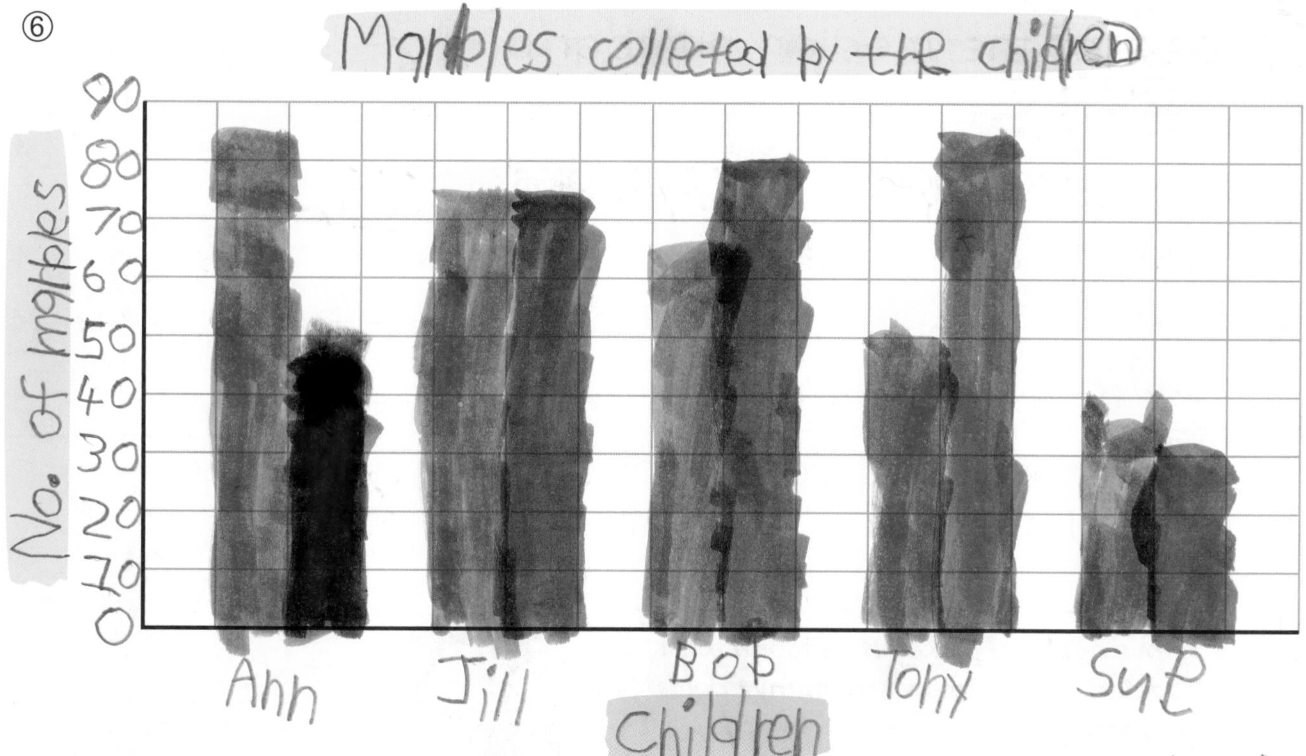

⑦ Who has the most marbles? Jill

⑧ How many green marbles do the children have in all? 310

⑨ Write a sentence to describe the graph.

So Jill has the marbles and Sue got the least marbles.

Judy asked a group of people about the number of apples they picked on a farm yesterday. Help her make a stem-and-leaf plot to show the data. Then answer the questions.

36 43 45 73 62 32 55 56 72 56 70 45 62 58 59 67 63 35 68 31 67 36 31 33 30 30 56 54 33 34 54 32 30 42 36 32 30 42 45 43

⑩ No. of Apples picked

Stem	Leaves
3	0 0 0 0 0 1 1 2 2 2 3 3 4 5 6 6 6
4	2 2 3 3 5 5 5
5	4 4 5 6 6 6 8 9
6	2 2 3 7 7 8
7	0 2 3

⑪ What is the median number of apples? 44

⑫ What is the mode number of apples? 30

⑬ What is the range of the number of apples? 43

⑭ How many people were asked in all? 40

⑮ How many people picked more than 60 apples? 9

⑯ *I love apples. I picked the second most apples. Do you know how many apples I picked?*

72

⑰ *Write a sentence to describe the stem-and-leaf plot above.*

The plots shows most peoples picked 30/40 apples yesterday.

See how many pails of honey were collected each month. Make a double bar graph to show the data. Then answer the questions.

	Apr.	May	Jun	Jul	Aug	Sep
No. of Small Pails	4	6	12	15	22	10
No. of Big Pails	3	7	10	20	25	3

⑱ No. of honey pails collected each month

No. of pails

Apr May Jun Jul Aug Sep

Month

⑲ Write a sentence to describe the graph.

The graph shows that a great amount of honey was collected in august.

⑳ ***If a big pail holds 1 L of honey, how much honey did we collect with big pails from April to September?***

68 L

28

Probability

- Predict the frequency of an outcome in a probability experiment.
- Determine how the number of repetitions of a probability experiment can affect the conclusion drawn.

Amy tosses two number cubes and calculates the sum. Help her complete the addition chart and list the possible outcomes. Then put a check mark in the circle if the sentence is correct; otherwise, put a cross.

①

2nd Cube \ 1st Cube	1	2	3	4	5	6
1		3	4	5		
2			5			8
3	4				8	
4		6				10
5			8	9		
6			9	10		

Possible outcomes:

②

a. 1 is one of the possible outcomes.

b. it is possible to get a sum greater than 10.

c. there are 12 possible outcomes in all.

d. there will be the greatest chance of getting 7.

e. it is unlikely to get either 2 or 12.

The children are going to toss two number cubes 40 times and calculate the sum for each toss. Check the children that have a reasonable prediction and explain. Amy Celine

③

Outcome \ No. of Times	Amy ✓	George	Celine ✓	Brian
2	1	8	1	4
3	2	7	1	6
4	3	6	4	1
5	4	5	4	1
6	6	4	5	3
7	8	3	7	7
8	6	2	5	7
9	4	1	5	2
10	3	2	4	0
11	2	1	2	5
12	1	1	2	4

④ Explain: It is more probable to get a number between 5 and 9 and less probable to get a smaller or bigger number.

Read what Brenda says. Help her predict the result.

⑤

If you toss a pair of number cubes 100 times and calculate the sum for each toss, how many times would you expect to get each outcome?

Outcome	No. of Times
2	3
3	6
4	8
5	11
6	14
7	19
8	23
9	30
10	35
11	44
12	50

Look at the spinners and read the sentences. Check the best predictions and explain.

⑥ *Spin me 50 times. Predict how many times the pointer will land on each section.*

Prediction	Car	Plane	Boat
A	17 times	16 times	17 times
B	20 times	15 times	15 times
C	18 times	9 times	23 times

Explain: ______________________

⑦ *Spin me 40 times. Predict how many times the pointer will land on each section.*

Prediction	Star	Heart	Diamond
A	18 times	6 times	16 times
B	11 times	17 times	12 times
C	25 times	9 times	6 times

Explain: ______________________

Judy predicts how many times the pointer will land on each section in 100 spins. Draw lines and colour the spinner to match her prediction.

⑧ *It will land on yellow about 12 times, green about 26 times, red about 26 times, and blue about 36 times.*

Each child tossed a coin 10 times and recorded how many times tails came up. Help the children complete the table and combine their individual results to determine a group result. Then answer the questions.

⑨

1	2	3	4	5	6
|||	卌	卌		||||	卌 ||	||

Children	1	2	3	4	5	6
No. of Tails	3	5	6	4	7	2

Group Result

Total number of tosses: 60

Total number of tails: 27

⑩

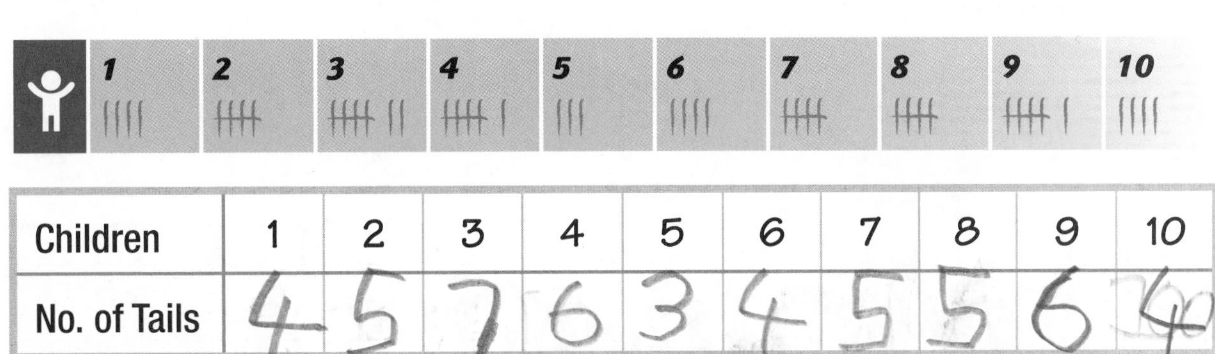

1	2	3	4	5	6	7	8	9	10
||||	卌	卌 ||	卌		|||	||||	卌	卌	卌		||||

Children	1	2	3	4	5	6	7	8	9	10
No. of Tails	4	5	7	6	3	4	5	5	6	4

Group Result

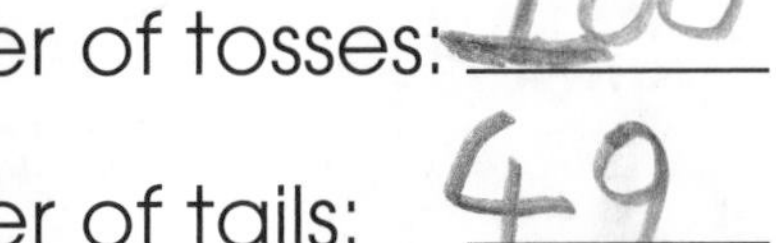

Total number of tosses: 100

Total number of tails: 49

⑪ *I think that the more probability experiments we have, the better the result will be. Am I correct?*

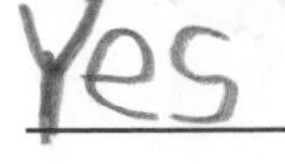

Yes

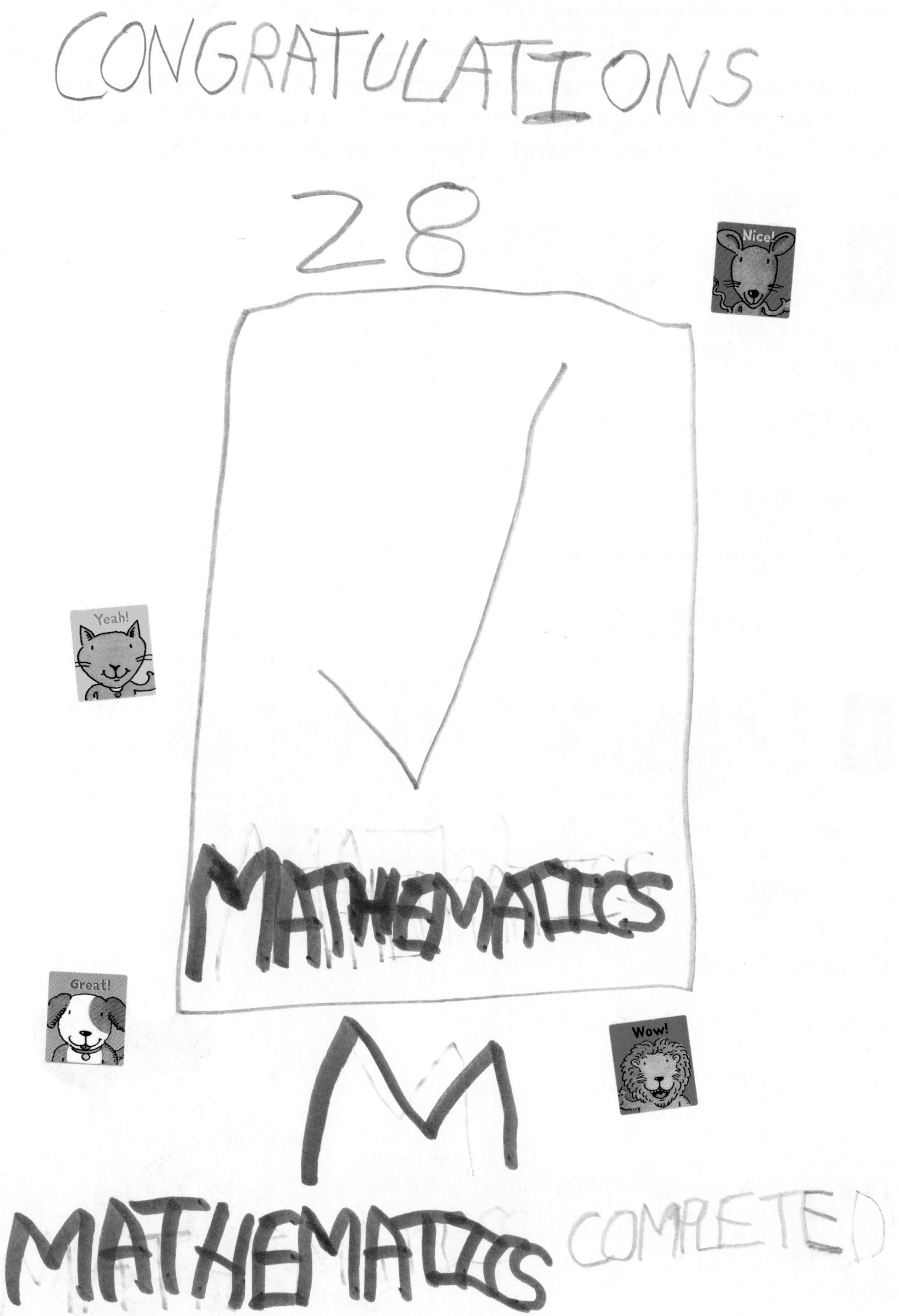

CONGRATULATIONS

28

MATHEMATICS

M

COMPLETED

ENGLISH

Tim *Horton*

Canada has more doughnut shops per person than any other country in the world! Why do we love doughnuts so much? It could be because of a man named Tim Horton.

Tim Horton's real name was Miles Gilbert Horton. He was born in Cochrane, Ontario in 1930. He loved to play hockey. When he was 19 years old, he joined the Toronto Maple Leafs and played with them for 17 years, helping the team to win the Stanley Cup four times.

In 1963, Tim decided to open a doughnut shop in Hamilton, Ontario. One year later, Tim invited a talented businessman, who used to be a police officer, to take over the running of the doughnut shop. Soon many cities in Canada had "Tim Hortons" shops. Why did Tim let another person take over his company? Well, Tim was still very busy playing hockey!

Soon after, Tim began to play for the New York Rangers, and later the Pittsburgh Penguins, and the Buffalo Sabres. Meanwhile, his doughnut business was getting bigger and more Canadians were eating doughnuts!

Sadly, Tim Horton died in a car accident in 1974. "Tim Hortons" is now the largest coffee and doughnut chain in Canada. There are more than 3000 shops all across Canada, as well as some in the United States and the United Arab Emirates.

A. Check the meanings of the underlined words as they are used in the passage.

1. joined: ____ fastened one thing to another
   __✓__ took part in
2. open: __✓__ start a business
   ____ unfold
3. running: ____ moving faster than walking
   __✓__ operation
4. chain: ____ connected metal links or rings
   __✓__ group of shops owned by the same company

B. Write numbers to put the events in order.

__4__ Tim played for the New York Rangers.
__5__ Tim died in a car accident.
__1__ Tim joined the Toronto Maple Leafs.
__2__ Tim opened his first doughnut shop.
__3__ Tim invited a partner to run the doughnut shop.

C. Do you think Tim Hortons would be as popular as it is without Tim's partner? Explain.

Yes Tim Hortons would be without Tims partner
Because Tim Hortons like him.

Nouns

A **common noun** names any person, place, thing, or animal.

Examples: officer city coffee deer

A **proper noun** is the name for a specific person, place, thing, or animal. It always begins with a capital letter.

Examples: Gilbert Hamilton Internet Bambi

D. Write the nouns in the correct groups. Write two more nouns in each group.

hockey

Tim Hortons

Stanley Cup

doughnut

Common Noun
hockey
doughnut
Mr. and mrs. Schwimmer
Giraffe

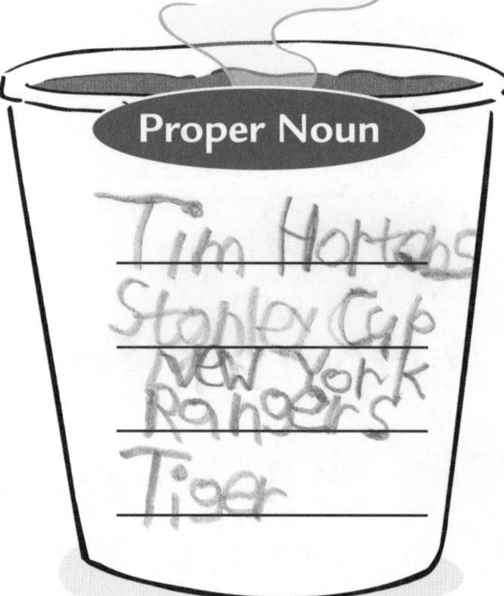

E. Rewrite the sentences by correcting the common and proper nouns.

1. Mr. and mrs. Schwimmer like chatting in a Coffee Shop.

   Mr. and Mrs. schwimmer like chatting in a coffee shop.

2. The Calgary flames is a very strong Hockey team.

   The calgary Flames is a very strong hockey team.

3. My Brother wants to be a Firefighter.

   My brother wants to be a firefighter.

Adjectives

A **comparative adjective** compares two things. It is formed by adding "er" to the end of the base form or "more" before it.

Example: This skirt is <u>cheaper</u> and <u>more beautiful</u> than that one.

A **superlative adjective** compares three or more things. It is formed by adding "est" to the end of the base form or "most" before it.

Example: Liz is the <u>smartest</u> and <u>most popular</u> student in class.

Some comparative and superlative adjectives are irregular.

F. Complete the table of adjectives.

Base Form	Comparative	Superlative
1. great		
2. talented		
3. famous		
4. sweet		

G. Fill in the blanks with the correct form of the given adjectives.

1. Dad is drinking (much) ____________ coffee than before.
2. The (late) ____________ score is surprising.
3. Sam is the (new) ____________ player on the team.
4. The store at the corner is (near) ____________ than the one on Beehive Road.
5. He is the (reliable) ____________ member in the club.

2

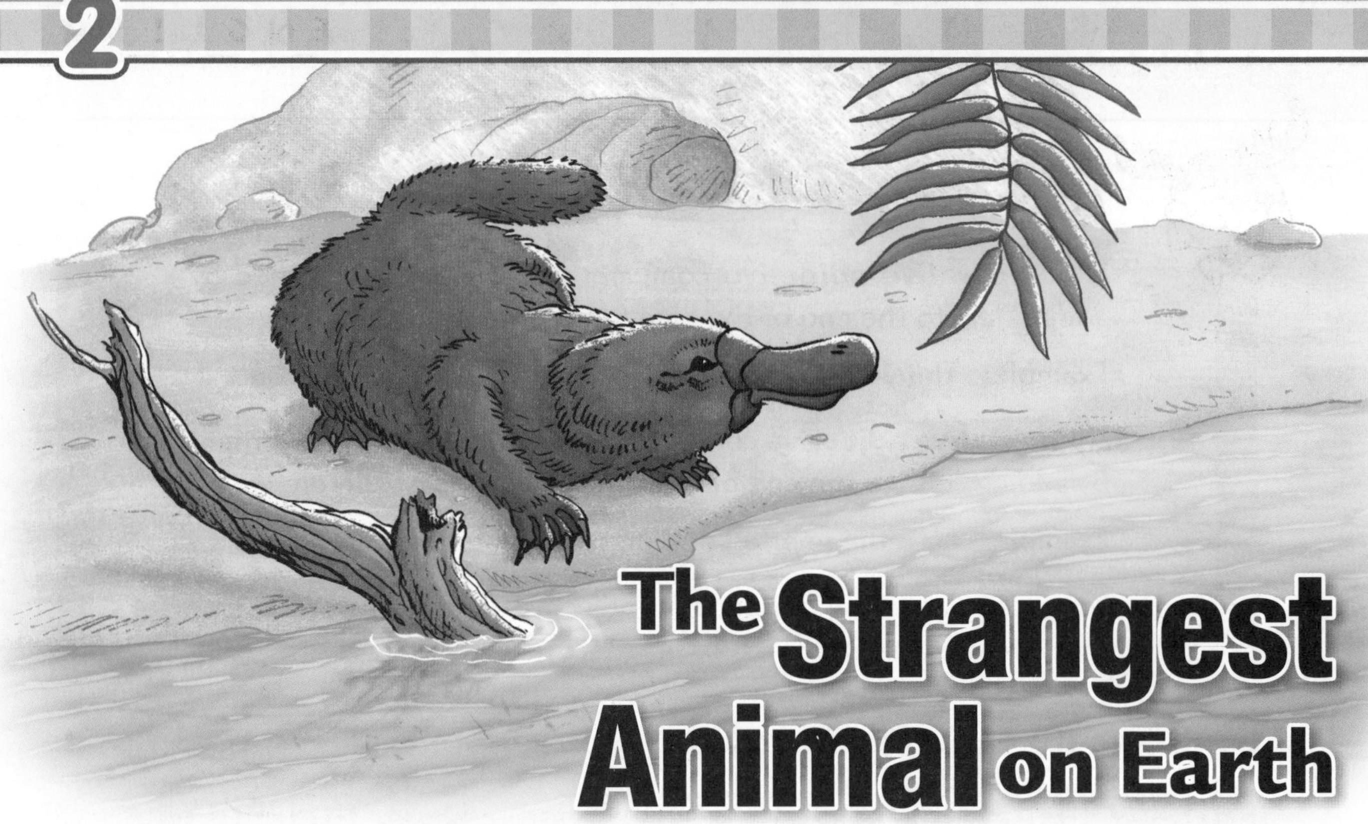

The Strangest Animal on Earth

What animal has fur and gives milk to its young like a mammal, but lays eggs like a bird or a reptile? What animal has webbed feet and a bill like a duck, but has a tail that looks much like a beaver's?

It's the duck-billed platypus, one of the strangest animals on Earth! Duck-billed platypi (the plural form of platypus) like to live in burrows near freshwater streams and ponds, and can be found only in eastern Australia and Papua New Guinea. They are about the size of a cat and weigh about three kilograms. They are good swimmers, but because their legs stick out at their sides, they walk like a lizard on land.

Duck-billed platypi like to eat meat, especially crayfish, worms, snails, shrimp, and other small animals from the water. They also eat small land rodents. Male platypi have a poisonous spike on each of their ankles which can be used to protect themselves from other animals, or to kill small animals for food. They have a lifespan of between 10 and 17 years.

This kind of animal, a warm-blooded mammal that lays eggs, is very rare. We call them monotremes. There used to be many kinds of monotremes, but they died out a long time ago. We can only see their fossils now. Today, there are only three living monotremes: the duck-billed platypus and two kinds of echidnas, or "spiny anteaters".

A. Complete the information about the duck-billed platypus.

1. Habitat Burrows near freshwater streams and ponds
2. Size About the size of a cat
3. Weight About 3 kg
4. Diet crayfish, worms, snails, shrimp, other small water animals and small land rodents
5. Lifespan between 10 and 17 years

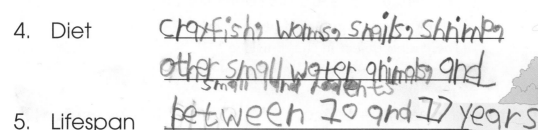

B. Answer these questions.

1. In what way does a duck-billed platypus resemble each of the following animals?

   a. a bird

   Its lays eggs.

   b. a duck

   It has webbed feet and bill.

   c. a beaver

   Its tail looks like a beaver.

2. What are the poisonous spikes on the ankles of the male platypus for?

   They are for protecting platypus from other animals or killing small animals for food.

Verbs

A **transitive verb** requires an object (the receiver of the action of the verb) to complete its meaning. An **intransitive verb** does not require an object to complete its meaning. Some verbs can be transitive or intransitive.

Examples: We sang the birthday song. (transitive)
("The birthday song" is an object in this sentence.)
We sang loudly together. (intransitive)
(There is no object in this sentence.)

C. Underline the verb in each sentence. Write whether it is transitive (T) or intransitive (I).

1. The duck-billed platypus swims well. I
2. They have legs sticking out at their sides. T
3. They love meat. T
4. Daniel eats a lot of meat. T
5. He seldom exercises. I
6. He sleeps ten hours a day. I

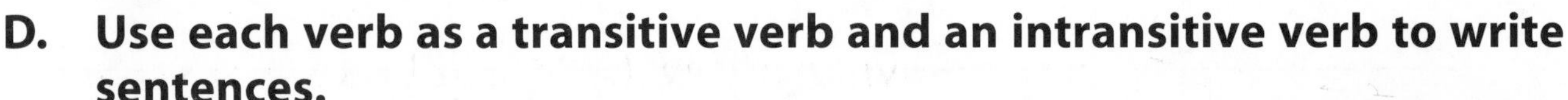

D. Use each verb as a transitive verb and an intransitive verb to write sentences.

1. **grow**
   Transitive: The plants grow in the garden.
   Intransitive: It is a growing pattern

2. **change**
   Transitive: The weather changes.
   Intransitive: The season changes.

Adverbs

An **adverb** describes a verb. Most adverbs are formed by adding "ly" to an adjective.

Example: The picture shows clearly what a duck-billed platypus looks like.

E. Complete the puzzle with adverbs formed from the clue words.

For adjectives ending in "y", drop the "y" and add "ily" to form adverbs.

Clue										
1. steady	S	T	E	A	D	I	L	Y		
2. glad	G	L	A	D	L	Y				
3. heavy	H	E	A	V	I	L	Y			
4. special		S	P	E	C	I	A	L	L	Y
5. proud			P	R	O	U	D	L	Y	
6. probable	P	R	O	B	A	B	L	Y		

F. Write a sentence of your own using each of the following adverbs.

1. softly

   The teddy bear is softly.

2. brightly

   The light is brightly.

3. terribly

   The fire is terribly.

3

Madagascar

A Strange Zoo

Madagascar is an island country about 480 kilometres east of southern Africa. It is famous for its unique fauna (animal life) and flora (plant life). There are so many things in Madagascar that you cannot find anywhere else on Earth!

Lemurs are the most famous of Madagascar's unique animals. They are a primitive type of monkey, and are related to humans. The fanaloka is a kind of civet cat and the tenrec is a kind of hedgehog unique to the island. Madagascar has hissing cockroaches, flying fox bats, bee-eating birds, and giant tortoises. Almost all of the reptiles and half of the birds on the island are not found anywhere else.

Madagascar has many strange and unusual plants. There are huge palms and many orchids. The national tree of Madagascar is the baobab tree. There are eight different species of baobab trees on the island.

Why does Madagascar have such special plants and animals? Madagascar used to be connected to Africa. About 165 million years ago, it broke off from Africa and began to drift away. The animals and plants back in Africa were changing over time, but those on Madagascar did not change as much. The flora and fauna have been separated from their ancestors for millions of years.

Many of Madagascar's unique plants and animals are extinct. We must make sure that we protect what is left.

A. Check the main idea of the passage.

- ✓ Madagascar was part of Africa millions of years ago.
- ✓ Lemurs are one of the unique animals in Madagascar.
- ✓ Madagascar has many species of unique animals and plants.
- ✓ The fauna and flora in Madagascar have not changed much over the last millions of years.

B. Fill in the blanks with words formed by unscrambling the letters in parentheses.

1. Madagascar has its own (quueni) qniqve animals and plants.
2. Many (sseepic) species of animals and plants on the island cannot be found anywhere else in the world.
3. The fauna and flora there are different from their (cessanort) ancestors.
4. Hissing cockroaches and flying fox bats are some (lanuuus) ynysyal animals living in Madagascar.
5. Millions of years ago, Madagascar was (notedccen) connectel to Africa.

Subjects

The **subject** of a verb is the person or thing that performs the action. It can be a noun or a pronoun.

Example: The habitats of many living things are being destroyed.

C. Underline the subjects in the sentences.

1. Many plants and animals are extinct.
2. World Wildlife Fund is involved in many conservation projects.
3. Dad promised to take me to the zoo this summer.
4. We can see many kinds of animals at the zoo.
5. I want to go on a pony ride.
6. My brother has two tortoises.

D. Write a suitable subject for each sentence.

1. ____________________ is rising in the east.
2. ____________________ waters the plants every day.
3. ____________________ has a new pet dog.
4. ____________________ like climbing up the fence.
5. ____________________ have not been to Africa.
6. ____________________ loves reading books about nature.

Objects

The **object** of a verb is the person or thing that receives the action. It is made up of the bare object and its modifiers. It can be a noun or a pronoun.

Example: Mrs. Franklin has donated <u>money</u> to WWF.

E. Check if the underlined words in the sentences are objects. Put a cross if they are not.

1. <u>Our cat</u> gave birth to three kittens. 
2. Grandpa bought a new cage <u>last Friday</u>. 
3. He has grown <u>some cherry trees</u> in his backyard. 
4. The beaver builds <u>its lodge</u> with tree branches. 
5. The cat has scared <u>the birds</u> away. 

F. Use each word as an object to write a sentence of your own.

1. monkey

   The monkey is on the tree.

2. reptiles

   The reptiles is a lizzard.

3. Africa

   Millions of years ago Madagascar was connected to Africa.

4. environment

   The environment is a job.

Velcro

An Amazing Invention

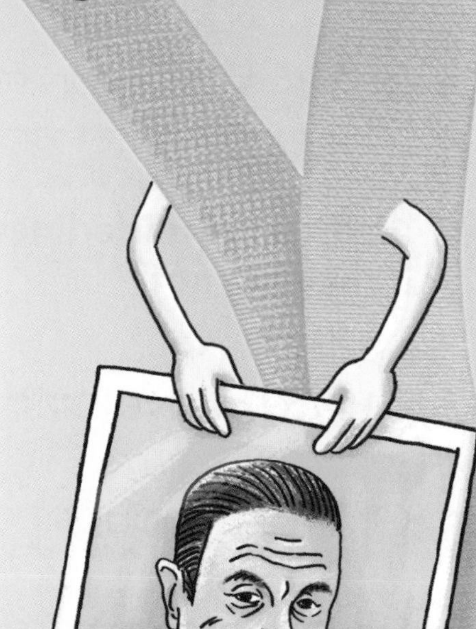

One day, a Swiss inventor named George de Mestral was walking in the woods. Later, he saw that many burrs had stuck to his wool pants. He wondered why they were hard to pull off. He looked at the burrs under a microscope, and saw that each burr was made up of tiny hooks. These hooks were sticking to the loops in the fabric of his wool pants.

The man decided that this was a good way to make things stick together. He took his idea to a textile designer in France. Together they invented a kind of "locking tape" fabric that fastened together using a system of hooks and loops.

But they did not know what to call it. Hook n' loop? Locking tape? It didn't seem quite right. At last, they decided to call this great invention Velcro. "Vel" comes from the word "velours", the French word for "velvet", and "cro" comes from "crochet", the French word for "hook".

Today Velcro is used everywhere, and many companies make it. But the word "Velcro" is a brand name, and belongs to the company started by George de Mestral.

You probably have a strip of hooks and a strip of loops to fasten your jacket, or your running shoes. But is your clothing made with real Velcro – or someone else's imitation?

A. Write "T" for the true sentences and "F" for the false ones.

1. George de Mestral was Swiss. T
2. He found many burrs on his wool pants after a walk in the woods. 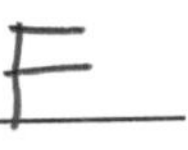
3. He realized that each burr was made up of tiny loops. F
4. He took his "hooks and loops" idea to a textile designer in France. 
5. They decided to call the invention "locking tape". 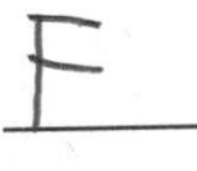
6. "Cro" comes from a Greek word meaning hook. 
7. The word "Velcro" is a brand name. 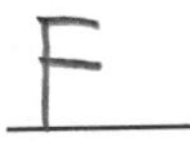
8. Velcro is only used on jackets and running shoes. F

B. Find words from the passage for the meanings below.

1. copy 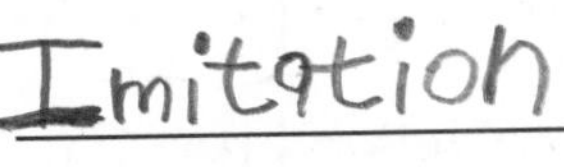
2. become attached Styck
3. an instrument for a larger view of things Mic~~ro~~soft
4. one who designs things as a profession Designer
5. prickly flower head that clings to clothing Byrr

Subjects and Predicates

A sentence is made up of a **subject** and a **predicate**.

One or more nouns together with their modifiers form the complete subject.

The predicate of a sentence describes what the subject is or what it does.

Example: Jim and his sister (subject) invented a massage device for their parents (predicate).

C. Put a vertical line between the subject and predicate in each sentence.

1. Grandpa invented a device that can trap mice.
2. He had looked at various types of mouse traps before he made his own.
3. My brother wants to invent something too.
4. He is thinking of inventing a device to replace the remote control for the TV.
5. He and his friend are looking for relevant information.

D. Underline the complete subjects in the sentences.

1. George and a French designer invented Velcro.
2. Hooks and loops are the basic idea of the invention.
3. My running shoes are fastened with Velcro.
4. I wear them to school every day.
5. Marco and Eric think that my shoes are cool.

E. Match the subjects with the predicates. Write the letters.

- (A) can minimize the risk of injury
- (B) toured around the world to show their work
- (C) has expanded its business over the years
- (D) mean a lot to the designer
- (E) have changed the way people live
- (F) is on sale this week

1. Many inventions ______ .
2. The armband ______ .
3. His company ______ .
4. Fastening your seatbelt ______ .
5. The award and the public's recognition ______ .
6. The designer and the producer ______ .

F. Complete the sentences with suitable predicates.

1. Her latest design ____ .
2. The industry ____ .
3. A lot of hard work ____ .
4. Many trials and errors ____ .

The Zzzzipper!

You probably use a zipper every day. We find zippers on our clothes, our boots, our school bags, and our pencil cases. Zippers are everywhere! What would we do without them?

People had to make do with buttons until about 100 years ago. The zipper was invented and patented on August 29, 1893 by an American mechanical engineer named Whitcomb Judson. He called it a "clasp locker". It was made using small hooks and loops. It didn't work very well, though. Although Judson displayed it at the 1893 Chicago World's Fair to a wide audience, not many people were impressed. He did sell 20 of these "clasp lockers" to the United States Postal Service to put on their mailbags, though.

In 1913, a Swedish engineer named Gideon Sundback produced a better version with metal teeth. He called it a "separable fastener" and sold many to the United States Army.

In 1923, B. F. Goodrich (a man famous for making rubber car tires) ordered 150 000 of them for his new product – rubber galoshes. He called the fasteners zippers because that was the sound he heard when the separable fastener was being pulled together.

The zipper invention got even better when it was made using a coil. Metal coils were easily bent out of shape, but in the 1960s, new flexible coils were being made out of synthetic material. The zipper was working better than ever!

A. Read the clues. Complete the crossword puzzle with words from the passage.

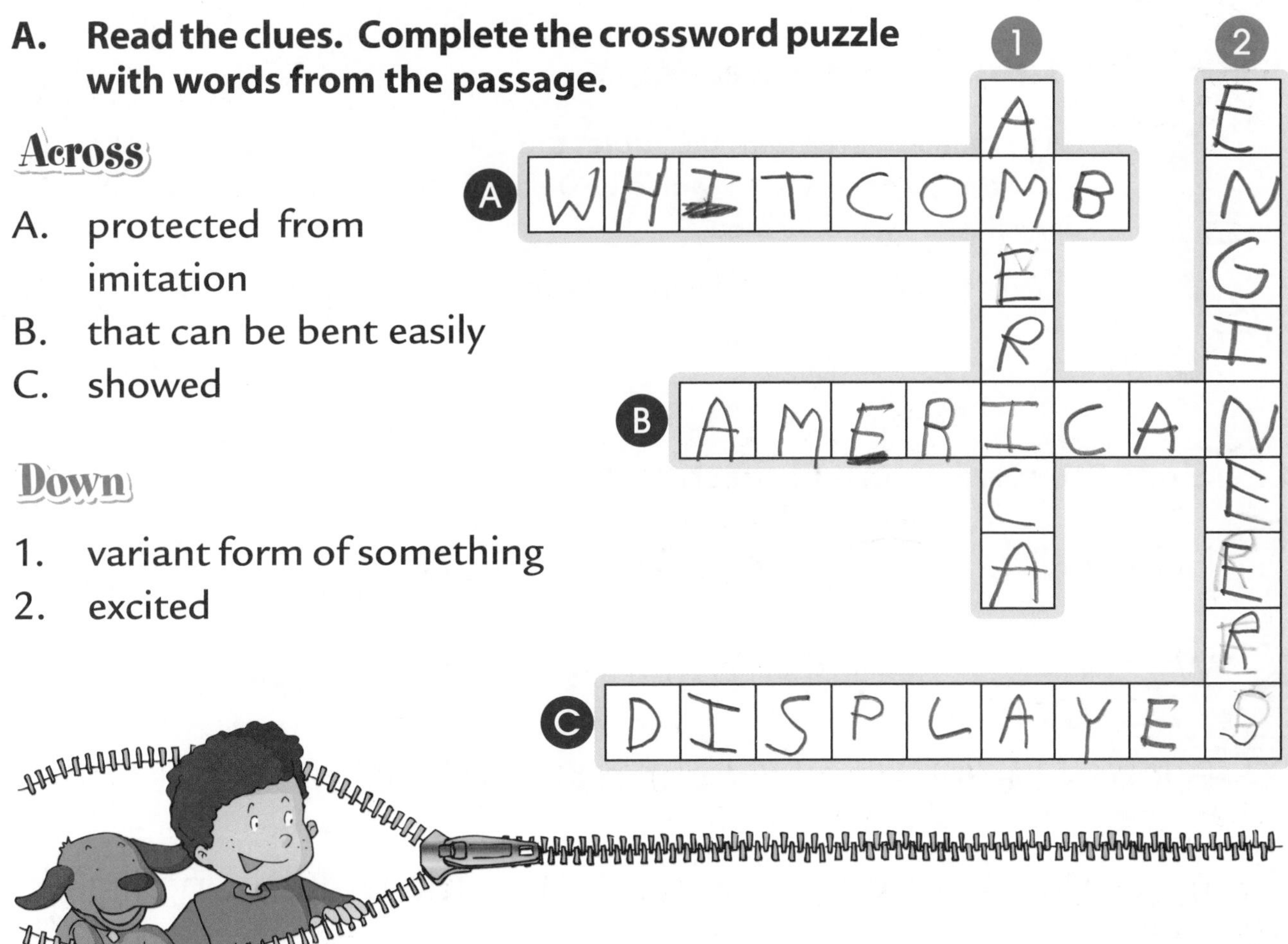

Across

A. protected from imitation
B. that can be bent easily
C. showed

Down

1. variant form of something
2. excited

B. Complete the table about the development of the zipper.

	Year	Event
1.	1893	Whitcomb Judson invented and patented the clasp locker.
2.	1913	Swedish engineer named Gideon Sundback produced a better version with metal teeth.
3.	1923	B. F. Goodrich called the separable fastener "zipper".
4.	1960s	New flexible coils were being made out of synthetic material.

Subject-Verb Agreement

A **verb** must **agree** with the **subject** in a sentence. If the subject is singular, a singular verb should be used. If the subject is plural, a plural verb should be used.

Examples: Maria wants to replace the buttons with a zipper.
We all agree with her.

C. Circle the correct verb for each sentence.

1. Daniel like / likes jackets with a zipper.
2. We need / needs 20 buttons to make the puppets.
3. Each of them have / has a bag of materials.
4. These stuffed geese was / were made by Kitty and Paula.
5. Do / Does they have enough for the show?

D. Check if the underlined words are correct. If not, write the correct words on the lines.

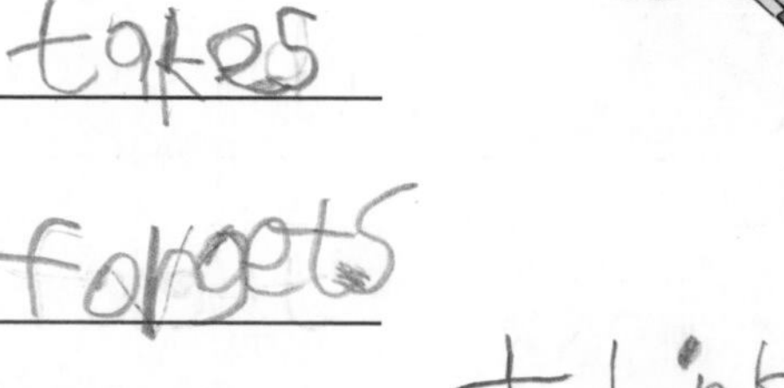

1. The zipper on my bag is broken. ____________
2. I have to buy a new bag for my hockey gear. ____________
3. It take time to find the right one. ____________
4. Little William always forget to zip his pencil case. ____________
5. I thinks he should get one without a zipper. ____________

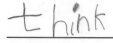

E. Write a suitable subject for each section.

1. It matches the boots.
2. It makes 100 000 zippers a day.
3. They were working on their project.
4. They do not need to work tomorrow.
5. He wants to design a new fastener.

F. Rewrite the following sentences. Change the singular subjects to plural and the plural subjects to singular. Make changes to the verbs and other words too.

1. The teachers are preparing for the Open Day.

   The teacher is preparing for the Open Day.

2. Some grade four students have invented this device.

   A grak 4 stydent has invented this device.

3. It is very useful on rainy days.

   They are very usefyl on rainy days.

4. These invitation cards look cute.

   This invitation card look cyte.

5. The speaker is going to demonstrate the invention.

   The speakers are going to demonstrate the invention.

6. That experiment has given us some insights.

   Those experiments have given us some insights.

6

Third Culture Kids

Emily St. Denny is 15 years old. She was born in Beijing, China, where her mother worked as a French teacher and her father taught English. When she was five years old, Emily and her family moved to Belgrade, Serbia. When she was seven years old, she moved to Nairobi, Kenya, where her little sister was born. Two years later, her family moved to Hong Kong, where she attended a French international school. After five years, the family moved to France.

Emily's mother was born in France. Emily's father is American. Emily says her little sister is very much French, like her mother. But after living in so many different places, Emily does not really know who she is. If pressed, she says she feels American more than anything else, as English is her first language. But she has never lived there! Welcome to the world of a "Third Culture Kid".

This term (shortened to "TCK") was made up in the 1960s by Doctors Ruth and John Useem. They used it to talk about the experience of mainly immigrant children growing up between two cultures: their culture of "origin" (or that of their parents), and the place they are currently living.

Today, TCK also refers to children who have travelled a lot and who are "culturally-blended". These are children who are familiar with many cultures and not as familiar with their parents'.

A. Complete the table about Emily.

	Age	Place of Residence
1.	Birth	Beijing, China
2.	5	Belgrade Serbia
3.	7	Nairobi Kenya
4.	9	Hong Kong
5.	14	France

B. Explain the following terms from the passage. Then use Emily's story as examples.

1. culture of origin

The culture of origin is the culture of the parents
Emily culture of origin French and American.

2. culturally-blended

Its means being familiar with many cultures. Emilys Familiar with the french, Chinese, serbian and African culture.

C. Write three things that you think Emily may be different from her classmates in France.

1. Emily was born in China.
2. Her father is american.
3. English is her first language.

Subject and Object Pronouns

A **subject pronoun** replaces a noun as the subject in a sentence. "I", "you", "we", "they", "he", "she", and "it" are subject pronouns.

An **object pronoun** replaces a noun as the object in a sentence. "Me", "you", "us", "them", "him", "her", and "it" are object pronouns.

Example: Sam keeps the cards in a box.
He keeps them in a box.

D. Circle the correct pronouns.

1. Emily was born in China. Now, he / she lives in France.

2. France is a beautiful country. It / He is famous for its wine.

3. Emily's dad loves French wine. It / He visited some vineyards in Burgundy last summer.

4. Her father and my dad want to make their own wine. He / They enrolled in a wine making course.

5. I / You always ask my mom for more orange juice and you / she will say to me, "Okay, but I / you have to finish your cereal first."

6. Mom and I like juice. We / She have fresh orange juice every morning.

E. Fill in the blanks with the correct pronouns.

Emily and I are classmates. I have known 1. her for almost a year. Emily and her family have lived in many places before. 2. They moved here to live with Emily's grandpa last year. 3. He owns a cake shop near our school. 4. It is about ten minutes away from school. Emily and I walk home together. 5. We stop by to say "bonjour" to her grandpa every day. I like 6. him very much as 7. he always treats 8. hys cakes and tarts.

F. Rewrite the sentences by replacing the underlined words with pronouns.

1. Emily's mother was born in France.

   She mother was born in France.

2. Emily's father speaks to Emily and Kelly in English.

   He speaks to them in English.

3. Emily and Kelly walk their dog to the park every day.

   They walk it to the park everyday

4. English is not widely spoken in France.

   It is not widely spoken in France.

Deborah Ellis:
Writing Books that Help Children

Deborah Ellis loves to write. One day she entered a writing competition held by a Canadian publisher. Her story did not win the competition, but the publishing company decided to publish it anyway. The book was called *Looking for X*. It was a real surprise then, when *Looking for X* won a Governor General's Literary Award the following year!

In 1997, Deborah spent time in Pakistan, working in refugee camps that housed mostly Afghan families. She heard stories of young girls who had to cut their hair off and dress up like boys in order to earn money for their families. At that time, women in Afghanistan were not allowed to leave their homes.

Deborah wrote *The Breadwinner*, a story about a young Afghan girl named Parvana. It became a huge success all around the world. Then Deborah's father said he wanted to know what happened next to Parvana, so Deborah wrote a sequel called *Parvana's Journey*. The series became a trilogy when Deborah wrote *Mud City*, the story of Parvana's friend Shauzia, in a refugee camp. All the money Deborah earns from the sale of these books goes to Women for Women in Afghanistan, Street Kids International, and UNICEF.

Deborah Ellis's books have helped readers better understand the difficult lives that many children have. She has said, "The world's children are a blessing to all of us. They are also our responsibility."

A. Match the words with the definitions.

1. publish C
2. refugee E
3. sequel B
4. trilogy A
5. blessing D

(A) group of three related works
(B) novel that continues the story of an earlier one
(C) print and distribute to the public
(D) something good that you are thankful for
(E) one forced to leave his or her country and seek protection

B. Write numbers to put the events in order.

2 *Looking for X* won a Governor General's Literary Award.
3 Deborah worked in refugee camps in Pakistan.
5 Deborah wrote *Parvana's Journey*.
4 Deborah wrote *The Breadwinner*.
1 Deborah wrote *Looking for X*.
6 Deborah wrote *Mud City*.

C. Explain what Deborah said in your own words: "The world's children... our responsibility."

The world's children are a blessing to all of us. They are also our responsibility.

Possessives

A **possessive pronoun** tells who possesses something or is related to someone.

Possessive pronouns: mine, yours, ours, theirs, his, hers

A **possessive adjective** tells to whom the noun that it describes belongs or is related.

Possessive adjectives: my, your, our, their, his, her, its

Examples: This is <u>my</u> cellphone. (possessive adjective)
This cellphone is <u>mine</u>. (possessive pronoun)

D. Circle the correct words.

1. Rob bought a copy of *Mud City* yesterday. He will lend me his / hers when he finishes reading it.
2. All of us bring my / our own lunch here. Have you brought your / yours ?
3. Do you know when your / yours parents will be back?
4. I can tie my / your own shoelaces but little Candy cannot tie hers / its .
5. My / Mine dog wags it / its tail when I come home.
6. Gena and Kelly clean their / theirs room once a week. We should clean our / ours too.
7. The twin brothers ride their / theirs bikes to school.

E. **Check if the underlined words are correct. If not, write the correct words in the speech boxes.**

1. Sue and <u>her</u> father volunteered to do the car wash. ✓
2. Look! The baby ducks are swimming after <u>theirs</u> mother. their
3. Will this dollhouse be <u>my</u>? mine
4. Do you think we can finish <u>ours</u> in two days? ✓
5. The actress donates <u>hers</u> income to charity. her
6. <u>His</u> story is published in today's paper. ✓

F. **Rewrite each sentence with a possessive pronoun or a possessive adjective.**

1. Is this your kite?
   Is this kite yours?
2. These are their toys.
   These toys are theirs.
3. That hat is hers.
   That is her hat.
4. This will be your desk.
   This desk will be yours.
5. Will this hamster be ours?
   Will this be our hamster.

A Letter from the School Nurse

Dear Parents,

There has been a confirmed case of conjunctivitis in your child's class.

Conjunctivitis, also called "pinkeye", is an infection of the membrane on the inside of the eyelid, and also covering the eyeball. It is caused by viruses or bacteria. Conjunctivitis is contagious. It is usually spread by touching the infected eye/eyes, and then touching other surfaces, such as a telephone, doorknobs, etc.

Symptoms include stinging, itching, or reddening of the eye/ eyes. There may be a white sticky discharge. When waking, the eye/eyes may have a crust and be difficult to open. Vision may be blurry.

If your child has any of these symptoms, please treat them for conjunctivitis. We suggest warm compresses on the closed eye/eyes for five to ten minutes, at least four times a day. This should be followed by antibiotic eyedrops ordered by your health care provider. Follow the doctor's instructions.

To prevent spreading, tell your children not to share washcloths, towels, pillows, or eye makeup. They should avoid touching their eyes and should wash hands frequently.

Thank you for your attention.

Yours sincerely,

Registered Nurse

A. Read the clues. Complete the crossword puzzle with words from the passage.

Across

A. prevent
B. often
C. become widely felt

Down

1. proved to be true
2. pads or cloths pressed on something
3. unclear

A: AVOID
B: FREEKENTLY
C: SPREAD
1: CONFIRMED
2: COMPRESSES
3: BLURRY

B. Fill in the blanks with words from the passage.

1. Conjunctivitis is a kind of eye Infection .

2. Olivia wrote the letter to the parents because she wanted to have their Attention.

3. Reddening of the eye(s) is one of the Symptoms of conjunctivitis.

4. Pinkeye is caused by Viryses or Bacteria .

5. Children should not share their towels or eye makeup because conjunctivitis is contagioys.

Prepositions

Some **prepositions** tell the time of an event or the location of something.

Examples: Alex goes skating <u>on</u> Thursdays.
There is some orange juice <u>in</u> the fridge.

C. Circle the correct prepositions.

The school nurse gave us a talk about conjunctivitis. She showed an eye model 1. at / on screen. The talk finished 2. at / on four o'clock. We were asked to submit a slogan for the "Protect Our Eyes" campaign 3. in / by next Friday. Our class will have a brainstorming session 4. on / in Monday morning.

Our class will join a sports camp for children with low vision 5. from / on July 10 to July 14 6. of / at W. Ross Macdonald School. We will act as volunteers to help the visually-impaired children 7. in / on the camp. We will guide them 8. between / to and 9. from / off the field every day. I look forward to the camp because I have not been involved in this kind of voluntary work before.

More on Prepositions

Certain **prepositions** are used after particular words or expressions.

Example: Mrs. Grant is very kind to us.

D. Fill in the blanks with the correct prepositions.

1. What's wrong __with__ your eyes?
2. Can you stop staring __qt__ me?
3. We may go sightseeing – it depends __on__ the weather.
4. Do not borrow face cloths __from__ others.
5. Mom is not ready yet. She is still looking __for__ her sunglasses.

E. Check if the underlined prepositions are correct. If not, write the correct words on the lines.

I ran to Ryan at the library this morning. He has been suffering from eye pain for three days. I am really sorry to him because he cannot take part in the swimming practice. His family doctor could not find the reason about the pain and referred him to a specialist. Ryan is very anxious at the swimming gala because the pain may prevent him to joining the competition.

1. into
2. ✓
3. for
4. ✓
5. for
6. ✓
7. qbout
8. from

English
A Worldwide Language

Languages change over time. New words are invented (like "mouse pad" or "blogging") based on new inventions. Other new words come from other languages. For example, when you tell your mother you are going to serve her a special Mother's Day breakfast of coffee and croissants with marmalade, and a side order of yogourt, you are using words from at least three other languages ("coffee" and "yogourt" are Turkish words, "croissant" is a French word, and "marmalade" is a Portuguese word)!

Of course, it is easy to know when some words we use come from other languages. For example, most of the names of Australian animals are from that country's aboriginal languages: kangaroo, kookaburra, koala, and wombat. Japanese foods, such as sushi and tempura are familiar to us, and so are their Japanese names. This is the same with many Chinese food words, such as dim sum and chow mein.

But you might be surprised to learn that some words you have been using for a long time are not originally English words. For example, "kindergarten" is a German word, "mosquito" is a Spanish word, "cinema" is a Greek word, "robot" is a Czech word, "orangutan" is a Malay word, and "sauna" is a Finnish word.

Even though these words were not English to begin with, they are now certainly a part of the ever-growing English language.

Words are fascinating things, don't you think?

A. Match the words with their language of origin.

1.  yogourt
2.  dim sum
3.  tempura
4.  mosquito
5. 

cinema
6.  kindergarten

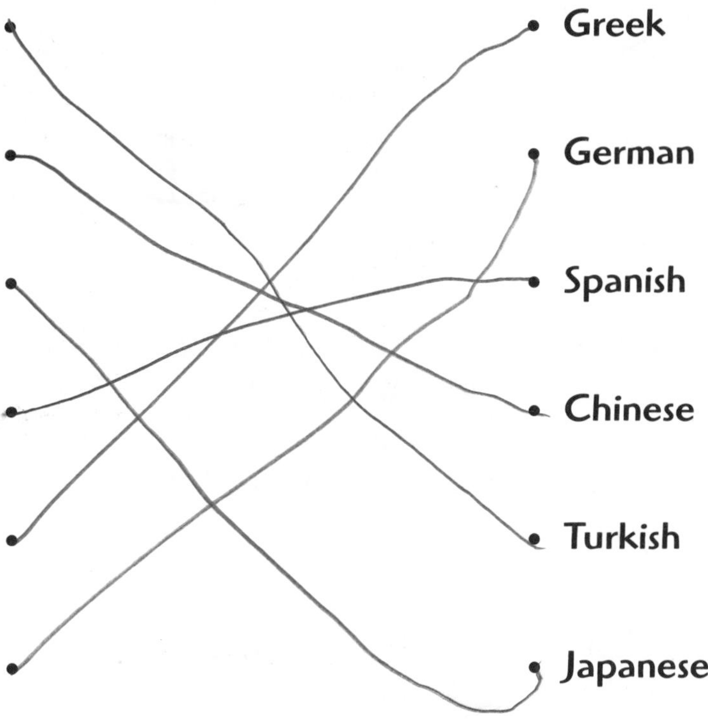

- Greek
- German
- Spanish
- Chinese
- Turkish
- Japanese

B. Circle the languages spoken in these countries in the word search.

Canada Germany France China
Japan Turkey Greece Czech Republic
Finland Portugal Spain Malaysia

p	F	r	e	C	z	M	a	y	F	i	n	n	T	u	r	G
o	i	S	p	z	J	a	P	o	r	t	u	g	u	e	s	e
r	n	p	G	e	r	l	G	r	e	e	k	F	r	e	C	r
t	n	a	e	c	J	a	p	a	n	e	s	e	k	k	z	m
F	i	n	i	h	e	y	a	n	c	s	C	h	i	n	e	a
e	s	h	S	p	a	n	i	s	h	c	h	e	s	i	o	n
C	h	i	n	e	s	e	E	n	g	l	i	s	h	o	n	h

The Simple Present Tense

The **simple present tense** talks about facts, present actions, and habitual actions. Most present tense verbs for third person singular subjects are formed by adding "s/es" to the base form.

Example: Donald <u>speaks</u> Spanish well.

C. Write "P" for sentences in the simple present tense and "O" for sentences in other tenses.

1. *Sesame Street* used to be my favourite TV program.

2. Many people grew up with the show.

3. How many of us learned our ABCs from the show?

4. Elmo is still my favourite character.

5. I have stuffed toys of all the characters in the show.

6. I put all of them on my bed.

7. My cousin plays with the toys whenever she comes to visit us.

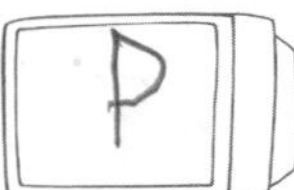

8. She likes Ernie the best.

9. I will show you the toys when you come to visit us next time.

D. Circle the correct verbs to complete the story.

I 1. have / has a new classmate. Her name 2. is / are Kim. She 3. will be / is from Korea. She 4. speak / speaks little English because her parents 5. talk / talks in Korean at home. They 6. run / runs a Korean restaurant near our school. It 7. serve / serves Korean food like kimchi and bibim bap. Kim 8. bring / brings her own lunch every day. Her lunch box 9. look / looks different from mine and the food 10. seem / seems to be very tasty.

E. Change the following sentences to the simple present tense.

1. Jack was interested in learning Korean.

   Jack is interested in learning Korean.

2. He wanted to buy a dictionary.

   He wants to buy a dictionary.

3. The children are playing word games at home.

   The childrens plays word games at home.

4. Sandy always won the game.

   Sandy always win the game.

Thailand's
Floating Lantern Festival

Thailand has a festival called Loy Krathong. "Loy" means "to float" and "krathong" is a lotus-shaped boat made of banana leaves. This festival usually takes place on the night of the full moon in November.

On this day, people in Thailand make krathongs. They put flowers, incense, and candles on their little boats, and then let them sail away on the water. They believe that the krathongs carry away bad luck.

Not only is Loy Krathong Festival a beautiful sight to see, but it is also a time of joy. Usually, there are firework displays. People do a traditional dance called Ramwong and sing the Loy Krathong Song on this day.

Loy Krathong Song (English translation)

The full moon of the twelfth month,
As water fills the banks,
We, all men and women,
Have really good fun on Loy Krathong Day,
Float, float the krathongs,
Float, float the krathongs,
And after we have floated our krathongs,
I invite you my dear,
To come out and dance,
Ramwong on Loy Krathong Day,
Ramwong on Loy Krathong Day,
Good merit brings us happiness,
Good merit brings us happiness.

A. Match the facts. Write the letters.

1. Loy Krathong D
2. krathong A
3. Ramwong B
4. Thailand E
5. candles C

- A a boat made from banana leaves
- B a traditional dance
- C light the boats
- D a festival
- E a country

B. Answer these questions.

1. When do people celebrate Loy Krathong Festival?

The people celebrate Loy Krathong Festival on the night of the full moon in November

2. What is the shape of a krathong?

It is lotus shape.

3. What do people put on their krathongs?

They put flowers increase and candles on their krathongs

4. Why do people let krathongs sail away on the water?

They believe in the krathongs will carry away the bad luck.

5. What else do people do apart from sailing krathongs?

They sing and dance.

6. Why is Loy Krathong Festival a beautiful sight to see?

The krathongs are lit with candles and there are fireworks display on this day.

The Simple Past Tense

The **simple past tense** shows what happened in the past. Most past tense verbs are formed by adding "d/ed" to the base form. Some stay the same or change in spelling.

Example: Uncle Lee toured around Asia last summer.

C. Check the sentences that are in the simple past tense.

1. Mr. Dixie went to Thailand. ✓
2. He likes sailing. ✗
3. The incense smells good. ✗
4. Did you see the pictures? ✓
5. We enjoyed the firework displays. ✓
6. They were magnificent. ✓

D. Circle the correct past form of the words on the left.

1. **celebrate**	celebrated	celebrateed	celebrate
2. **throw**	throwed	threw	thrown
3. **cost**	costed	cast	cost
4. **carry**	carry	carryed	carried
5. **float**	float	floated	floaten

E. Fill in the blanks with the past form of the correct words.

be explain teach cut
pick give say roll
bring show

Last week, Mrs. Powers 1. toygh us to make Thai krathongs in the Arts and Crafts lesson. She 2. gave each of us a plastic bowl and some coloured paper. We 3. [illegible] our own glue and scissors. She 4. Showed us some samples of krathongs and 5. explained to us how to make them. All of them 6. were beautiful. I 7. picked some red and yellow paper and 8. cut the edges in zigzag lines. Then I 9. rolled the tips to make them curl. Mrs. Powers 10. said that I had done a good job.

F. Use the past form of each word to write a sentence of your own.

1. see I see a cronovirus.
2. fill I fill a bucket.
3. wear I wear a Police offrer.
4. stop I stop the thief.

Happy "Wet" New Year

These days, Thailand celebrates the calendar New Year on the first day of January. But it wasn't always this way: Thailand used to celebrate its new year in April with the Songkran Festival. This festival starts on April 13 and lasts from three to ten days, depending on which part of Thailand you are in.

Thai people believe that the New Year, or springtime, is a time to "throw out the old and bring in the new". Songkran is "Spring Cleaning Day" across Thailand; it is part of their religious beliefs that useless items will bring bad luck if not thrown away.

The Songkran Festival is celebrated with water. On the afternoon of April 13, people carefully clean their images and statues of Buddha. Young people show respect to their elders and seek their blessings by pouring scented water into the hands of parents and grandparents.

The Songkran Festival is also a time of fun and joy. Everyone throws water on each other on the streets! Why? There were legends about serpents that sprayed water on the land. If these serpents sprayed a lot of water, there would be a lot of rain. Some people believe that throwing water at people is another way of asking for rain and they need the rain for farming. Whether or not this is true does not seem to matter to the people of Thailand on the day of the Songkran Festival – they are having a splash!

A. **Write "T" for the true sentences and "F" for the false ones.**

1.  People in different parts of Thailand celebrate the Songkran Festival for different periods of time.

2.  People throw away useless items at Songkran.

3.  They believe that getting rid of useless items will bring them luck.

4.  People clean their Buddha statues at the Songkran Festival.

5.  People poured scented water into the hands of their children to show their care.

6. F Some people believe that throwing water at people is another way of asking for wealth.

B. **Check the main idea of the passage.**

 Thailand celebrates New Year on January 1.

 People in Thailand respect their elders.

 People in Thailand celebrate New Year with water.

C. **Imagine it is the Songkran Festival in Thailand. Will you throw water at others? Why or why not?**

No! becayse I dont want their shirt to get wet.

The Future Tense

The **future tense** shows what will happen in the future. The verb is formed by adding "will/shall" before the base form of the verb. "Will" can be used with all subjects while "shall" is used with "I" or "we".

Example: My Thai pen pal will come to Canada at Easter.

D. Underline the future tense verbs in the following sentences.

1. My grandparents will visit Thailand next week.
2. We shall see them off at the airport.
3. They will stay at a resort near the beach.
4. Grandpa will take many photos with his digital camera.
5. Grandma will enjoy a quiet time there.
6. They will send us postcards.
7. They will be back for Christmas.

E. Circle the correct words to complete the paragraph.

Katherine 1. will / shall visit us in New Year. She will 2. spend / spent a week here. Dad will 3. takes / take us on a ski trip in Barrie. We 4. will / are join a beginner's program there. Dad will 5. be / being there to watch us. He 6. will / shall take his new video camera with him and 7. record / recording the trip.

F. Look at Andrew's New Year's resolutions. Write them in complete sentences.

1. make my bed
2. eat fewer candies
3. brush teeth twice a day
4. not make Mom angry
5. go running once a week
6. share toys with Johnny

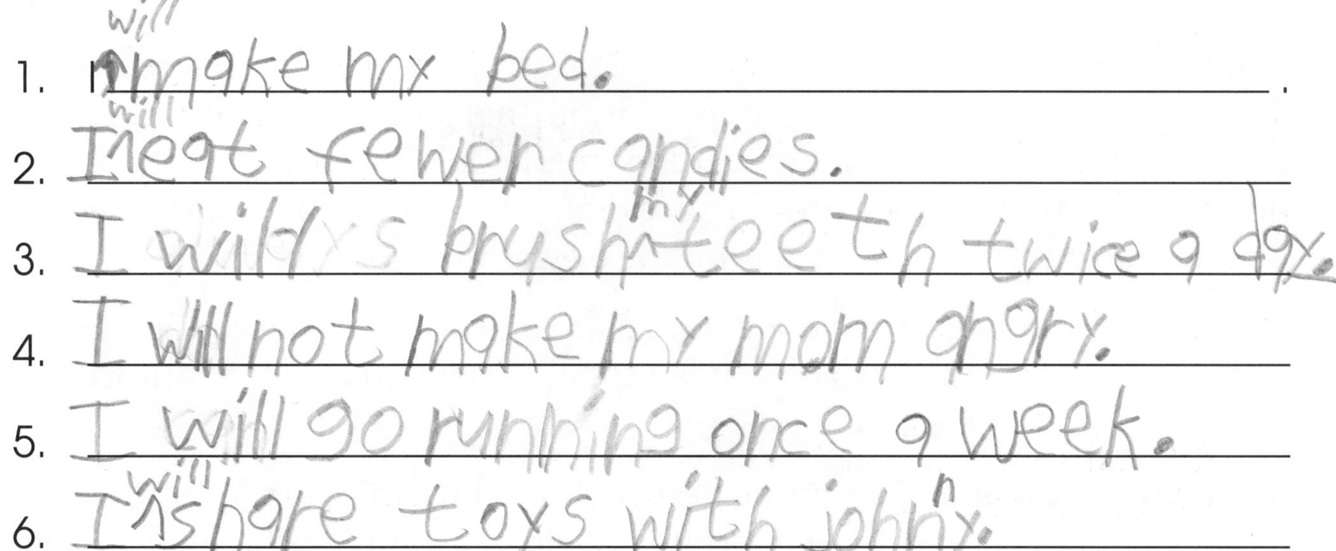

G. What are your New Year's resolutions? List three of them in the future tense.

1. ______
2. ______
3. ______

People have been writing about the "lost city" of Atlantis for centuries. Some say it was an ancient civilization that disappeared into the sea. Others say it was a place where real-life "merpeople" lived, and perhaps still do ("mer" is the French word for "ocean"). Do you think Atlantis is a real place? Do you think it still exists on the ocean floor somewhere?

Many people now believe that there is a place on Earth that can be traced back to the famous legend of Atlantis. It is a small Greek island called Santorini in the Mediterranean Sea.

Santorini is an island of stunning beauty. It has lowlands and lovely beaches at one end, but it rises up to enormous steep cliffs at the other end. When you stand on the cliffs and look out, you can see another, much smaller island.

Geologists (people who study the Earth) say this island's unusual shape is because of a volcano. Centuries ago, the island had a huge volcano on it. When it exploded around 3500 years ago, it blew the island apart.

Archaeologists have found evidence of an ancient town on Santorini. If you go there, you can see for yourself; there are walls and steps of buildings. Pot shards and cooking utensils and pieces of furniture have also been found.

Is this evidence of Atlantis or simply evidence that people lived on that lovely island centuries ago?

A. Read the clues. Complete the crossword puzzle with words from the passage.

Across

A. story handed down from the past

B. impressive

C. periods of 100 years

Down

1. proof
2. broken pieces of pottery, glass, etc.
3. implements or containers for everyday use at home

1 EVIDENCE
2 SHARDS
3 UTENSILS
A LEGEND
B STUNNING
C CENTURIES

B. Answer these questions.

1. What is so special about the landscape of Santorini?

It has lowlands and lovely beaches at one end but steep cliffs at the other end.

2. Why do some people believe that Santorini was Atlantis?

There is evidence of an ancient town of Santorini

Sentences (1)

A **sentence** gives a complete thought about someone or something.

A **telling sentence** makes a statement. It ends with a period.

Example: Santorini is a small island in Greece.

An **asking sentence** asks a question. It ends with a question mark.

Example: Have you been to Greece?

C. Write "T" for telling sentences, "A" for asking sentences, and "I" for incomplete sentences.

1. Do you know where Santorini is? A
2. Santorini, a beautiful island. I
3. Atlantis may never have existed. T
4. Are you interested in archaeology? A
5. Shall we go to the library? A
6. Just a legend. T
7. The landscape on the island is unique. T

D. Put the correct punctuation marks at the end of the sentences.

Have you been to the new Greek restaurant ? My parents took me there for dinner last night . It was the first time I had tried Greek food , Do you know what "Horta" is ? It is boiled greens . It tastes good with lemon, vinegar, and oil . Would you like to try it ?

E. Change the telling sentences to asking sentences and asking sentences to telling sentences.

1. There is a volcano on the island.
   Is there a volcano on the island?

2. The volcano did not explode in the last decade.
   Did the volcano not explode in the last decade?

3. People can find evidence of explosion.
   Can people find evidence of explosion?

4. Will Donald go to the beach this weekend?
   Donald will go to the beach this weekend.

5. Can we go boating on the lake?
   We can go boating on the lake.

F. Write two telling sentences and two asking sentences about the lost city of Atlantis.

Telling Sentences

1. People have been writing about the lost city of atlantis for centuries.
2. Pot stands and cooking utensils and pieces of furniture have also been found.

Asking Sentences

3. Do you think atlantis is a real place?
4. Is this evidence of atlantis or simply evidence that people lived on Ehatlovely island centuries ago?

The Snake Dens of Narcisse

The little town of Narcisse, Manitoba is known to herpetologists all over the world. Herpetologists are people who study snakes and other reptiles. The area around Narcisse has the world's largest population of the red-sided garter snake. It is the largest community of any snakes in the world!

Around Narcisse, the ground is made with a porous rock called limestone. There are a lot of crevasses and caves underground, which make cozy dens. The garter snake spends the winter there. It is the only reptile that can survive in such a cold place, thanks to these warm winter dens. There are more than 30 snake dens in a 12-square-kilometre area around Narcisse, which is the home of well over ten thousand snakes.

Once the snow is gone, male garter snakes come out of the dens. The female snakes appear soon after, and mating season begins. It lasts for about three weeks. During this time, the snakes will form large wriggling balls together. It is an extraordinary sight to see. When mating season is over, the snakes will slither away to nearby fields and wetlands for the summer to feed.

Female garter snakes will give birth to as many as 40 offspring, but over three-quarters of them will not survive through the winter. Cold temperatures, predators, and poaching are problems. Many snakes are also killed when they try to cross the highway. Snake tunnels have been built under the roads to help protect the snakes of Narcisse.

A. Give one-word answers to the questions.

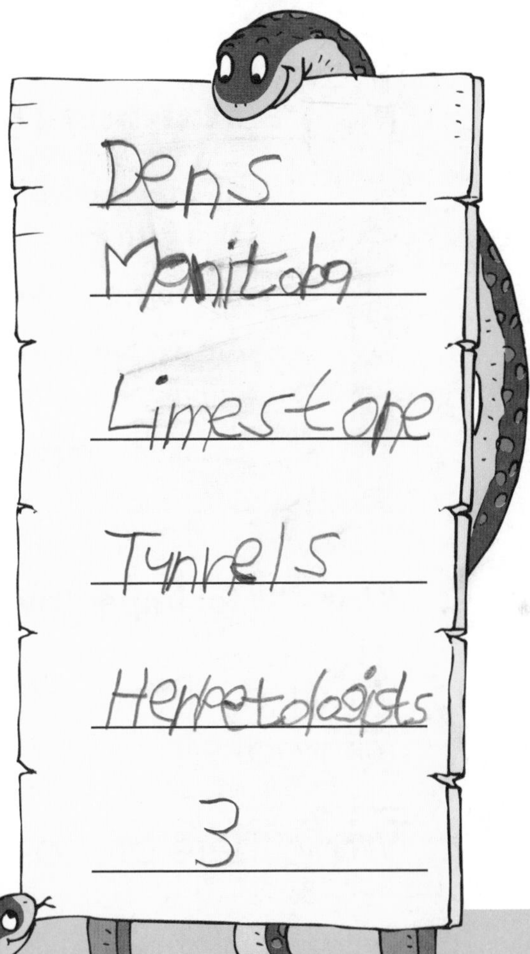

1. Where do snakes live? Dens
2. In which province is Narcisse? Manitoba
3. What is the ground of Narcisse made with? Limestone
4. What has been built to help protect the snakes in Narcisse? Tunnels
5. What do we call the people who study snakes and other reptiles? Herpetologists
6. How many weeks does the mating season of garter snakes last? 3

B. Write an effect for each of the following causes.

1. Narcisse has the world's largest population of the red-sided garter snake.

   Narcisse is known to herpetologists all over the world.

2. The crevasses and caves in the limestone make cozy dens.

   The garter snake is the only reptiles that can servive the cold winter in Nacrisse.

3. There are poachers for the garter snakes.

   Many snakes are killed.

Sentences (2)

An **imperative sentence** makes a request or gives an order. It ends with a period. The subject "you" is left out.

Example: Listen to me.

An **exclamatory sentence** expresses a strong feeling, such as surprise, happiness, or anger. It ends with an exclamation mark.

Example: That snake is real!

C. Write "I" for imperative sentences and "E" for exclamatory sentences.

1. What a big wriggling ball the snakes have formed!
2. Wow, there are so many snakes in the cage!
3. Take a picture of the snake.
4. Stay away from the bush.
5. Read the tag and write down the name of the snake specimen.
6. The snake is really long!
7. Do not stand beyond the railing.
8. I've never seen a snake with such a big head in my life!
9. Tell me the time, please.

D. Change the following questions to imperative sentences.

1. Could you show me your ticket?

   You could show me your ticket!

2. Will you take off the jacket?

   Take off the jacket!

3. Can you stop running?

   Stop running!

4. Would you wait for me at the exit?

   wait for me at the exit!

E. Look at the picture. Write three exclamatory sentences to show your feelings if you were one of the children.

1. Oh no the snake!
2. The snake is in the bushes!
3. We cant go!

14

Ogopogo

Canada's Lake Monster

You have probably heard of Nessie, the shy monster that lives in Loch Ness, Scotland. But did you know Canada has its own "Loch Ness Monster"? It is called Ogopogo, and it lives in the long, deep Lake Okanagan in British Columbia.

The Salish Native people in British Columbia have known about this lake monster for more than 100 years, long before the Loch Ness Monster became known to the world. These First Nations people called it N'ha-a-itk. Every time they needed to go onto the lake, they would look carefully for the monster before setting out. Sometimes they would throw food into the lake, so the monster would like them and leave them alone.

In 1942, the monster became known as Ogopogo. These days, we think Ogopogo is more of a friendly lake creature than a scary monster. Just like Nessie, the Loch Ness Monster, Ogopogo is believed to have a snake-like body, with several humps, a green outer skin, and a large, goat- or horse-like head. Its body is about half a metre in diameter and five or six metres long. Some people who claimed they saw it said it looked like a log! Some scientists think Ogopogo could be a kind of ancient water serpent or a primitive whale.

What do you think? Is Ogopogo a friendly creature – or just a funny story?

A. Match the related words.

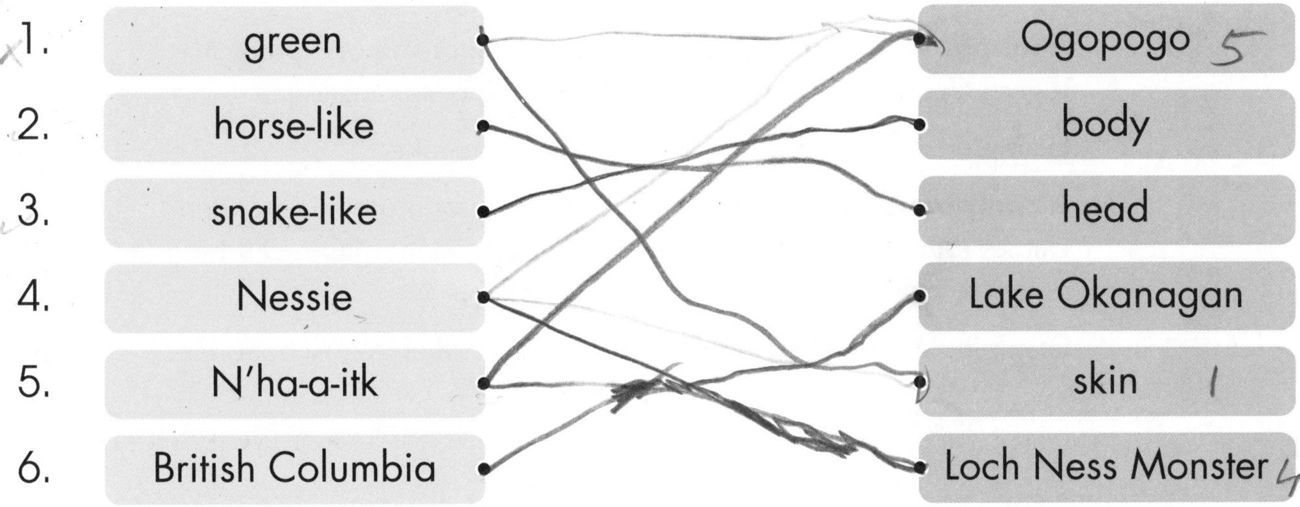

1.	green	Ogopogo
2.	horse-like	body
3.	snake-like	head
4.	Nessie	Lake Okanagan
5.	N'ha-a-itk	skin
6.	British Columbia	Loch Ness Monster

B. Write "T" for the true sentences and "F" for the false ones.

1. Canada has a lake called Lock Ness. ____
2. The name "Ogopogo" was adopted in 1942. ____
3. The First Nations people called the lake monster Ogopogo. ____
4. People would throw food into the lake to attract the lake monster. ____
5. Nessie and Ogopogo are believed to be the same kind of creature. ____
6. Ogopogo has several humps on its body. ____
7. Its body is about five or six metres in diameter. ____
8. Some scientists believe that Ogopogo could be a kind of primitive whale. ____

Simple and Compound Sentences

A **simple sentence** is made up of one subject and one predicate. It gives a complete thought about someone or something.

Example: Uncle Greg has a cottage near the lake.

A **compound sentence** is made up of two or more independent clauses joined by a conjunction. An independent clause can be a sentence by itself.

Example: We visit him every summer and he takes us on a boat ride.

C. Colour "S" for simple sentences and "C" for compound sentences.

1. They want to go to Lake Okanagan and they'll stay in the lakeside town for a few days.

2. Loch Ness is known for its monster Nessie and Lake Okanagan is famous for its Ogopogo.

3. The head of Ogopogo is like a horse but its body is like a snake.

4. The lake is 169 kilometres long and up to 300 metres deep.

5. Do you think it is a friendly creature or is it just a myth?

6. Ogopogo could be a kind of primitive whale.

7. The monster looks weird but cute.

D. Add subjects or predicates to make simple sentences.

1. The lake monster is called ogopogo .
2. Lake Huron saw the ogopog .
3. My sister and I watch TV In the night.
4. My dad and I go boating on the lake.
5. Everyone took a picture of the statue.
6. It is just a myth.

E. Complete the sentences with the related clauses to make compound sentences.

- we will watch it tonight
- Mom wants to go shopping
- his sister chose to be Snow White
- we call it Ogopogo

1. The First Nations people call the lake monster N'ha-a-itk but we call it og o pog o .
2. Benjamin picked a costume of the lake monster and his sister chose to be snow white .
3. Dad wants to go fishing this Saturday but Mom wants to go shopping .
4. Uncle Henry gave us a DVD yesterday and we will watch it tonight.

15

Cheese Rolling

Great Britain's Extreme Sport

You have probably heard of tomato throwing and the polar bear swim. But have you ever heard of the sport of cheese rolling?

Cheese rolling is an event that takes place every spring at Cooper's Hill, Gloucestershire (a county in England, west of London). People say that cheese rolling is one of Great Britain's oldest customs. Some say the custom started even before the Romans lived in that country 2000 years ago. Most say cheese rolling has been going on for at least a couple of centuries as a celebration of the onset of summer.

Each year, thousands of spectators come to Cooper's Hill to watch people chase a seven-pound round of Double Gloucester Cheese down the hillside. There are separate races for men and women, and now uphill races for boys and girls too. The winners get to keep the rounds of cheese they have tried so hard to catch. However, no one ever catches the cheese because it hurtles down the slope at nearly 110 kilometres per hour!

It is all quite funny to imagine people chasing a little wheel of cheese as it rolls down a hill, but perhaps it is not so funny to see it because Cooper's Hill is very steep. Every year, several of the cheese-chasers tumble down the hill. Often, people suffer broken bones. But this has not stopped the event from taking place.

Chasing cheese. Would you do it?

A. Complete the crossword puzzle with words from the passage that are synonyms of the clue words.

Across

A. onlookers

Down

1. beginning
2. maybe
3. dashes
4. fall
5. traditions

A: SPECTATORS
1: ONSET
2: PERHAPS
3: HURTLES
4: TUMBLE
5: CUSTOMS

B. Answer these questions.

1. Describe how the event goes.

The participant chase a seven pound round of Gloucester cheese down the hillside and try to catch it.

2. What are the prizes for the winners?

The winners will get the rounds of cheese they have tried to catch the prizes.

3. Do you think the event should stop? Explain.

no becayse the rounds of cheese is still rolling down the hill.

Capitalization

We use **capital letters** for:

- the first word in a sentence.
- proper nouns.
- titles.
- days, months, holidays, and events.
- races, nationalities, religions, and languages.

C. Rewrite the following paragraph by using capitalization correctly.

this year, the warwick cheese festival will take place from friday, june 16 to sunday, june 18. this annual event is the biggest cheese festival in north america, attracting tens of thousands of canadians and visitors from all over the world. you can sample over 100 kinds of cheese made all over quebec at the festival. attendees are invited to vote for the people's choice prize of the year.

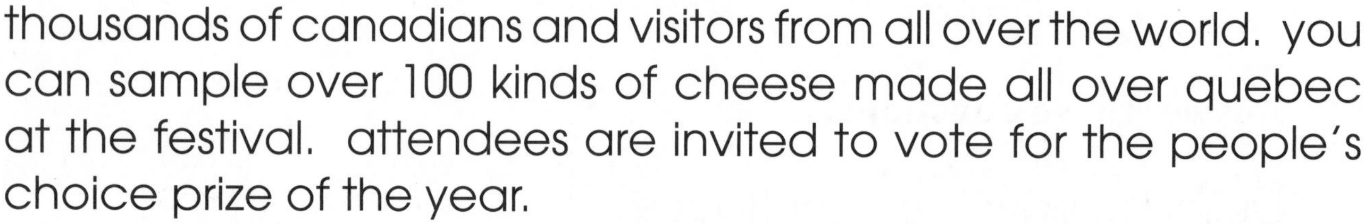

This year, the Warwick Cheese Festival will take place from Friday, June 16 to Sunday, June 18. This annual event is the biggest Cheese Festival in North America, attracting 10s of 000s of Canadians and visitors from all over the world. You can sample 100 kinds of Cheese made all over Quebec at the festival. Attendees are invited to vote for the peoples choice prize of the year.

Commas

We use the **comma** to:

- separate words or phrases in a series.
- separate adjectives before a noun.
- follow transition words.
- set off a direct quotation.
- set off words in apposition.

Example: Mr. Merlot, the committee chairman, said to the members, "We should find a new, safer location for next year's event." However, Mr. Anderson, Mr. Powers, and Mrs. Streep disagreed.

D. Add commas where needed in the following sentences.

1. Vincent shouted, "I shall return next year."
2. Bridget Carlson last year's, winner presented the prize to Jason.
3. The participants have to chase a big heavy, round of cheese down the hillside.
4. The slope, the stones, and the speed, have caused some cases of injuries.
5. Mr. Douglas their team leader, explained to them, why they had lost.
6. Unfortunately, the contest was put off, because of the nasty weather.

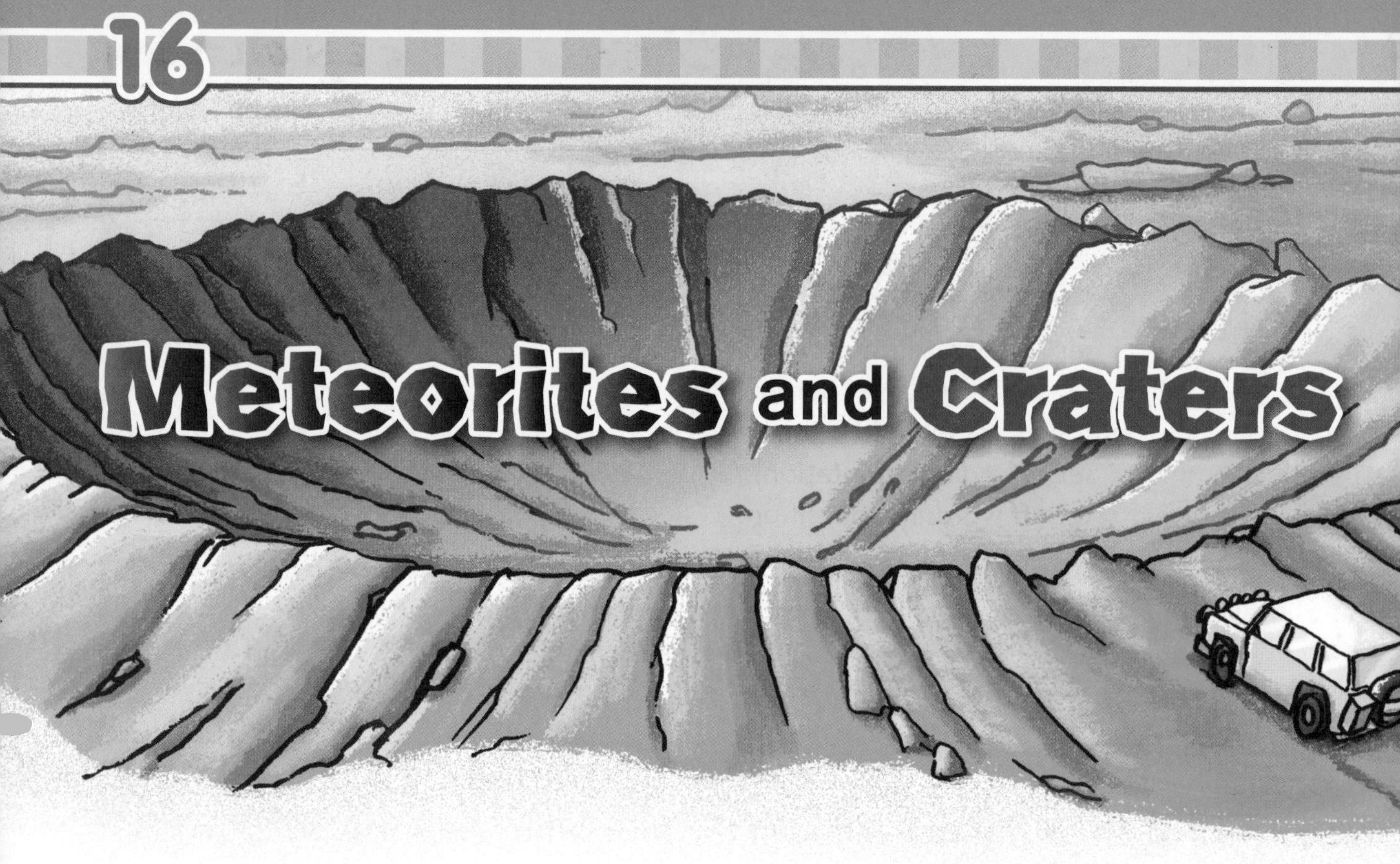

Meteors are large rocks that speed through space and fly into the Earth's atmosphere with a streak of bright light. Usually they break into pieces before they hit the Earth. If they land, we call them meteorites. If the meteorite is big, it will cause a lot of damage to our Earth. Some people believe that dinosaurs died out because a large meteorite hit the Earth millions of years ago.

When a meteorite hits the Earth, it forms a crater. Barringer Meteor Crater is in the United States, near the town of Winslow, Arizona. It is the best example of a crater that is easy to see. It is about 1200 metres in diameter and 170 metres deep. Scientists say this crater was made about 50 000 years ago, and was created by an iron meteorite that was only 30 m in diameter. That is a pretty small piece to make such a large crater!

We know of at least 120 craters around the world. Some are very old, and can only be seen when viewed from space. There is a crater in the Gulf of Mexico. It is 180 kilometres wide. Some scientists think this was the place where the meteorite which killed the dinosaurs landed.

Some people think that Hudson Bay is actually a crater. This would make it the largest crater on Earth by far. Do you believe it?

A. Write "F" for facts and "O" for opinions.

1. Dinosaurs died out because a large meteorite hit the Earth millions of years ago.

2. Meteors break into pieces before they land on the Earth.

3. Barringer Meteor Crater was formed about 50 000 years ago.

4. Barringer Meteor Crater is about 1200 m in diameter.

5. The iron meteorite that created the Barringer Meteor Crater was small.

6. There are at least 120 craters that we know of in the world.

7. Some craters can only be seen when viewed from space.

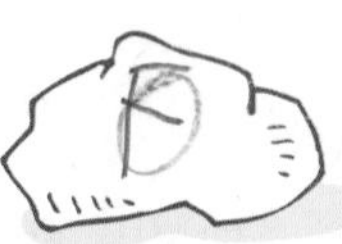

B. Find words from the passage for the meanings below.

1. loss of value and usefulness ____________

2. long, thin line ____________

3. the longest line across a circle ____________

4. come against something with force ____________

5. reached the ground ____________

Quotation Marks

Quotation marks are used in pairs. They can be used to:

- contain the exact words of a speaker or from a book.
  Example: "Freeze!" the FBI agent said.
- indicate the titles of songs, books, movies, newspapers, etc.
  Example: Do you watch the latest series of "The X Files"?

C. Add quotation marks where needed in the following sentences.

1. My dad is a great fan of Star Wars.
2. Dragon Rider is a must-read for you.
3. Wendy asked, Did dinosaurs have feathers?
4. Issac has read Harry Potter and the Goblet of Fire three times already.
5. The magician said, Count one to ten with me and then you will see.
6. All your performances were exceptionally good, the judge commented.
7. He added, Everyone deserves a big round of applause here.
8. They sang Dancing Queen in the singing contest.

Apostrophes

We use the **apostrophe** to:

- show possession.
  Example: Mike's brother has to wait for us there.
- form contractions.
  Example: He isn't tall enough to get on the ride.

D. Check whether the underlined words are possessives (P) or contractions (C).

		P	C
1.	"The Invaders" <u>isn't</u> an easy game to play.		✓
2.	<u>I'll</u> beat you in the next game.		✓
3.	We will meet at <u>Joe's</u> place tomorrow.	✓	
4.	The <u>teacher's</u> explanation was very clear.	✓	
5.	<u>Dad's</u> telescope is very powerful.	✓	
6.	They <u>didn't</u> understand how that crater was formed.		✓

E. Add apostrophes where needed in the following sentences.

1. Candys uncle is a professor at the University of Toronto.
2. The children dont want to stop the game.
3. Theyre going to be late.
4. Mr. Greens farm is near Hudson Bay.
5. Bryans dog doesnt like this model dinosaur.

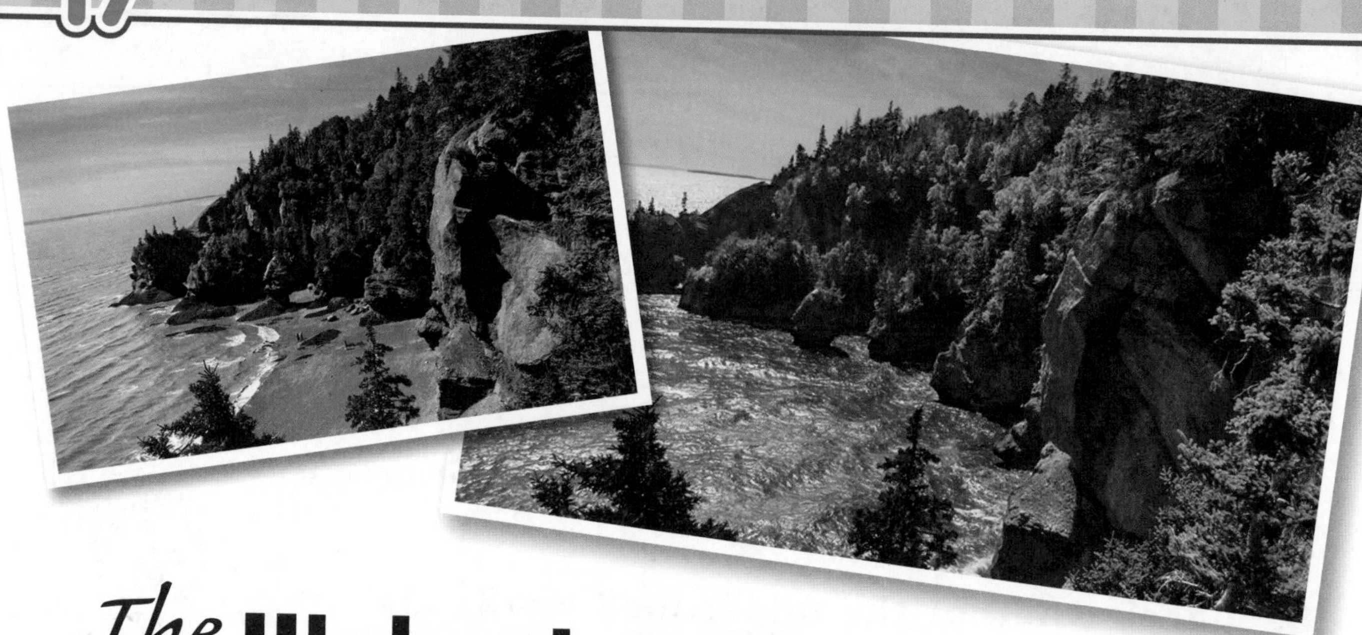

The Highest Tides on Earth

The sizes of ocean tides are different around the world. A typical tidal range is one or two metres. The Bay of Fundy, between New Brunswick and Nova Scotia, has one of the most extreme tidal ranges. The Minas Basin at the eastern end of the Bay of Fundy has the highest tides in the world. There, the tidal range is between 12 and 16 metres!

The main reason for the immense tides in the Bay of Fundy has to do with the shape of the Bay of Fundy-Gulf of Maine coastline and the continental shelf, which is a shelf of land that juts out into the Atlantic Ocean, making the sea floor shallower.

People from all over the world come to the town of Wolfville, Nova Scotia, to see the tide for themselves. At low tide, the tiny harbour of Wolfville is empty. The mud flats of the sea bottom extend for several kilometres. In summer months, migrating shorebirds feast on the worms and crustaceans exposed at low tide.

When the tide is rushing in, tidal bores often form in the St. Croix, Meander, and Salmon Rivers, which empty into the Minas Basin. Then people can watch the awesome sight of a wave of water travelling in the opposite direction of these rivers' current. Soon enough, however, the action starts moving in the opposite direction. High tide has arrived once again and the water will soon start moving out once more – in its never-ending and always fascinating cycle.

A. Fill in the blanks with words from the passage.

1. Usually, a tidal range is one or two metres.

2. The Bay of Fundy has Immencee tides.

3. The enormous tides of the Bay of Fundy are caused by the shape of the bay's Costland and the continental shelf.

4. At low tide, the mud flats of the sea bottom extend for several kilometres.

5. In summer, worms and crustaceans are exposed at low tide.

6. The tide rushes in and out in an endless cycle.

B. Write the main idea of each paragraph.

Paragraph One: The bay of Fundy has the highest tides in the world.

Paragraph Two: The main reason of the immense tide in the Bay of Fundy has to do with the shape of the bay of Fundy-Gulf of maine coastline which makes the sea floor shellow.

Paragraph Three: Wolfvile in Nova scotia people from all over the world to come and see the tide and megriting bird to feast on the animal expost at low tide in summer.

Paragraph Four: The high tide rushes in and then moves out. This repeats and forms a never ending cycle.

Connecting Words

We use **connecting words** to join ideas together. Some connecting words are used to add, contrast, show sequence, and conclude ideas.

Example: At low tides, the water will move out <u>and</u> some crustaceans will be exposed on the sand.

C. Circle the correct connecting words in the following sentences.

1. If / Since you want to see the highest tides of the world for yourself, you can go to Wolfville in Nova Scotia.

2. Nova Scotia may be a bit far to you and / but it is worth it.

3. Uncle Ray took some pictures of the tides. However / Also , he drew a few sketches of the scene.

4. Although / Because I did not see the tides for myself, I could imagine how massive they must have been.

5. Amy and I have not seen Uncle Ray when / since he left for Calgary in January.

6. He said that he would come back for Christmas and / or we could meet him in Calgary this summer.

D. Use these connecting words to join the related sentences below.

and but after because if

- I did not expect they would reach that high
- he will record the tidal bores
- it is a long ride to get there
- the waves subsided
- Dad takes us

1. I was shocked by the heights of the tides because I did not expect they would reach that high.
2. The water became very calm after the waves subsided.
3. The tides are beautiful but it is a long ride to get there.
4. I would love to go there again if dad take us. tidal bores.
5. I will ask Dad to take a video camera with him and he will record the tidal bores.

18

The Longest Train Ride

Did you know you can travel all the way from London, England to China by train? It is one of the longest regularly scheduled train rides in the world! This train journey passes through many cities, including Paris in France, Berlin in Germany, Warsaw in Poland, Moscow in Russia, Ulaanbaatar in Mongolia, and Beijing in China.

In the past, people taking this journey had to take a hovercraft from Dover, England to the coast of France, and then get back on a train. But now, the train goes through the Channel Tunnel, connecting England with France.

The longest run of this journey without changing trains is the Trans-Siberian Railway. This railway network actually has four routes connecting Moscow with the Russian Far East, Mongolia, China, and beyond.

The Trans-Siberian route runs from Moscow to the Russian Far East at Vladivostok. It is 9288 kilometres long and crosses eight time zones.

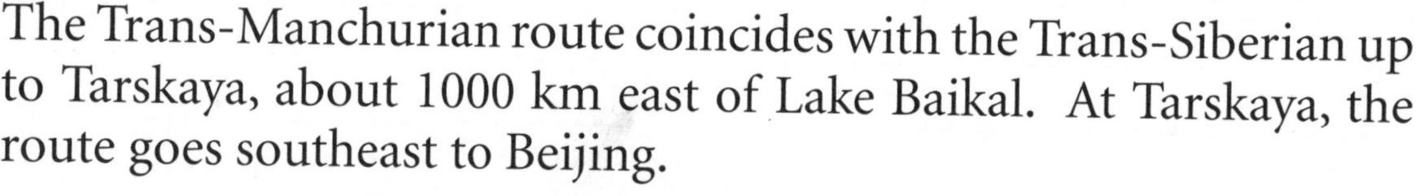

The Trans-Manchurian route coincides with the Trans-Siberian up to Tarskaya, about 1000 km east of Lake Baikal. At Tarskaya, the route goes southeast to Beijing.

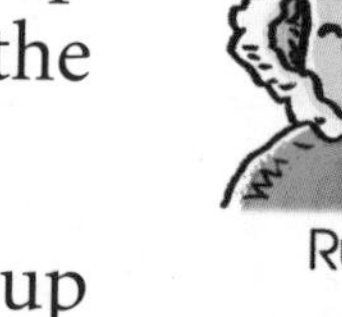

The Trans-Mongolian route coincides with the Trans-Siberian up to Ulan-Ude on Lake Baikal's eastern shore. Then it heads south to Ulaanbaatar, and then Beijing.

In 1991, a fourth route, the Baikal-Amur Mainline was completed. This line branches off from Tayshet to Khabarovsk, in Russia's Pacific Northeast.

A. Match the cities with their countries.

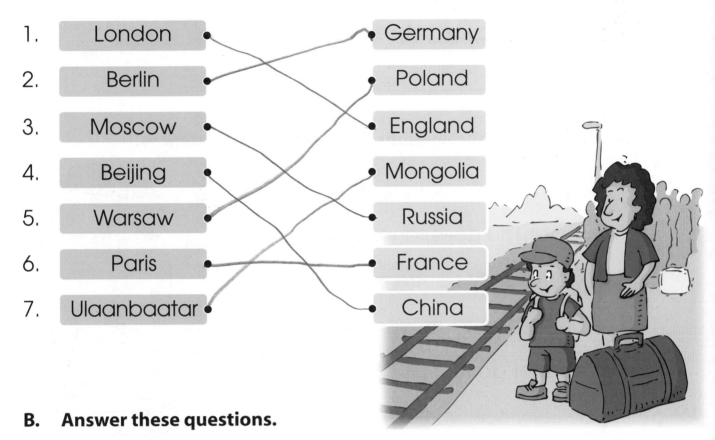

	City	Country
1.	London	Germany
2.	Berlin	Poland
3.	Moscow	England
4.	Beijing	Mongolia
5.	Warsaw	Russia
6.	Paris	France
7.	Ulaanbaatar	China

B. Answer these questions.

1. What is so special about the Trans-Siberian Railway?

It is one of the longest regularly scheduled train rides in the world!

2. What allows people to travel from England to France by train?

The channel tunnel allows people to travel connecting england with france.

3. From where do these routes branch off?

a. Trans-Manchurian Tarskaya

b. Trans-Mongolian Ulan-Ude

c. Baikal-Amur Mainline Tayshet

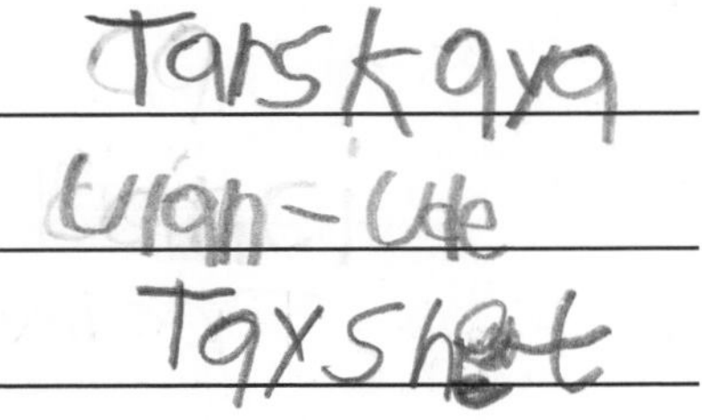

Abbreviations

An **abbreviation** is the shortened form of a word or words.

Example: December → Dec.

C. Underline the abbreviations in the following sentences.

1. A bag of potatoes weighs more than 4 kg.
2. Mrs. Sorenson goes to work by train.
3. The community centre is on Sunshine Rd.
4. P. 3 of the handouts went missing.
5. We cannot go to P.E.I. by train.
6. Uncle Larry has worked for Jubilee Co. for six years.
7. The Street Festival starts from Friday, Jul. 10.
8. Lt. Paddington gave each officer a map.

D. Write the abbreviations for the words and the standard forms for the abbreviations.

1. Mountain Mt.
2. compact disc CD.
3. Boulevard Blv
4. centimetre cm
5. U.S. USA
6. Jr. Junior
7. Tue. Tuesday
8. Ltd. Limited

Contractions

A **contraction** is a single word that is formed by combining and shortening two words. An apostrophe is used to replace letters.

Example: He has lost his day pass for the train.
<u>He's</u> lost his day pass for the train.

E. Form contractions from the following pairs of words.

1. there is ___theres___
2. do not ___dont___
3. should not ___Shouldnt___
4. they will ___theyll___
5. we are ___were___
6. you have ___youve___
7. did not ___didnt___
8. I am ___Im___
9. will not ___willnt___
10. that is ___thats___

F. Fill in the blanks with some of the contractions you formed in (E).

1. ___were___ going to the train station. Do you want a ride?
2. ___thats___ ridiculous. How could he have done that?
3. Can you see that? ___theres___ something behind the black curtain.
4. You ___didnt___ miss Lily. She is the tallest girl on the team.
5. ___Dont___ listen to him. He is a liar.
6. Polly was sick. She ___cant___ go to the show.

19

The Great Wall of China

The Great Wall of China was first built over 2200 years ago by the Emperor of the Qin (Ch'in) Dynasty. This warrior created his empire by defeating and uniting seven warring states. Then he connected four old fortification walls that had been built 500 years earlier to defend against the invading tribes.

Over the years, the Great Wall of China was built, rebuilt, and added to. The wall we see today is actually farther south than the first Great Wall. It was made with masonry, hard-packed earth, granite, bricks, and rocks. All the construction was done by hand! The wall varies in thickness, from about 4.5 to 9 metres.

A major rebuild took place from the end of the 14th century until the beginning of the 17th century, during the Ming Dynasty. The wall was expanded to 6400 kilometres. Watchtowers and cannons were built onto it.

The Great Wall of China is the biggest feat of engineering and construction ever undertaken. It stretches from Shanhai Pass on the Bohai Sea in the northeast part of China to the southeastern portion of Xinjiang province, in the far west. Today, it is a major tourist attraction. It is not only proof of our construction capabilities, but also a reminder of a history of warring and separation.

A. Choose the correct answers. Circle the letters.

1. The Great Wall of China was built by a Chinese B .

   A. dynasty B. emperor C. tribe

2. The Great Wall was built to A against the enemy.

   A. defend B. invade C. unite

3. The present wall is farther C than the first Great Wall.

   A. north B. east C. south

4. C were added onto the wall during the Ming Dynasty.

   A. Paintings

   B. Windows and doors

   C. Watchtowers and cannons

5. Which of these were not used to build the wall?

   A. masonry and granite

   B. bricks and rocks

   C. steel and wood

B. "It is not only proof of our construction capabilities, but also a reminder of a history of warring and separation." What does it mean? Explain in your own words.

It means that there is the great wall.

Prefixes

A **prefix** is a group of letters placed at the beginning of a base word to change its meaning.

Example: The prefix "un" of "unstable" changes the base word "stable" to its opposite.

C. In each group of words, circle the one that contains a prefix. Then write the prefix on the line.

1. invade include insignificant In
2. defend defrost deduct De
3. unwise unite undertaken Un
4. pressure prepaid precise Pre
5. disappear disaster discipline Dis

D. Use each prefix you have identified in (C) to form a new word. Use the new word to write a sentence of your own.

1. In Insignificant
2. De Defrost

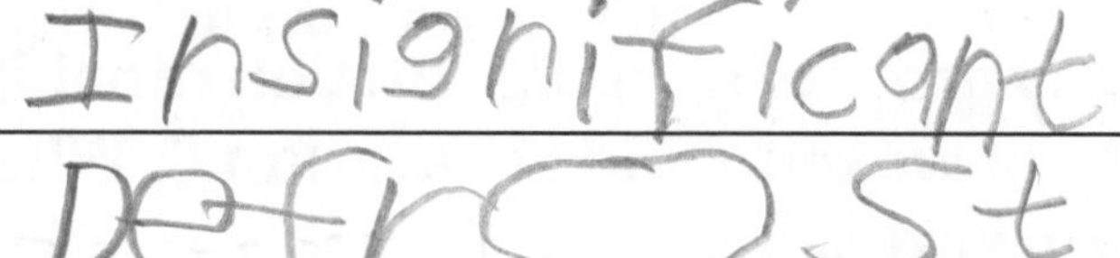

3. Un Unwise

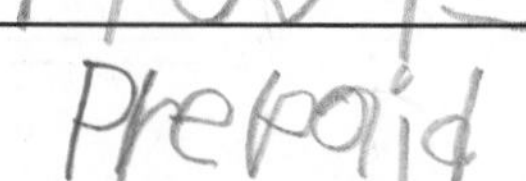

4. Pre Prepaid

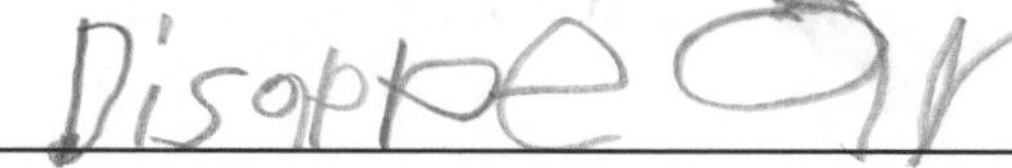

5. Dis Disappear

Suffixes

A **suffix** is a group of letters placed at the end of a base word to change its meaning.

Example: The suffix "er" of "reminder" changes the verb "remind" to a noun.

E. Complete the crossword puzzle with the base words of the clue words.

Across

A. provincial
B. construction
C. thickness
D. attractive

Down

1. noticeable
2. uniting
3. historical
4. earlier

F. Add a suffix to each of the following words to form a new word. Use the new word to write a sentence of your own.

big connect expand actual

1. big biggest
2. connect connnecting
3. expand expanded
4. actual actual s

Tulipomania

Have you ever heard of tulipomania? It means that people went crazy for tulips, all at the same time. This is not a joke. It really happened.

About 400 years ago, tulips were becoming the most popular flower in Holland (a part of what is now called the Netherlands). Rich people spent a lot of money building lavish gardens. It seemed that the more tulips they put in their gardens, the richer they felt. This made the price of tulip bulbs go higher and higher. If the price of a tulip bulb cost 50 florins (Dutch money) on Monday, it might cost 100 florins by Wednesday.

People started to think they could make a lot of money selling tulips. Now, both rich and poor people wanted tulips. If people did not have money, they traded their jewellery, their land, and their animals to buy tulip bulbs.

In late 1636, tulipomania reached its climax. One single tulip could be sold for 6000 florins, two horses, and a coach. At that time, 6000 florins would buy 50 tonnes of butter!

Soon after, tulip traders found that people were no longer willing to pay such high prices for tulips. The bubble burst. Tulips became almost worthless. People who had paid a lot of money for their tulips lost everything.

It seems hard to believe that people would spend so much money for a flower. Tulipomania was a baffling event, but it is something we can learn from.

A. Check the true sentences.

1. Tulipomania is only a story. F
2. Holland is a part of the Netherlands. T
3. All people in Holland spent a lot of money building lavish gardens. 
4. They were once willing to pay any price for tulips. T
5. People even traded their animals for tulip bulbs. 
6. Tulipomania was most serious in 1936. F
7. Florin is a kind of tulip. 
8. A single tulip once cost more than a horse. T

B. Quote a sentence from the passage to support each of the following sentences.

1. A tulip once cost a fortune.

A single tulip cost sold $6000 florins.

2. The price of tulips went up quickly.

If the price of a tulip bulb cost 50 florins on monday, it might cost 100 florins by wednesday.

3. People would pay any price for tulips.

If people did not have money, they traded their jewellery, their land, and their animals to buy tulip bulbs.

Compound Words

A **compound word** is formed when two words are put together to form a new word of a different meaning.

Example: flower + pot → flowerpot

C. Underline the compound words in the paragraph. Then circle them in the word search below.

This morning we got up early because we had to meet Grandma and Grandpa at the airport. They went to the Netherlands to celebrate Grandma's 50th birthday. I saw Grandma coming out from the gate before anybody else. I was attracted by her big tulip hairpin. Grandpa said they had been upgraded to business class because the economy class had been overbooked. How lucky they were!

G	r	h	u	p	g	r	a	d	e	d	G	a
r	h	a	i	r	p	i	n	h	d	p	r	i
a	b	i	r	h	d	a	y	a	G	r	a	r
n	i	r	o	a	b	o	b	i	r	a	n	p
d	r	o	v	e	r	b	o	o	k	e	d	o
e	t	t	G	r	a	n	d	m	a	d	p	r
b	i	r	t	h	d	a	y	a	n	y	a	t

D. Unscramble the letters to form compound words.

1. price + less (essl) Priceless
2. grass + hopper (popher) grasshopper
3. thunder + storm (morst) thunderstorm
4. fare (rafe) + well farewell
5. worth (rowth) + while worthwhile
6. marsh (sharm) + mallows marshmallows
7. table (letab) + cloth tablecloth

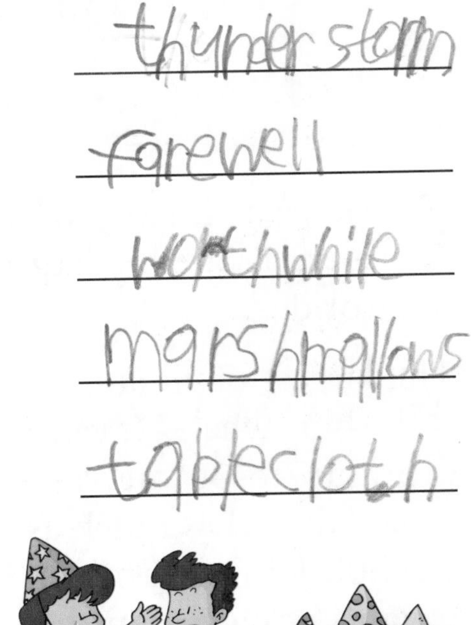

E. Fill in the blanks with the compound words you formed in (D).

1. We threw Tim a farewell party yesterday.
2. We bought some marshmallows for dessert.
3. Mom laid the new floral-patterned tablecloth on the table.
4. Can you see the grasshopper on that tulip?
5. Wendy was late because of the thunderstorm.
6. She said that it was worthwhile coming all the way from downtown.
7. To me, our friendship is Priceless.

21

The Largest of All

Do you know which animals are the largest in the world?

The largest of all animals is the blue whale. It can grow up to 30 metres in length and as much as 140 000 kilograms in weight, heavier than the biggest dinosaur. As you know, the blue whale lives in the ocean. Then, what is the largest land animal? The answer is the African elephant. The heaviest was recorded to be approximately 12 000 kg.

The largest and heaviest bird is the ostrich, which also lives in Africa. It can be more than two and a half metres tall and can weigh 145 kg, but it cannot fly like most other birds can. The wandering albatross, however, is the bird that has the widest wingspan, measuring almost three and a half metres. It flies over its home of Australia.

Reptiles and snakes can be very big too. The saltwater crocodile of Australia is the largest of all living reptiles. It is so big that it weighs as much as 25 adult humans! It can take any animal up to the size of a water buffalo. The anaconda snake, found in South America, is the heaviest snake. It can be eight metres long and weigh as much as three humans. The Komodo dragon, which is the world's largest lizard, can grow to three metres long and weigh as much as two humans.

A. Complete the chart.

Animal	Description	Measurement
1. blue whale	the largest of all animals	up to 30 m in length and 140 000 kg in weight
2. African elephant	The largest land animal	Approximately 12000 kg
3. ostrich	The largest and heaviest bird	More than 2 and a half m tall and can weigh 145 kg
4. wandering albatross	The bird with the widest wingspan	Measuring almost 3 and a half m
5. saltwater crocodile	The largest of all living reptiles	Weighs as much as 2.5 adult humans
6. anaconda snake	The heaviest snake	8 m long can be and weigh as much as 3 humans
7. Komodo dragon	The world's largest lizard	Grow to 3m long and weigh as much as 2 humans

Synonyms and Antonyms

A **synonym** is a word that is similar in meaning to another word.

Example: rush – dash

An **antonym** is a word that is opposite in meaning to another word.

Example: win – lose

B. State whether each pair of words are synonyms or antonyms.

1. grow shrink antonyms
2. leave return antonyms
3. fault mistake synonyms
4. goal objective synonyms
5. almost nearly synonyms

C. Fill in the blanks with the correct synonyms of the words in parentheses.

powerful arid scorching consume

1. Wild ostriches inhabit the (dry) arid African savannahs and deserts.
2. The ostrich, with its long, (strong) Powerful legs, is a fast runner.
3. Ostriches (eat) consume mainly seeds, roots, grass, and flowers.
4. Ostrich parents huddle their chicks under their body to protect them from the (hot) scorching sun.

D. Underline the antonym of the word in parentheses in each sentence.

1. Saltwater crocodiles are highly intelligent animals. (dumb)
2. The African elephant is threatened with extinction because of poaching and habitat destruction. (creation)
3. The wandering albatross can make shallow dives for food. (deep)
4. Although the anaconda snake is large, it is not venomous. (non-poisonous)
5. Komodo dragons are ferocious hunters that eat almost any animals, including humans. (gentle)

E. Complete the paragraph with synonyms or antonyms of the words in parentheses.

prey feeding gulp
tiny lunges

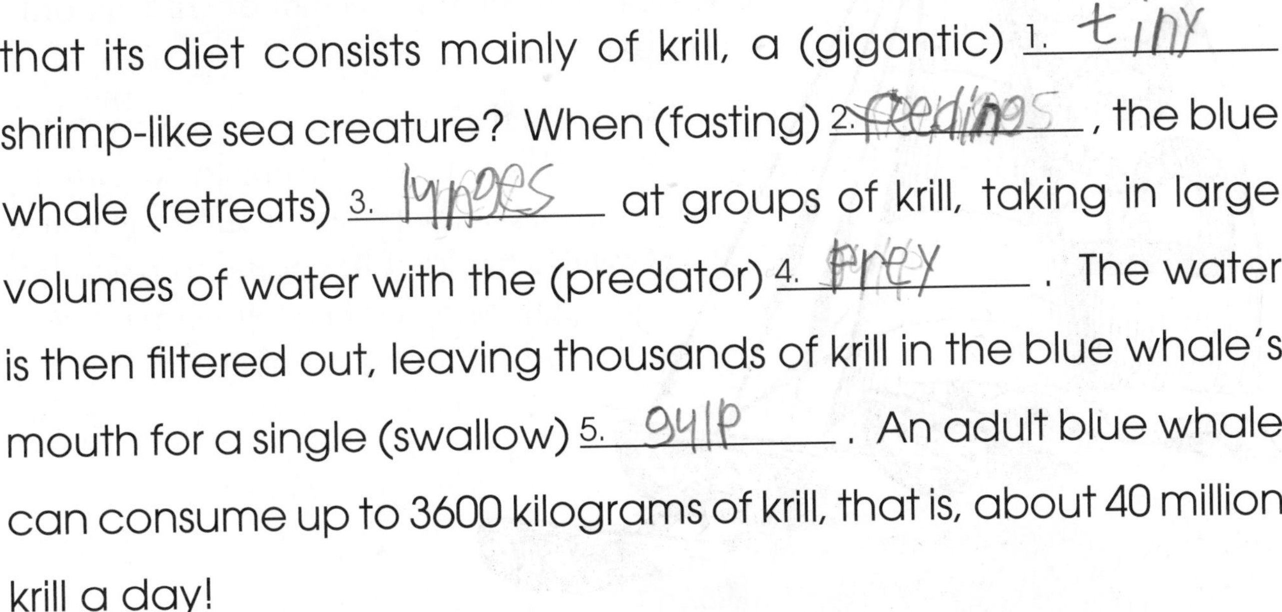

Knowing that the blue whale is the largest animal on Earth, can you believe that its diet consists mainly of krill, a (gigantic) 1. tiny shrimp-like sea creature? When (fasting) 2. feedings, the blue whale (retreats) 3. lunges at groups of krill, taking in large volumes of water with the (predator) 4. prey. The water is then filtered out, leaving thousands of krill in the blue whale's mouth for a single (swallow) 5. gulp. An adult blue whale can consume up to 3600 kilograms of krill, that is, about 40 million krill a day!

Ellen MacArthur

The Fastest Female Solo Sailor in the World

On February 7, 2005, Ellen MacArthur, a 28-year-old British woman, sailed around the world. Actually, sailing around the world is no longer an extraordinary feat. People have been doing it in sailboats and cruise ships for ages. But Ellen broke the world record by finishing the sailing in 71 days, 14 hours, 18 minutes, and 33 seconds – and she did it all by herself!

But this was not Ellen's first experience as a record-breaker. In the 2001 Vendée Globe race, she sailed around the world solo in 94 days. At that moment, she became the fastest woman and youngest person to sail solo around the world.

During this trip, she videotaped her experiences. She suffered from loneliness much of the time. If there was a problem, she had to fix it herself. For example, during a storm, Ellen was injured by a flying object inside her small cabin. She had to stitch up the cut herself. She was a cook, sailor, doctor, repairperson, mechanic – and her only companion.

When asked about her achievement, Ellen said it was not an easy thing to do. But the support of the public around the world was what kept her going to reach her goal. She thanked her team on land which made it possible.

A. Check the meanings of the underlined words as they are used in the passage.

1. **ages**
   - [x] A a very long time
   - [ ] B lengths of time that a person has lived
2. **record**
   - [ ] A videotape
   - [x] B best performance ever reached
3. **race**
   - [ ] A a subdivision of humankind sharing physical characteristics
   - [x] B contest
4. **trip**
   - [x] A a journey
   - [ ] B stumble
5. **fix**
   - [x] A repair
   - [ ] B fasten something firmly to something

B. Write the main idea of each paragraph.

Paragraph One: Ellen MacArthur broke the world reord by sailing around in 71 days, 14 hrs, 18 min and 33 sec.

Paragraph Two: Ellen was the fastest woman and youngest person to sail solo around the world.

Paragraph Three: Ellen was lonely and has to fix problems herself during the trip.

Paragraph Four: Ellen will continue her goal of breaking other records with the support of people around the world.

Homophones

A **homophone** is a word that sounds the same as another word, but has a different meaning and spelling.

Example: sail – sale

C. Circle the homophones of these words in the word search.

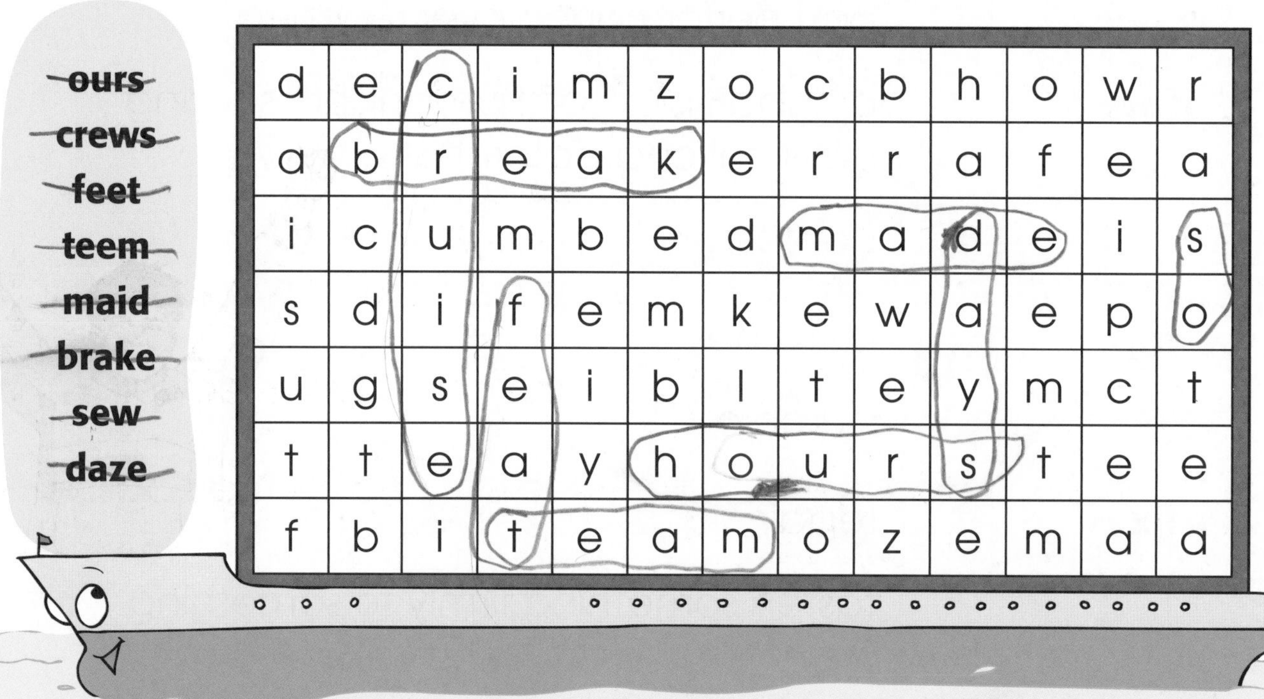

ours
crews
feet
teem
maid
brake
sew
daze
d e c i m z o c b h o w r
a b r e a k e r r a f e a
i c u m b e d m a d e i s
s d i f e m k e w a e p o
u g s e i b l t e y m c t
t t e a y h o u r s t e e
f b i t e a m o z e m a a

D. Fill in the blanks with homophones of these words.

peak blew role sealing knight

1. Peter can touch the ____________ of the cabin.
2. We want to ____________ at Uncle John's note.
3. Kylie likes the ____________ of the sea water.
4. Uncle John thinks that it is tranquil to sail at ____________ .
5. Kylie helped him ____________ up the sail on the mast.

Frequently Confused Words

We may be confused by words that have similar spellings or that sound alike. To ensure that we use the proper word, we can look it up in the dictionary to clarify the meaning.

Examples: His boat is bigger <u>than</u> ours.
We should check the weather first. <u>Then</u> we will decide if we go sailing tomorrow.

E. Circle the correct words for the following sentences.

1. Its / It's such a good day to go sailing.
2. We should waste / waist no time and set sail to the island.
3. Feel free to seek advise / advice from your leaders.
4. A team of boats with colourful sails sailing off the coast is an awesome site / sight .
5. It seems that the rope is a bit loose / lose .
6. He wants to take a beginner's coarse / course before we go sailing again.
7. Everyone except / accept Daniel enjoyed the sailing trip.
8. Whose / Who's cap is this?
9. Maybe / May be we should take it to the "Lost and Found".

On November 7, 1872, the Mary Celeste left New York to sail to Italy. Captain Briggs, his wife and daughter, and seven crew members were on board. But something terrible happened. The captain of another ship found the Mary Celeste floating in the middle of the Atlantic Ocean on December 4, 1872. There were no people on the wooden sailing ship and they were never found.

What happened? Why did the crew and passengers leave the ship? There were no obvious reasons. The Mary Celeste was undamaged. Everything was neat and tidy, with no sign of fighting. There was plenty of food and drinking water and no sign of fire or smoke damage. But Captain Briggs, his family, and the crew abandoned the Mary Celeste very quickly. We can tell because there was half-eaten food on the table. The crew also left all their clothing behind. Even their boots were beside their beds.

How and when did the people leave? Although some people claim that the lifeboat was still on the ship, others say it was missing. The captain's journal was still on the ship and the last entry was made on November 24. So, we can only guess that they left sometime between then and December 4.

An investigator, Mr. Flood, went to the ship several times to search for the answers to all the questions. But he could not find anything. No one else has solved the mystery either.

What do you think happened to those people on the ship?

A. Match the words with their meanings. Write the letters.

1. crew D
2. obvious B
3. abandoned E
4. entry A
5. investigator C

(A) item written
(B) clear; easily seen
(C) person who looks into something
(D) all people working on a ship
(E) deserted

B. Answer these questions.

1. How many people had gone missing when the Mary Celeste was found?

   10 people had gone missing when Mary Celeste was found.

2. How do you know the people left the ship very quickly?

   a. There was half-eaten food on the table.

   b. The crew also left all their clothing behind.

   c. Even their boots were beside their bed.

3. What happened on these days?

   a. Nov. 7, 1872:

   The Mary Celeste left New York to sail to Italy.

   b. Nov. 24, 1872:

   captain briggs made the last century in the captains journale

   c. Dec. 4, 1872:

   The captain of another ship found the Mary Celeste floating in the middle o the Atlantic Ocean.

Journals

A **journal** is a daily written record of things happened and experiences.

C. Imagine you are Captain Briggs. Write a journal for November 24, 1872.

You can write about an event that might lead to the abandoning of the ship later on.

November 24, 1872

Captain briggs has been made the last or final century in the captains Journal before Captain briggs has been left the Ship At the Mystery.

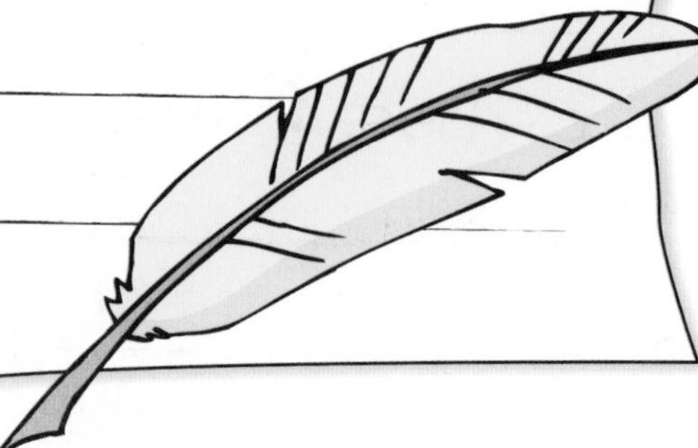

Forming Questions

We can begin a question with a question word like "What", "When", "Where", "Who", "Whom", "Whose", "Why", or "How".

Example: <u>Where</u> was the ship found?

D. Complete the questions with question words.

1. ___Why___ did the crew and passengers leave the ship?
2. ___Where___ can we see the northern lights?
3. ___Who___ are those things in the corner?
4. ___Who___ can solve the problem?
5. ___How___ does this machine work?
6. ___Who___ did you call just then?
7. ___Why___ can't you join us?
8. ___Whose___ journal is this?

E. You have a chance to ask Mr. Flood, the investigator, five questions about the mysterious case of the Mary Celeste. What will you ask him? Use the question words you have learned.

1. What happened?
2. Why did the crew and passengers leave the ship?
3. Where was the ship found?
4. How and when did the people leave?
5. What do you think happened to those people on the ship?

24

Inukshuk

Have you ever seen an inukshuk? If you have seen the flag of Nunavut, you have seen one. The word "inukshuk" means "likeness of a person" in Inuktitut, the language of the Inuit people.

An inukshuk is a stone figure made by balancing rocks on top of each other. Inuksuit (the plural form of inukshuk) are an important part of Inuit culture and are created for various reasons. Depending on how the rocks are placed, an inukshuk may be built to warn others of nearby dangers, mark a place of respect, such as a gravesite, or show directions for later travellers to follow.

Building an inukshuk is an important part of hunting for the Inuit people. An inukshuk may be built to give other hunters information about the location of caribou herds or spook the caribou during the hunt, causing the animals to run to an area where other hunters lie in wait.

An inukshuk may be large or small, and the rocks used will be of any size and shape. An inukshuk may consist of only one stone too, although most are made of several rocks. It is forbidden to destroy or remove an inukshuk.

There are important things to consider when building an inukshuk. The rocks must fit together in harmony, and balance each other. Those making the inukshuk must work together. In Canada's Arctic territories, one can still see these amazing structures. Some are centuries old, still standing as a symbol of harmony and cooperation.

A. Fill in the blanks with words from the passage.

1. An inukshuk is the symbol on the flag of Nunavut.
2. An inukshuk can show travellers Directions.
3. Inuksuit are important to the lives of Inuit people, especially Hunters.
4. People build inuksuit with rocks of any Size and Shape.
5. The rocks must Balance each other when building an inukshuk.
6. Removing or destroying an inukshuk is Forbidden.
7. An inukshuk stands as a symbol of Harmony and Cooperation.
8. Some inuksuit found in Canada's Arctic territories are centuries old.

B. List five uses of an inukshuk.

1. To warn others of nearby dangers.
2. Mark a place of respect.
3. To show travellers directions.
4. To tell hunters information about the location.
5. To spook caribou causing them to run where hunters lie in wait.

Tricky Usage

Some words often cause confusion. Be sure to check the correct usage of these words in the dictionary to avoid mistakes.

Example: They are <u>already</u> for the competition. (✗)
They are <u>all ready</u> for the competition. (✔)

C. Read the explanations and complete the sentences with the correct choices. You may change the form where necessary.

1. **among and between**

"Among" refers to more than two people or things while "between" refers to two people or things.

a. ________ the six stones, the bottom one is the biggest.

b. You need to put one flat stone ________ the two round ones.

2. **lay and lie**

"Lay" is a transitive verb meaning "to place something down". "Lie" is an intransitive verb meaning "to rest in a certain position".

a. The doctor asked me to ________ down on the bed.

b. Please ________ the picnic blanket on the grass.

3. **raise and rise**

"Raise" means "to make higher". You have to do something to something else. "Rise" means "to get up".

a. They all rise when there is a score.

b. They are raise the flags of the teams they support.

4. **bring and take**

"Bring" means "to carry from a more distant place to a nearer one". "Take" means the opposite.

a. Please bring the drinks over here.

b. I helped Dad take the garbage out today.

5. **good and well**

"Good" is an adjective and it describes nouns. "Well" is an adverb and it describes verbs.

a. The necklace is good on you.

b. He dances well .

6. **amount and number**

"Amount" is used with uncountable nouns whereas "number" is used with countable nouns.

a. A large number of beads were used to make this belt.

b. There is only a small amount of sugar in the dessert.

Rainforests are called "the lungs of the world" because we breathe oxygen with our lungs, and the dense growth of trees in rainforests makes the much-needed oxygen.

Rainforests can be divided into four layers. The forest floor is the ground level. It is very dark down there because very little sunlight gets past all the leaves in the trees above. When dead leaves and animals are on the ground, they are broken down into organic matter by the heat and the many small insects.

The understorey starts from the ground to about 20 metres. It is made up of the trunks of taller trees, plants, and smaller trees. It is still quite dark at this level, so the trees grow slowly. Some of these trees grow tall and pointed at the top to reach the sunlight. Other plants, like vines, cling onto the trees and get a free ride toward the sunlight.

The canopy layer is made up of the limbs and leaves of trees. This is a very thick layer: 20 to 50 m off the ground. Insects, birds, reptiles, and monkeys live in this layer. This layer of leaves and branches catches the sunlight and also most of the rain.

The top layer is called the emergent layer. The top of the tallest trees can stretch more than 50 m high. These trees are old and big but there are not too many of them. These trees have huge leafy heads that stretch wide because they have more room to grow.

A. Name the layers of the rainforest, from the bottom (1) to the top (4). Then match the activities with the layers by writing the letters in the boxes.

1. The forest Floor [C]
2. The understorey [A]
3. The canopy [D]
4. The emergent [B]

(A) Vines cling onto trees to reach the sunlight.

(B) Huge leafy heads of trees stretch wide.

(C) Dead leaves are broken down into organic matter.

(D) Insects, birds, reptiles, and monkeys live here.

B. Answer these questions.

1. Why are rainforests called "the lungs of the world"?

The dense growth of trees there makes the oxygen that we breathe our lungs.

2. What breaks down the dead leaves and animals on the ground of the rainforest?

Heat and small insects break down the dead leaves and animals on the ground.

3. Why are some trees in the understorey pointed at the top?

They want to reach the sunlight.

Writing Paragraphs

A **paragraph** is a group of sentences that express a common idea. It is made up of a topic sentence and body sentences.

A **topic sentence** introduces the main idea. Usually, it is the first sentence in a paragraph. It tells us what to expect in the rest of the paragraph.

C. For each paragraph, check the appropriate topic sentence.

1. Rainforests clean and recycle water. The rainforest plants remove carbon dioxide from the atmosphere and give out much of the Earth's oxygen. Rainforests affect the greenhouse effect, which traps heat inside the atmosphere.

 Rainforests are important to the Earth's ecology.

 Rainforest plants generate much of our oxygen.

2. The whole restaurant was decorated like a real rainforest. There were monkeys swinging in the trees. A crocodile kept opening and closing its mouth and an elephant kept curling up its trunk. There was a big aquarium filled with colourful fish. We could also hear the sounds of different animals, such as birds, gorillas, and elephants.

 I felt as if I were in a rainforest.

 Dad took us to a special restaurant for lunch.

D. Write a topic sentence for each of the following paragraphs.

1. Topic sentence: They went to the myseum that they are watching the movie stars.

You can find wax figures of famous people in the museum – Elvis Presley, John Lennon, John F. Kennedy, and Pierre Elliot Trudeau, to name a few. These figures were carved in detail. You may find your favourite movie stars standing beside you. So, be prepared.

2. Topic sentence: She went to the beach and she putted on her out in the sun.

I woke up early and put on my "out in the sun" T-shirt. Mom had already finished packing our food and drinks. Dad loaded everything into the trunk and off we went. It took us almost an hour to get to the beach.

3. Topic sentence: He is alone in the forest and the rabbit came in the forest.

He went into the forest alone after his wife passed away. His children had tried to convince him to come home time and again but he refused to leave. Mr. Sanderson has not had his hair cut since he left home 20 years ago. He finally came out on their 30th wedding anniversary.

Our Window Box Herb Garden

My family lives in a small apartment. We do not have a backyard, but we love plants. One day, Mom and I decided to make a window box herb garden.

First, we went to the library to read about how to grow herbs in window boxes. Then we went to the gardening store and bought a long window box with a long "dish" that fits under it, some soil, and packets of seeds. Then we went for a "coffee talk" at a doughnut shop and talked about what delicious meals we would make with our herbs.

At home, we put some small stones into the bottom of the box. The stones allow extra water to drain out of the soil and into the dish under it. If there is no drainage, the soil gets soggy and the herbs do not grow well.

Mom and I both love pizza, so we made sure to plant a lot of basil. I love the smell of fresh basil! We also planted rosemary, which tastes good with roast lamb. That smells wonderful too. We planted mint because Mom wanted to try making fresh mint tea. We planted dill too because it goes so well in potato salad.

We placed the window box on top of the fridge and waited for the seeds to sprout. Then we put the box on the shelf outside the kitchen window to get sunlight. My mom and I love to smell our fresh herbs. We couldn't wait to see them grow and prosper!

A. Colour the herbs that the writer planted. Then write the herbs for the dishes.

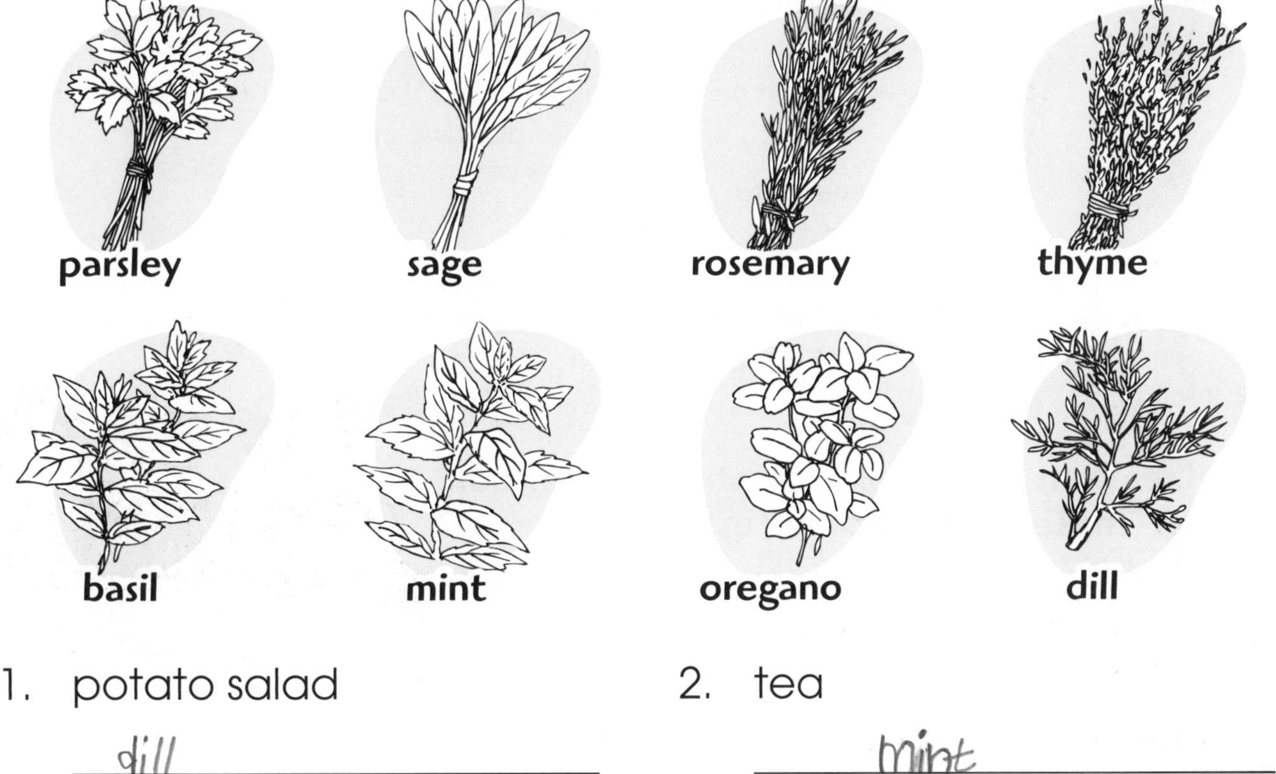

1. potato salad

dill

2. tea

mint

3. roast lamb

rosemary

4. pizza

basil

B. Put what the writer and her mom did in order. Write the letters on the lines.

A They put the box on the shelf outside the kitchen window.

B They placed some stones in the box and planted the herbs.

C They read about how to grow herbs in window boxes.

D They put the box on top of the fridge and let the seeds sprout.

E They bought a window box, some soil, and packets of seeds.

C E B D A

Narrative Writing

In **narrative writing**, we tell a story, true or imagined. We usually write the events in the order in which they happen. We may tell the story in either the first person (using "I" or "we") or the third person (using "he", "she", "it", or "they"). To plan, we should:

- think of a general storyline.
- set the time and place for the story.
- list the events in the story in the order in which they happen.
- include a concluding paragraph that wraps up the story or leads the reader to think more about it.

C. Create an outline for a narrative composition on "The Last Day of School" in the third person.

Topic: The last day of school

General storyline: This is the summer holiday and they are packing the books and everything.

Time and place: The school ends early and begins late.
The story takes place at school.

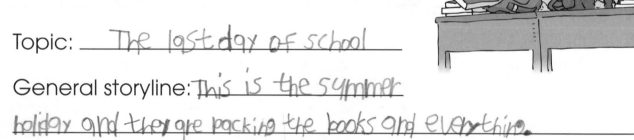

Events: The events are...
Canada day: Fireworks in Canada
America day: Fireworks in America
Pakistan day: Fireworks in Pakistan
India day: Fireworks in India

Conclusion: The School is finally ended.

Paragraphs in a Narrative Composition

Introductory paragraph: This sets up the story. It tells where and when the story takes place, who is involved, and what the story is about.

Body paragraphs: They contain details of the events.

Concluding paragraph: This ends the story.

D. Based on your outline in (C), write a finished copy of your story.

Title: Summer holiday

Introduction: The story takes place outside.

Body paragraphs: The people is saying bye to each other because this is the summer holiday and The events are...
canada day: Fireworks in Canada
America day: Fireworks in America
Pakistan day: Fireworks in Pakistan
India day: Fireworks in India.

Conclusion: Now Everyone is having the break.

Our Summer at the Farm

Last summer, my parents took my little sister and me to my grandpa's old farmhouse. Grandpa was born in the house. He says that when he was a boy, there were many farmers living in the area around the old farmhouse. There are not so many now.

Mom wanted to plant a vegetable garden, so Grandpa tilled the soil before we arrived. In late May, we planted onions, potatoes, peas, beans, carrots, leeks, corn, and Chinese cabbages. By the end of June, there were a lot of weeds in our garden, so we had a lot of hoeing to do.

The onions came up first. By the middle of July, we had so many onions! We ate them in salads and egg sandwiches, and gave a lot away. But where were our carrots, leeks, and Chinese cabbages? Grandpa said the grasshoppers had eaten the tops off them! But at least they did not get the peas and beans.

By the middle of August, the grasshoppers were starting to eat the leaves off all the potato plants, so we picked the potatoes quickly, and they were small. We ate a lot of potato salad. Small potatoes are yummy! The corn did not get very big, either. There were just too many weeds. But we still had fun eating our own delicious potatoes, onions, peas, and beans.

By the end of August, our garden was empty. But the memories of our special summer on the farm will be with us forever!

A. Write "T" for the true sentences and "F" for the false ones.

1. The writer went to his grandpa's farmhouse with his parents and brother. F
2. There are not many people living around their farmhouse now. T
3. The writer's grandpa tilled the soil before they arrived. T
4. Carrots were the first to come up. F
5. Some of their vegetables were eaten off by grasshoppers. T
6. The carrots, leeks, and Chinese cabbages were untouched by the grasshoppers. F
7. They gave many vegetables away. T

B. Write one thing that the writer and his family did in each period of time.

1. Late May

   They planted different types of vegetables.

2. Late June

   They hoed their vegetable garden.

3. Mid-July

   They made salads and egg sandwitches with the onions They had grown.

4. Mid-August

   They picked the potatoes.

Descriptive Writing

Descriptive writing describes a person, a thing, or an event in great detail to create a picture in the reader's mind. We can make our writing more interesting by using vivid adjectives and adverbs.

C. Write two adjectives to describe each of the following nouns.

1. farmhouse ________ , ________
2. garden ________ , ________
3. grandpa ________ , ________
4. day ________ , ________

D. Underline the adverb in each of the following sentences. Then circle its synonym.

1. The field needs tilling and watering badly.
   desperately / well
2. The weeds are almost as tall as my sister.
   mostly / nearly
3. The birds are chirping cheerily in the trees.
   happily / loudly
4. They really enjoyed the rural experience on the farm.
   truly / actually

Using Senses in Descriptive Writing

We may develop our **descriptive writing** according to our senses – sight, hearing, touch, and sometimes smell and taste too.

E. Complete the table by listing and describing what you sensed in your last outing, e.g. a day at a farm, the zoo, or the beach.

	What you sensed	Description (in detail)
Sight	Book	I see the book
	couch	I see the couch
Hearing	class	I heor the class
	Sink	I heor the Sink
Smell	Rice	I smell the rice
	Waffle	I smell the waffle

F. Based on the table in (E), write a short paragraph about the outing. Be as descriptive as you can.

The World Is Ours

Venezuela! France! Sudan!
China and Afghanistan!
I'll go here, then I'll go there.
I want to learn about everywhere!

I want to ask, "How are you feeling?"
In Ushuaia and Darjeeling.
I'll play soccer with kids like me
From the Amazon River to the Caspian Sea.

Come with me!
The world is ours!
We'll learn – we've got secret powers.

In Vietnam, we'll plant some rice.
Then fly to Tibet, and touch the skies.
We'll make our way to Timbuktu –
Tuktoyaktuk and Kalamazoo!

Iceland! Spain! Cambodia!
Ethiopia! Bolivia!
Indonesia! Mexico!
So many places we will go.

We'll have fun, but we'll take a stand
When our friends need help in far-off lands.
It's up to me. It's up to you.
Together we will make it true.

The world is mine.
The world is yours.

The world is ours.

A. Complete the crossword puzzle with words from the passage that rhyme with the clue words.

Across

A. Afghanistan
B. go
C. there
D. me

Down

1. Cambodia
2. you
3. eyes
4. ours

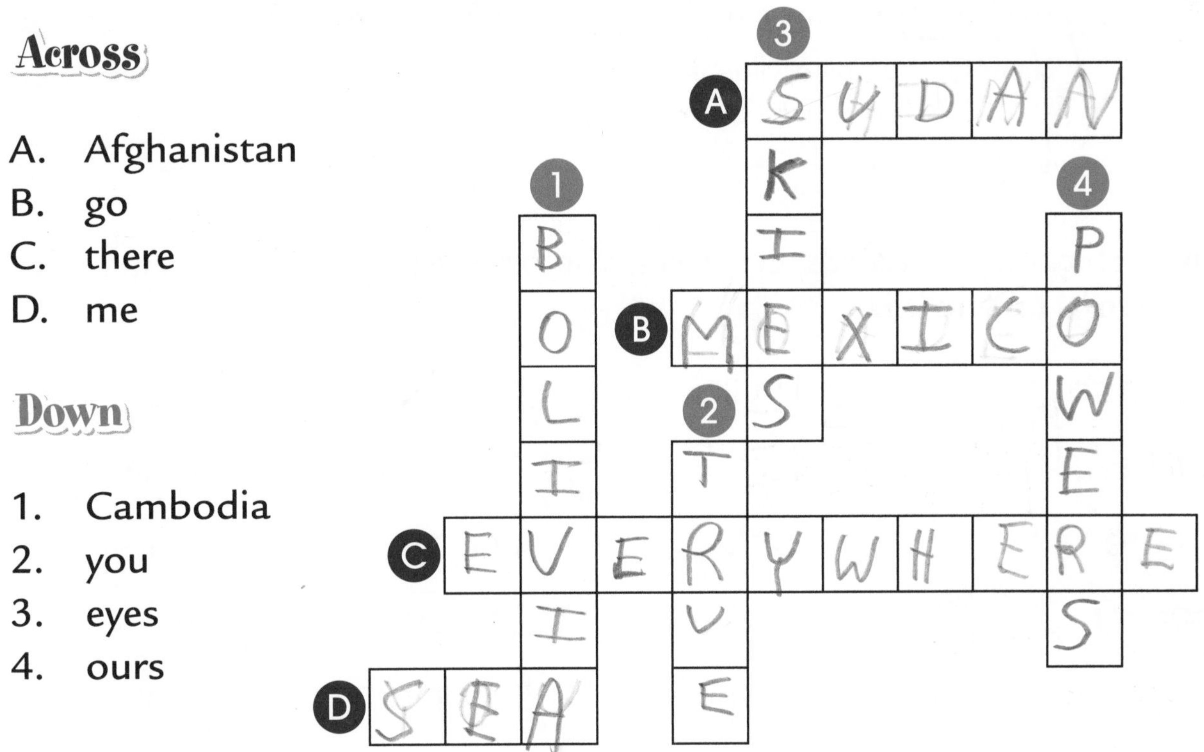

B. Complete the verse that can be added after the fourth one "In Vietnam...Kalamazoo!"

A verse is a group of lines forming a unit in a poem.

In England, we'll have fish and chips.

In vietnam we'll plant some rice. Then fly to Tibet and touch the skies. We'll make our way to Timbuktu– Tuktoyaktuk and Kalamazoo!

Writing Poems

Rhyme is one of the most frequently used tools in **poems**.

Example: Sunshine, blue sky, lullaby,
It is time to say goodbye.

C. In each group of words, cross out the one that does not rhyme with the word on the left.

1.	**Canada**	Lydia	~~conquer~~	Australia
2.	**there**	fair	chair	~~dead~~
3.	**plane**	~~plan~~	drain	rain
4.	**soccer**	locker	sober	~~sorry~~
5.	**popcorn**	warn	~~poppy~~	horn
6.	**dream**	~~dim~~	supreme	scream

D. Add a line that rhymes with each of the given ones.

1. Roll, roll, roll the snow.

Row, row, row your boat.

2. In goes my favourite lemonade.

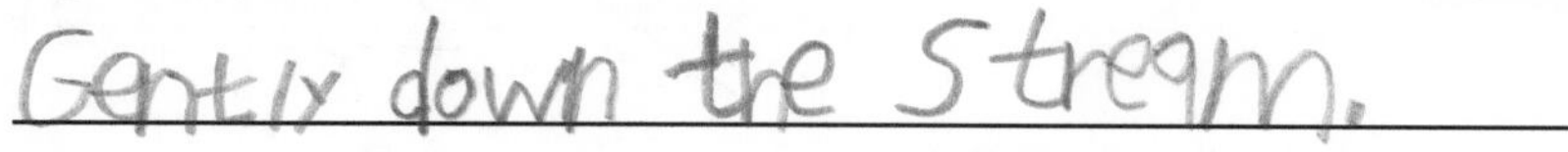

Gently down the Stream.

3. Look at this and look at that.

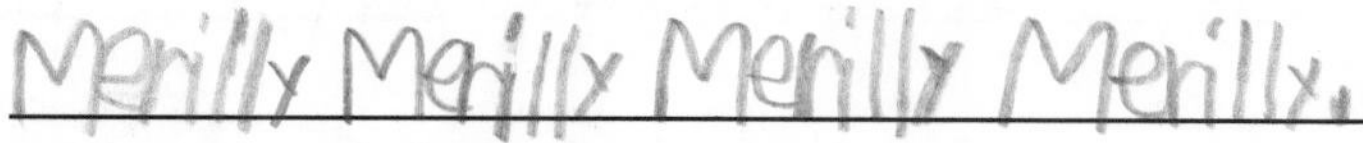

4. From the Rocky Mountains to the St. Lawrence River.

Gently down the stream Gently down the stream.

Acrostic Poems

An **acrostic poem** is a poem in which the first letters of the lines form a word or words. The word or words formed is usually the theme of the poem.

Example: Eric is an active boy.
Riding his bike with buddy Roy.
Into the woods and around the park.
Can't stop until it's dark.

E. Write an acrostic poem with your first name. Make the lines rhyme where possible.

U Umair is my name
M Mario is from Super Mario
A Aarib is my brother
I I am the boy
R Ramadan and Eid is my favorite celebration

F. Write another acrostic poem, this time with your favourite season.

A Autum is my favorite season
U Unit 1 and Unit 2
T Trees with leaves on it
U Unit 1 and Unit 2
M My birthday is on autumn
N No rains an snows

CONGRATULATIONS

28

ENGLISH

E

ENGLISH COMPLETE

SOCIAL
STUDIES

Medieval Peasants and Knights

In medieval times, the lives of all people were governed by a four-tier social structure called the feudal system, with the king at the top and peasants at the bottom. The roles and daily lives of people in different tiers were very different.

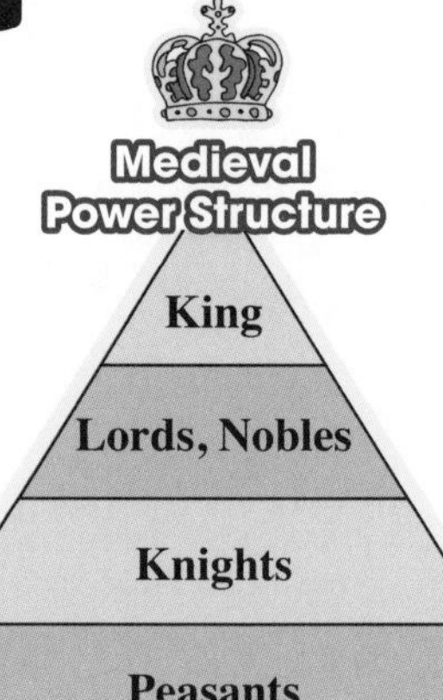

A. Read what the peasant and the knight say. Then complete the comparison chart.

I was born a peasant because my parents are peasants. I live in a village on my lord's manor. I was required to swear an oath of loyalty and obedience to my lord. I work for my lord in exchange for protection and the use of his land. I am a farmer. I have to pay rent in the form of goods and labour services to my lord.

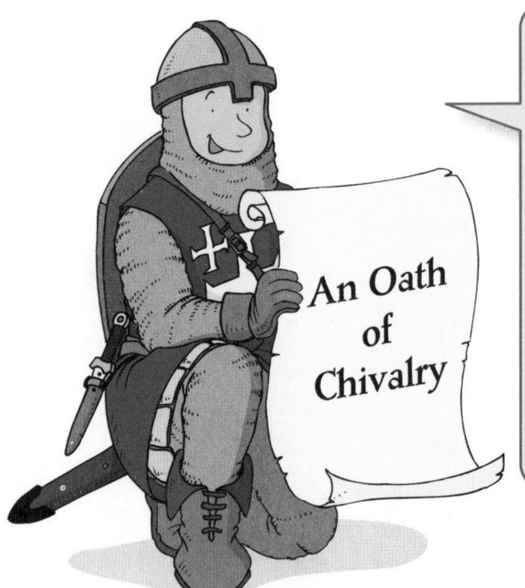

I was born the son of nobles. I was sent to the lord's castle to begin training for knighthood when I was seven and have been living there ever since. When I became a knight, I took an oath of chivalry by which I promised to defend my lord and the weak, and be loyal and brave. I am a warrior. I received a land grant called a fief from my lord and in return I will provide military services when demanded by my lord.

The Life of a Peasant and a Knight

	Peasant	Knight
Parents' social status	Peasant	Nobles
Where they grew up	A Village On The Lords Manor	The Lords Castle
What oath they swore	An oath of Loyalty and obedience to the lord	An oath of Chivalry
What they received from their lords	Protection and the use of land	A Fief/Land Grants
What they did for their lords in return	Paid rent in the form of Goods And Labour	Military

B. Write the letters in the correct spaces in the Venn diagram.

- **A** *spent most time on outdoor work, such as ploughing, sowing, and hedging*
- **B** *spent most time honing his weapon skills and horsemanship*
- **C** *had to wake up early in the morning*
- **D** *ate more vegetables than meat*
- **E** *believed in God*
- **F** *ate more meat than vegetables*
- **G** *used a variety of tools, such as flails, scythes, and sickles*
- **H** *used many different weapons, such as swords, lances, and battle-axes*

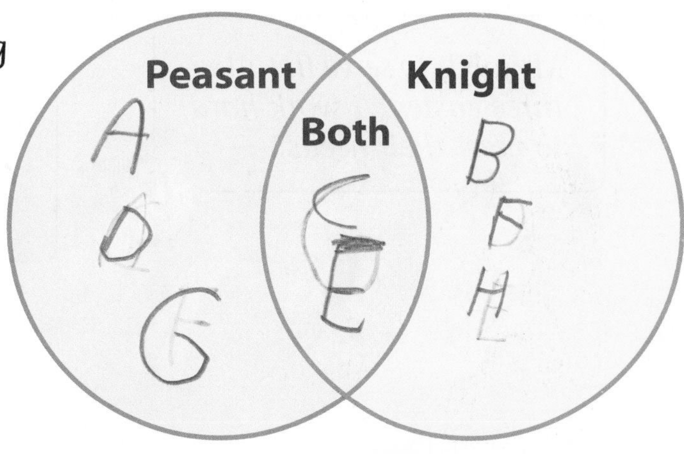

Medieval India and Today

Medieval India followed a social structure that organized people according to castes, much like the feudal system in medieval Europe. The level to which one belonged depended on which level the person's family was in. Unlike today's women, the status of women in medieval India, no matter which caste they belonged to, was very low.

A. Look at the diagram of the caste system. Identify the castes to which the four people belong. Write the letters in the circles.

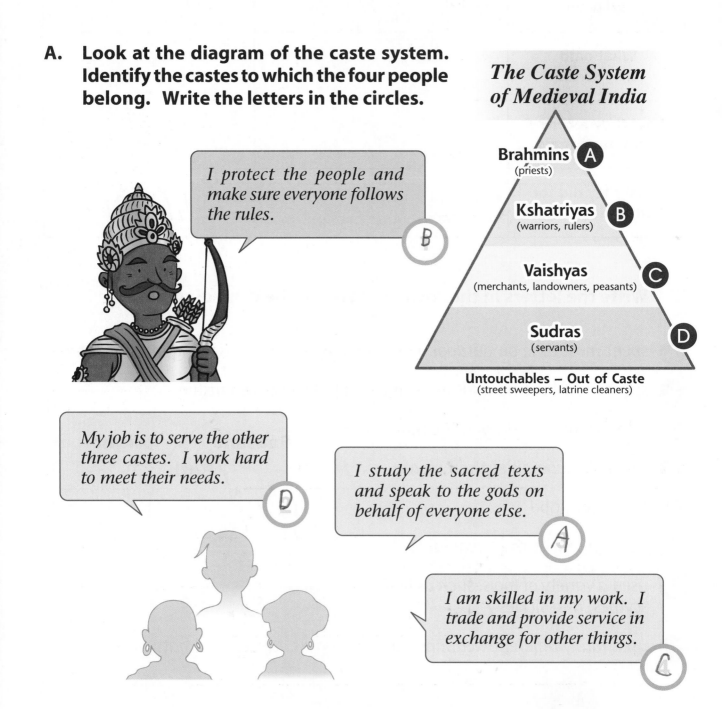

The Caste System of Medieval India

Brahmins (A)
(priests)

Kshatriyas (B)
(warriors, rulers)

Vaishyas (C)
(merchants, landowners, peasants)

Sudras (D)
(servants)

Untouchables – Out of Caste
(street sweepers, latrine cleaners)

I protect the people and make sure everyone follows the rules. (B)

My job is to serve the other three castes. I work hard to meet their needs. (D)

I study the sacred texts and speak to the gods on behalf of everyone else. (A)

I am skilled in my work. I trade and provide service in exchange for other things. (C)

B. Read what the women say. Write "Yes" or "No" to complete the chart.

Medieval Indian Woman

I belong to the Sudra caste. My family is very poor. I do not receive any education. I am a servant in a priest's house. I prepare the meals, take care of the kids, and clean the house. My parents found me a husband in the same caste. My work is harder now because I also have to take care of my husband, my children, and my house. I don't have any rights and I'm not allowed to go anywhere or do anything I like. I can never move up to a higher caste.

We were friends in the university. After graduation, we chose the fields we'd like to work in and now we have our own careers. We married the men we love. We share with our husbands the responsibilities of taking care of our kids and household chores. We work hard and we now enjoy a better quality of life. We can afford going on a family trip every year. We like having gatherings and going to the movies together when we have spare time.

Today's Women

	Medieval Indian Women	Today's Women
Chance to Receive Education	No	Yes
Choice of Marriage	No	Yes
Rights and Freedom	No	Yes
Household Responsibilities	Yes	Yes
Leisure Time	No	Yes
Chance to Improve Life	No	Yes

Pollution: Medieval Times and Today

Pollution has long been an environmental problem, which has inevitably led to many health hazards. As population grew and industry developed in medieval times, so did pollution and its related health problems.

A. Put the different kinds of pollution in the correct time periods. Write the letters in the boxes.

Pollution

- A *animal waste dumped everywhere causing land pollution*
- B *burning of wood and coal for fuel causing air pollution*
- C *motor vehicles, trains, and aircraft causing noise pollution*
- D *human and farm waste discharged directly into rivers and streams causing water pollution*
- E *chemicals used intensively on farms causing soil pollution*
- F *horse-drawn carriages on streets at night causing noise pollution*
- G *emissions and waste from modern industries causing air, land, and water pollution*

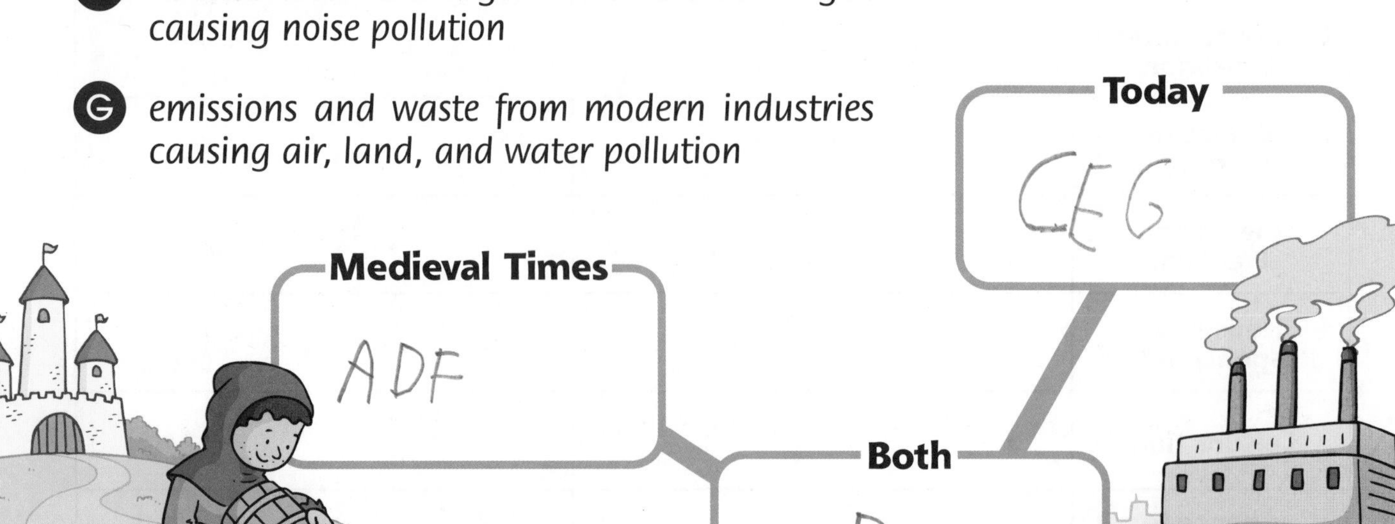

B. Check the circles to show the common diseases in medieval times and those found today.

Poor sanitation and pollution are interrelated. Polluted environments provide ideal conditions for the spread of many diseases.

Asthma

a chronic inflammatory disease caused by genetic and environmental factors

- ✓ Medieval Times
- ○ Today

Dysentery

a viral, bacterial, or parasitic infection transmitted through consuming contaminated food or water

- ✓ Medieval Times
- ○ Today

Leprosy

a chronic bacterial infection transmitted through moisture from the nose and mouth

- ✓ Medieval Times
- ○ Today

Measles

a viral infection of the respiratory system spread through respiration

- ✓ Medieval Times
- ○ Today

SARS

a viral respiratory disease transmitted through direct contact or inhalation

- ○ Medieval Times
- ✓ Today

Plague

a bacterial infection spread by rats and rat fleas, direct contact, or contaminated food

- ✓ Medieval Times
- ○ Today

Influenza

an infectious viral disease transmitted through direct contact or inhalation

- ✓ Medieval Times
- ○ Today

Typhoid

a bacterial disease transmitted through consuming food or water contaminated with feces

- ✓ Medieval Times
- ✓ Today

Malaria

an infectious disease spread by mosquitoes

- ✓ Medieval Times
- ✓ Today

Communication: Past and Present

Some communication methods used in the past are still in use today, and thanks to advances in technology, communication tools have improved over the years.

A. Fill in the blanks to complete the timeline. Then answer the question.

Timeline of Communication Tools

phone
typewriter
radio
computer

- **3000 BCE** — papyrus and reed pen, communication drum
- **105 CE** — paper
- **1400 CE** — printing press
- 1800
- **1838** — telegraph
- **1860s** — Typewriter (**1930s version**)
- **1876** — telephone
- **1896** — Radio (**1950s version**)
- 1900
- **1927** — television
- **1946** — electronic Computer (**1990s version**)
- **1973** — mobile Phone
- 2000
- **present**

Name one of the communication tools in the past that we still use today.

Mobile Phone

B. Draw lines to match the communication tools and means used in the past with the present ones. Then answer the question.

Communication Tools and Means

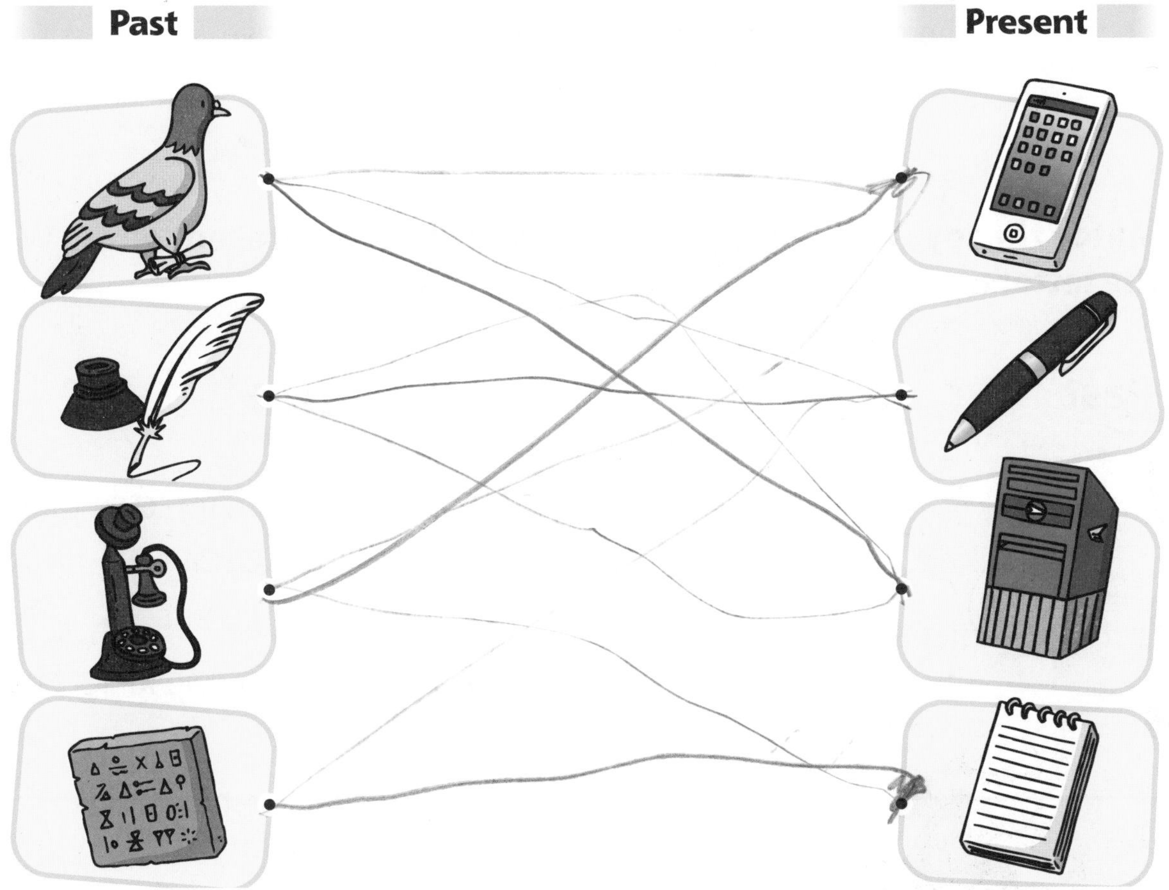

Choose one pair of communication tools or means above and explain how the present one helps improve communication.

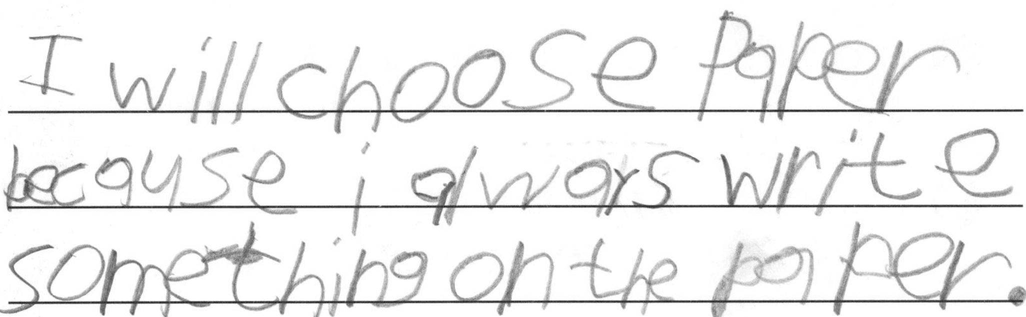

I will choose Paper
because i alwars write
something on the paper.

5

Toys and Games: Past and Present

Many toys and games played by children in the past are still played by children today, and while advances in technology have led to improvements in these toys and games, they have also given rise to problems.

A. Match the toys and games from the past with the present ones. Write the letters.

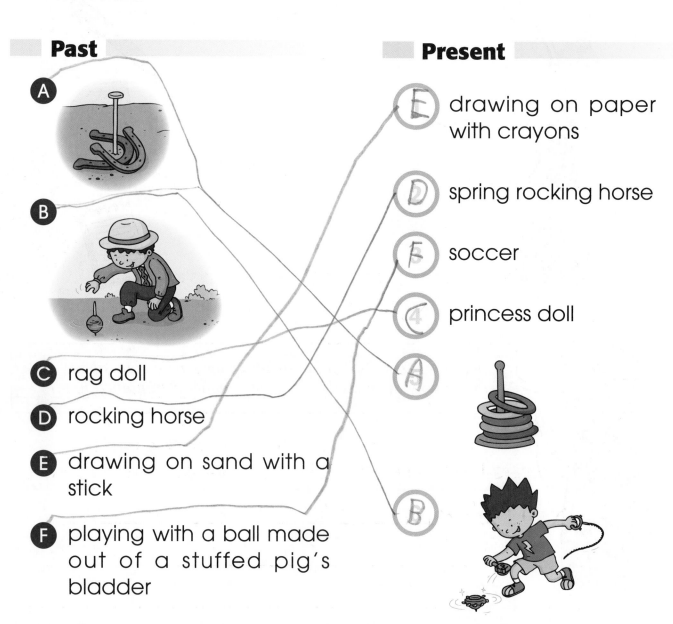

Past

A

B

C rag doll

D rocking horse

E drawing on sand with a stick

F playing with a ball made out of a stuffed pig's bladder

Present

E drawing on paper with crayons

D spring rocking horse

F soccer

C princess doll

A

B

B. Identify the characteristics of the toys and games in the past and the present. Write them in the correct columns.

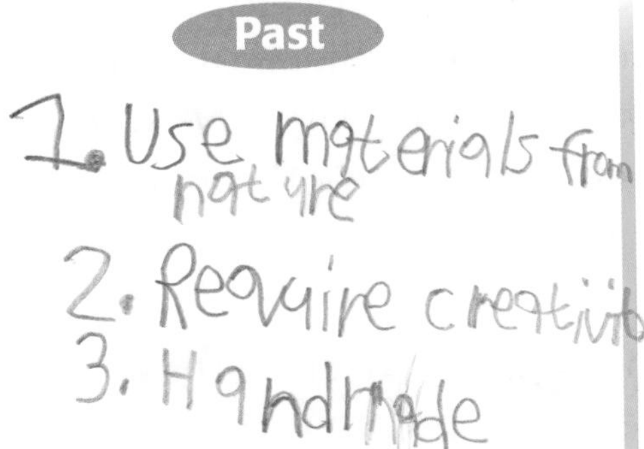

Characteristics of Toys and Games

Past	Present
1. Use materials from nature	1. Automaded
2. Reqaire creativity	2. More durable
3. Handmade	3. Electronic
	4. Run on batteries

- electronic
- run on batteries
- handmade
- automated
- more durable
- use materials from nature
- require creativity

C. Answer the questions.

1.

I don't have to go out to play ball games with friends because I can play ball games on my tablet. I like playing this video game anytime and anywhere.

If Jason keeps being attached to his tablet, what negative effects will there be on him?

There will be negative effects on his health because he stays mostly indoors and will not get the required exercise.

2. Do you think the changes in toys and games have contributed to the prevalence of childhood obesity? Why?

Yes because he is playing.

6

Farming Practices: Past and Present

Farmers in the past used simple tools and machines that were powered by humans or animals. Today, with modern machines, chemical fertilizers, and pesticides, farmers are able to produce crops in large quantities in less amount of time. However, there are costs to such practices.

A. Identify the things used for farming in the past that are still in use today and the ones that are only used today. Write the letters.

Things for Farming

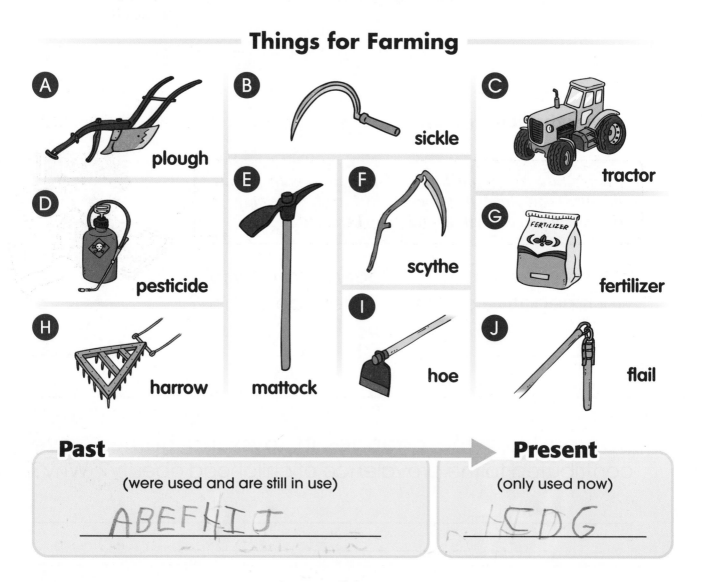

A plough

B sickle

C tractor

D pesticide

E mattock

F scythe

G fertilizer

H harrow

I hoe

J flail

Past → **Present**

Past (were used and are still in use)	Present (only used now)
ABEFHIJ	~~H~~CDG

B. Fill in the blanks with the items in (A).

In the old days, simple tools were used in farming. To break up the earth, farmers used 1. Mattock and 2. Hoe. If they had oxen or horses, they could use 3. Plough and 4. Harrow drawn by these animals to save them time and effort. In harvesting, they used 5. Sickle and 6. Tractor to cut grass and reap their crops. 7. Scythe with jointed sticks were used for threshing.

Although these tools are still used by some farmers today, big machinery is largely employed on most farms. 8. Tractor are used to draw ploughs and harrows to break up the soil. They are also used to pull combine harvesters to reap, thresh, and winnow grain crops in a single process. In order to ensure large yields and great profits, 9. Fertilizer and Flail are used to maintain soil fertility and 10. Pesticide to kill pests.

C. Read what the farmer says and answer the question.

While modern farming practices have brought me big profits, there are also negative consequences. For example, the overuse of fertilizers has resulted in salt build-up and contamination of groundwater. Can you think of another negative impact of modern farming practices?

Pesticide to kill pest but sometimes they also kill other organisms that are good for the soil.

Education: Past and Present

Education today has changed much from what it was in the past. Yet, there are some aspects that have remained the same.

A. Identify the differences between education in the past and the present. Some practices have remained unchanged. Write the letters in the Venn diagram.

Education

- **A** *receive and submit school assignments online*
- **B** *use computers and tablets in class*
- **C** *breaks between classes*
- **D** *write on slates with chalk*
- **E** *learn from teachers*
- **F** *classrooms dimly lit and poorly heated or ventilated*
- **G** *different age groups in the same classroom*
- **H** *learn reading, writing, and arithmetic*
- **I** *use books*
- **J** *detention as a form of punishment*

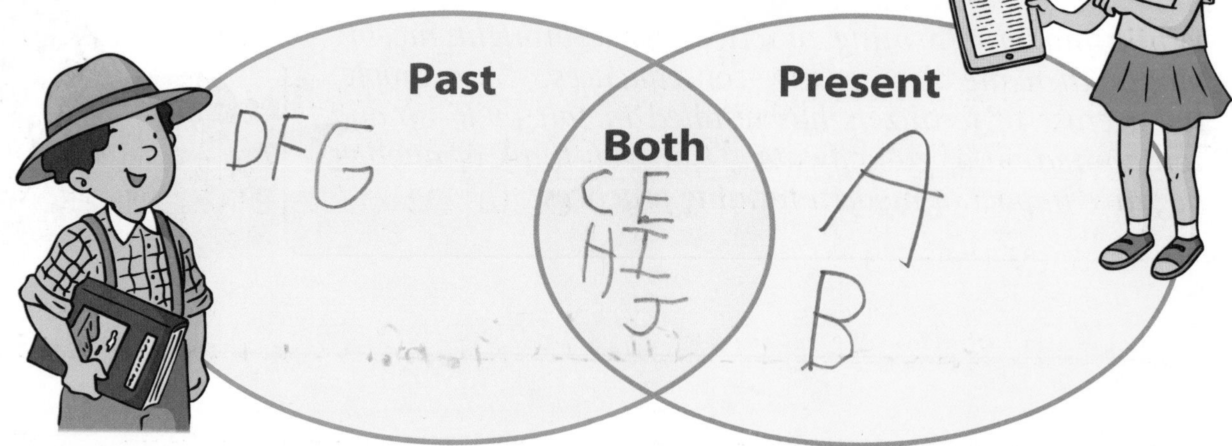

B. Write about your school. Then answer the question.

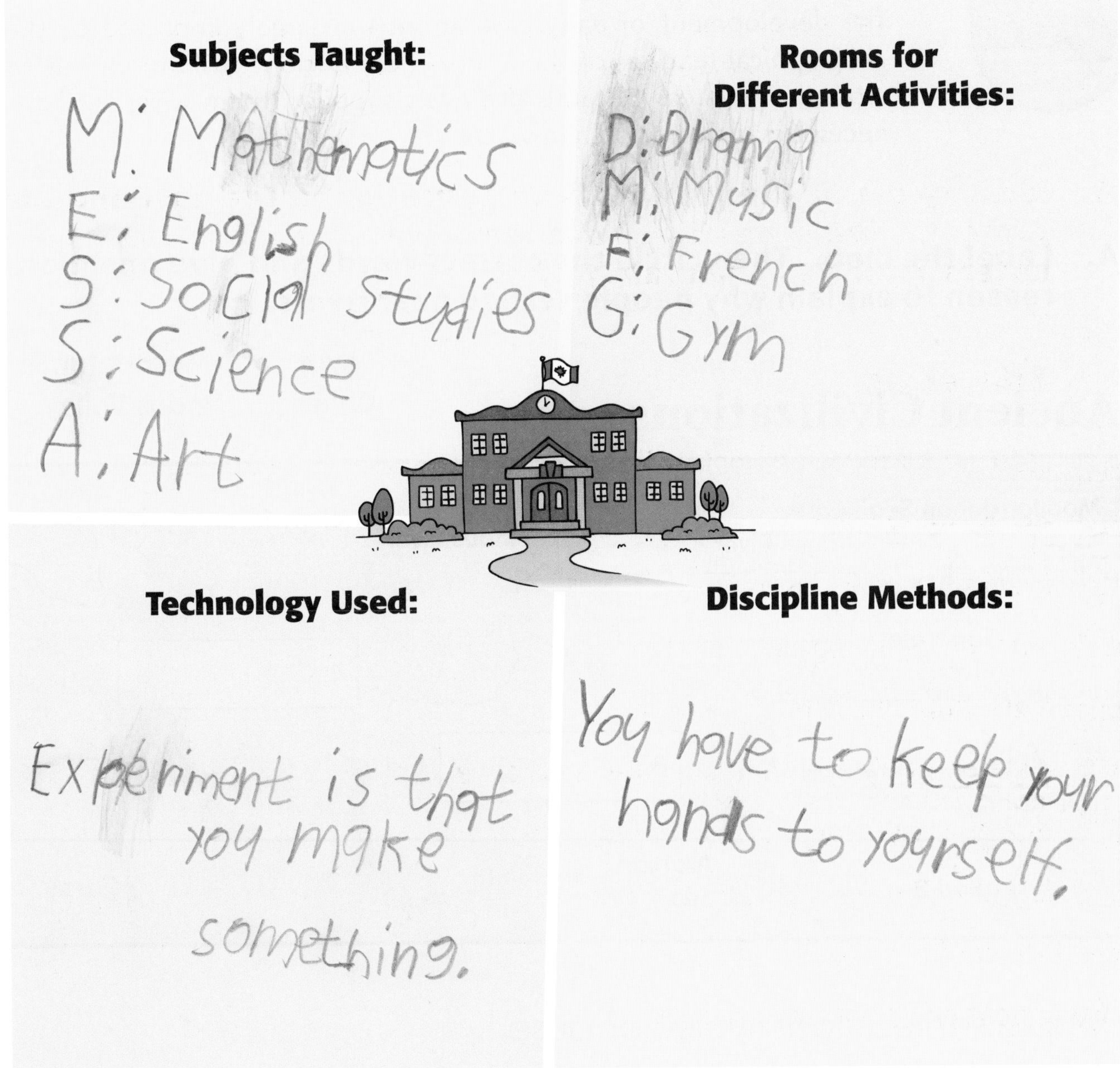

Subjects Taught:
M: Mathematics
E: English
S: Social studies
S: Science
A: Art
Rooms for Different Activities:
D: Drama
M: Music
F: French
G: Gym
Technology Used:
Experiment is that you make something.
Discipline Methods:
You have to keep your hands to yourself.

Schools in the past did not have specific rooms for students' activities, but schools nowadays do. Do you think it is beneficial to students if a school has different rooms for different activities?

Yes! There are different teacers in the class.

8 Civilizations along the Rivers

The development of early civilizations was largely impacted by the geographical features of the land. These ancient civilizations settled around river areas because the rivers supplied them with the basic necessities such as food and water.

A. Label the map. Then circle the correct words and give one more reason to explain why people settled near rivers.

Egypt **Mesopotamia**
China **Indus Valley**

Ancient Civilizations

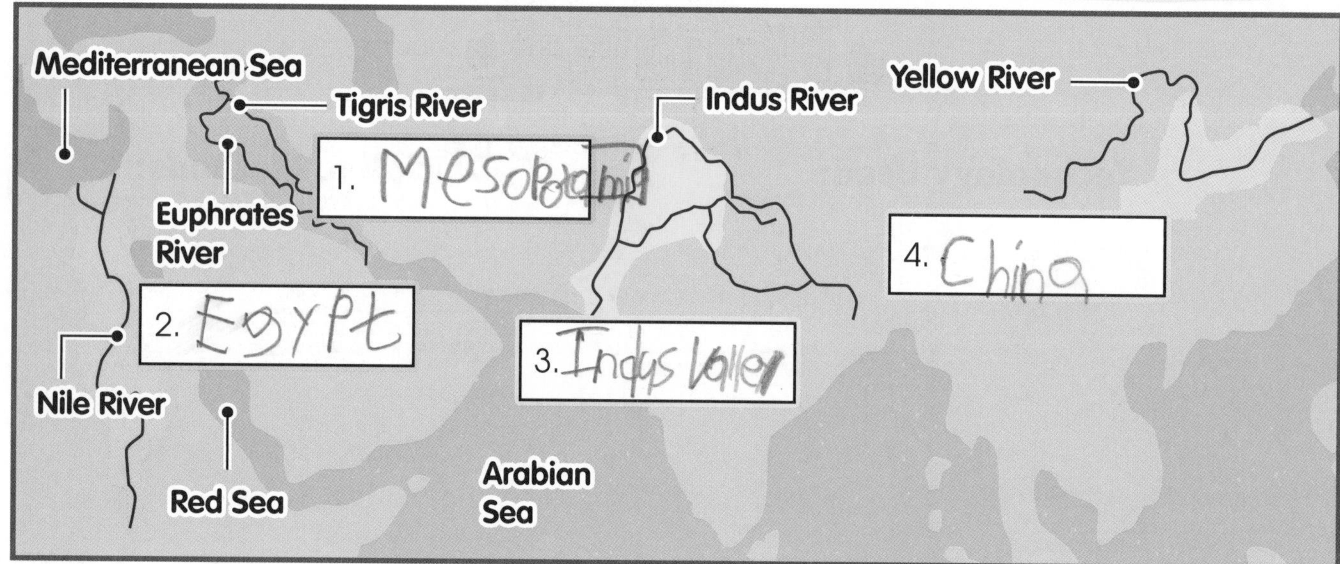

People settled near rivers because...

- rivers provided them with **fresh / salty** water to drink.
- rivers provided water for growing **crops / flowers** .
- they could **swim / travel** along the rivers to other places.
- they could **keep / hunt** the animals coming to drink water.
- They could swim/surf on the river.

B. Read the magazine below. Answer the question.

Indus Valley

Yearly flooding of the Indus River formed an enormous fertile plain where the Indus Valley Civilization developed. The river provided water for irrigating crops. It was also a link to the Arabian Sea, and boats were used for transportation of materials for trading. The Himalayan Mountains and the Arabian Sea sheltered the land from attack and disease.

Ancient Egypt

The Nile River was a reliable source of water for farming. It also helped promote trade between Upper and Lower Egypt and other lands to the south. Seasonal flooding of the Nile provided the Egyptians with rich soil and washed away waste. The Mediterranean Sea, the Red Sea, and the surrounding deserts served as natural barriers against diseases and war.

List three ways in which the two civilizations above are similar.

Similarities between the Indus Valley and the Ancient Egypt civilizations:

- They both depended on the rivers for farming.
- They both use the river for transportation.
- They both had natural barriers against diseases and war.

9

The Impact of Natural Events on Early Civilizations

Flooding created fertile land as the cradle of some major early civilizations, including Ancient Egypt. However, natural events, together with some cultural, social, and political factors, also contributed to the weakening and downfall of many civilizations.

A. Identify the natural events and fill in the blanks to complete the descriptions.

Natural Events	1	2	3	4
Earthquakes	eruption	Athens	Alexandria	rainfall
Volcanic Eruptions	Crete	Greek	tsunamis	famine
Drought	volcano	war	agriculture	Mediterranean
Tsunamis	Minoan	revolt	shoreline	drought
			saltwater	climate

1. [ ] Around 1645 BCE, a ________ on the island of Thera (present day Santorini, Greece) erupted. The Minoans of Thera and the nearby island of ________ abandoned their homes and left. The disastrous ________ had significantly weakened the ________ civilization.

2. [ ] In 464 BCE, a powerful earthquake shook the Ancient ________ city-state of Sparta. It not only damaged much of the city-state but also contributed to the ________ of the Helots, the breakdown in the relation between Sparta and ________, and the ________ with Athens that ensued.

3. Tsunamis ___Tsunamis___ usually come with earthquakes. In 365 CE, a tsunami was triggered by two successive earthquakes off the coast of Greece and it devastated the city of ___Alexandria___, Egypt and the surrounding villages and towns, and permanently changed the ___Shoreline___. ___Saltwater___ that flooded the farmlands had made ___Agricuture___ impossible for many years.

4. Drought ___Drought___ could be as devastating as tsunamis. ___Climate___ change led to the drop in ___Rainfall___, and prolonged periods of severe drought meant ___Mediterranean___. Around 1200 BCE, many ___Famine___ civilizations, including Ancient Greece, suffered greatly from drought and disappeared from the region.

B. Answer the question.

You know that flooding created fertile land which people of many early societies depended on, but flooding could also have adverse effects on them. Write one negative impact of flooding on early societies.

Flooding could damage and wash away crops.

10

Architecture in Ancient Egypt

People in early societies used materials readily available to them to construct permanent structures and dwellings. Even monumental structures as magnificent as the pyramids of Ancient Egypt were built with materials found from the environment, with the help of simple tools.

A. Bricks were widely used for construction in Ancient Egypt. Put the sentences in order to show how bricks were made. Write 1 to 5.

Making Sun-dried Bricks

5 *Strong bricks ready for construction were made.*

1 *Mud was collected from the Nile River nearby.*

3 *The mixture was put in standard-sized wooden moulds.*

2 *The mud was mixed with straw.*

4 *The mixture in the moulds was left to dry and harden in the hot sun and the desert heat of Egypt.*

B. Write "T" for the true statements about Ancient Egypt and "F" for the false ones.

1. Sun-dried bricks were used to build palaces. T
2. Burned bricks were not made because of the scarcity of fuel. T
3. Basalt was used in building city walls. F
4. Palm trees provided lots of wood for construction. F
5. Limestone could be found in abundance and was used in building pyramids. T
6. Granite was hard to cut with simple tools so it was reserved for tombs and temples. T

C. **Look at the tools. Decide what they were used for in Ancient Egypt. Write the letters.**

Building and Construction Tools in Ancient Egypt

- **A** *used with a mallet to shape stone*
- **B** *for making bricks of the same size and shape*
- **C** *used with a chisel to cut or shape stone*
- **D** *for smoothing walls*
- **E** *ensuring that constructions are vertical*
- **F** *for making precise right angles in construction*
- **G** *enlarged when saturated with water to split rock*

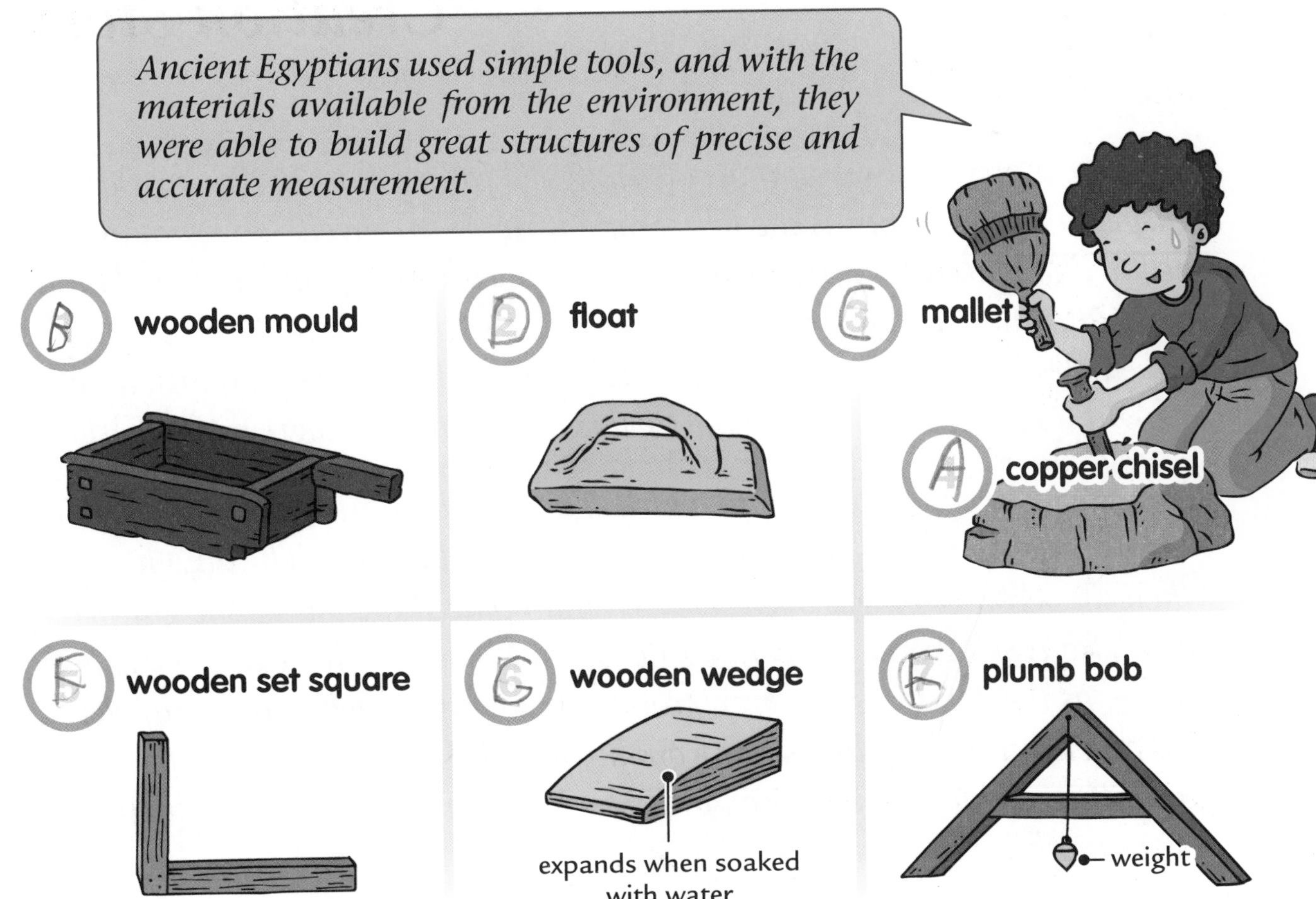

Creation Stories and the Environment

Different First Nations in Canada have their own versions of creation stories. As stories were passed down the generations through storytelling, even the creation story of one culture has many versions, but they all reflect how people of each of these cultures think about the world and how they view themselves in relation to the land and the natural environment.

A. Read this version of the Haudenosaunee creation story and fill in the blanks to complete the sentences.

In the beginning, there was only Sky World, and in the world far below it was water everywhere.

One day, a pregnant woman accidentally fell from a hole in Sky World. She grasped at some plants as she fell. Some water birds saved Sky Woman from the fall and placed her on the back of a turtle. To provide land for Sky Woman to live on, other animals tried to dive deep down the water to the ocean floor to find earth. Many were unsuccessful and sacrificed their lives. At last, an otter brought up earth and put it on the turtle's back. From that grew Turtle Island.

Later, Sky Woman gave birth to a girl. The daughter grew up and gave birth to twin sons, one right-handed and the other left-handed. The daughter died when the second son was born. Sky Woman placed the plants she grasped as she fell from Sky World on her daughter's grave. Soon, corn, beans, and squash, known as the Three Sisters, grew from her daughter's head, and strawberries and other medicinal plants grew from her feet. Her daughter was later known as Mother Earth. Time passed and Sky Woman passed away. She became Grandmother Moon in the sky.

The right-handed twin, known as the Creator, created many good things on Earth, including gentle hills and rivers and beautiful roses. Then he created human beings. The left-handed twin altered his twin brother's creations, like adding thorns to roses, and made all the bad and disturbing creations, including snakes.

1. The Haudenosaunee believe that the human world was created with the help and sacrifice of Animals.
2. If the animals had not saved Sky Women from falling, human beings and the world we live in would not have been created.
3. The earth placed on the turtle's back grew and grew to become Sky Women, which is today's North America.
4. The staple food and medicine human beings depend on to stay alive grew from the grave of Mother Earth.
5. The good twin created all the good things in the human world.

B. Answer the question.

First Nations people believe that all things in nature, including human beings, are connected in the Web of Life. Human beings have to respect and give thanks to everything in the environment, and take only what we need for survival from nature. We have the responsibility of protecting the Earth and being its stewards. Explain these beliefs with the help of the Haudenosaunee creation story.

First nations people believe that the Earth was created before the Existense of human beings with the sacrifice of animals so with the why it is responsibility of the human beings to respect everything in nature.

Canada's Provinces and Territories

Canada has ten provinces and three territories. Apart from the national capital, each province or territory has its own capital city.

A. Identify the provinces and territories of Canada. Write their short forms in the circles.

Map of Canada

Provinces

AB	Alberta
BC	British Columbia
MB	Manitoba
NB	New Brunswick
NL	Newfoundland and Labrador
PEI	Prince Edward Island
NS	Nova Scotia
ON	Ontario
QC	Quebec
SK	Saskatchewan

Territories

NU	Nunavut
NT	Northwest Territories
YT	Yukon

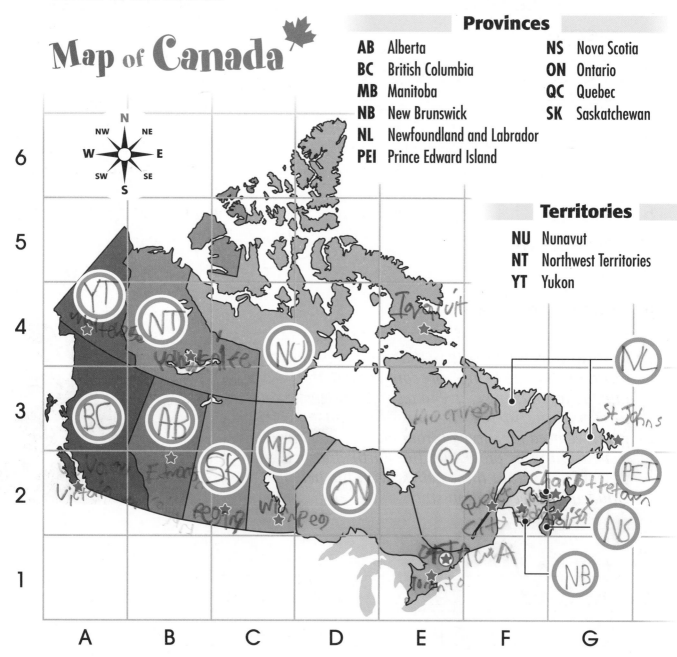

B. Look at (A) again. Write the locations of the capital cities. Then draw lines to match the provinces and territories with their capital cities.

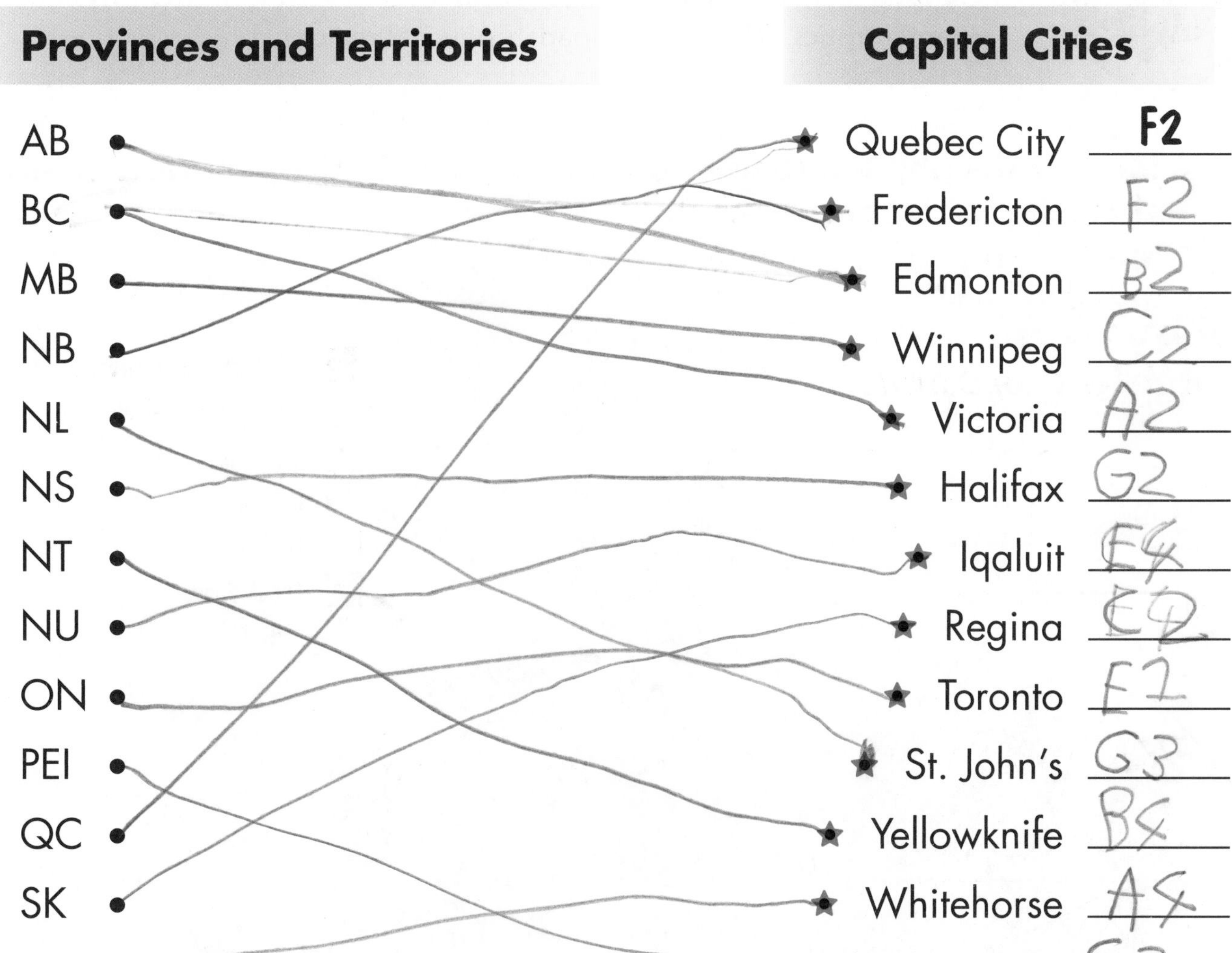

C. Fill in the blanks with the help of the map.

1. Ottawa, the national capital of Canada, is ______________ of Toronto.
2. ______________ is east of New Brunswick.
3. Saskatchewan is ______________ of Yukon.
4. There are ______________ provinces west of Ontario.
5. ______________ is the largest province.

13

Canada's Physical Regions

Canada can be divided into areas of land that share physical characteristics. These are Canada's physical regions.

A. Identify the physical regions on the map and in the pictures. Then circle the correct answers.

Physical Regions of Canada

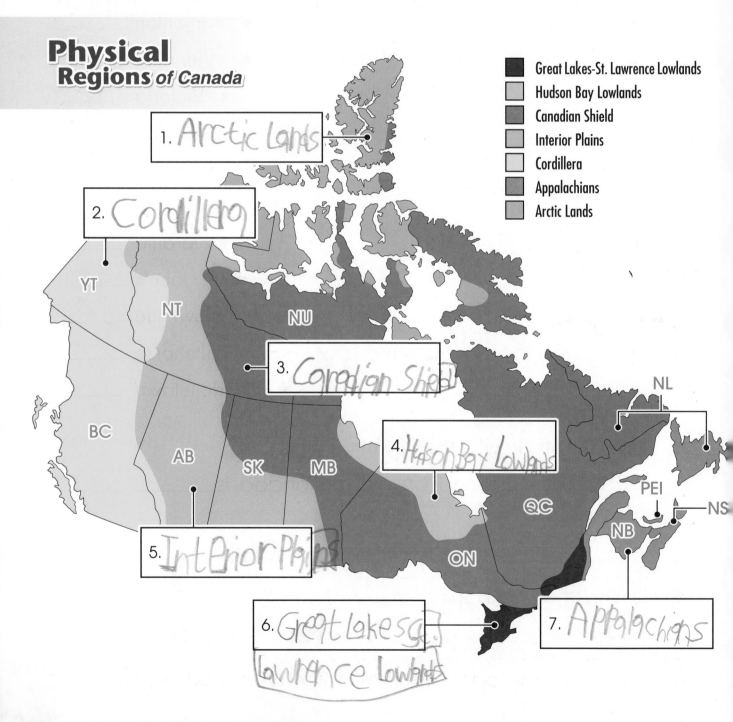

- Great Lakes-St. Lawrence Lowlands
- Hudson Bay Lowlands
- Canadian Shield
- Interior Plains
- Cordillera
- Appalachians
- Arctic Lands

YT NT NU BC AB SK MB ON QC NL PEI NS NB

1. Arctic Lands
2. Cordillera
3. Canadian Shield
4. Hudson Bay Lowlands
5. Interior Plains
6. Great Lakes St. Lawrence Lowlands
7. Applachians

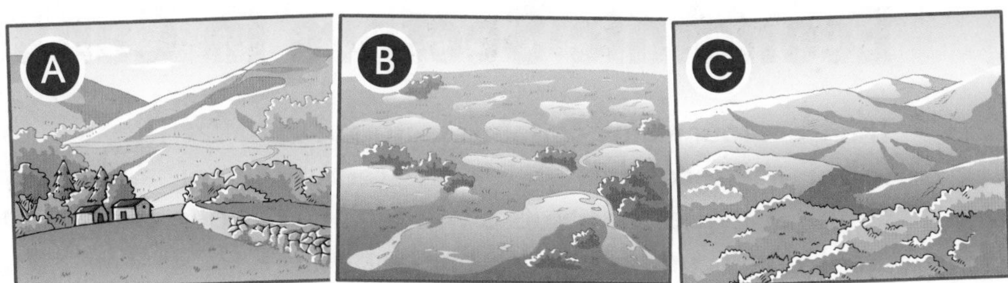

A Great Lakes-St. Lawrence Lowlands :
lush and fertile **gardens** / **farmlands**

B Hudson Bay Lowlands :
coastal wetlands with lots of **swamps** / **trees**

C Appalachians :
eroded **soil** / **mountains** and large bays

D Interior Plains :
rich deposits of oil and **dinosaur** / **fish** fossils

E Cordillera :
rugged mountain ranges and **plateaus** / **lakes**

F Arctic Lands :
little / **mostly** permanent frozen ground

G Canadian Shield :
lakes, thick forests, and **ancient** / **newly-formed** rocks

Economic Sectors in Canada

There are four main economic sectors in Canada. They are: the primary sector, the secondary sector, the tertiary sector, and the quaternary sector. Each sector has its own specific activities, and the four sectors are strongly correlated with one another.

A. Name the four economic sectors. Then circle the correct words and match the examples with the sectors.

Economic Sectors

Examples

construction **mining** **research** **entertainment**

1. 

   P__________ Sector

   - extracts or produces **refined** / **raw** materials
   - e.g. __________

2. 

   S__________ Sector

   - processes raw materials into **goods** / **data**
   - e.g. __________

3. 

   T__________ Sector

   - provides **services** / **produce** and support
   - e.g. __________

4. 

   Q__________ Sector

   - involves transfer of **raw materials** / **information**
   - e.g. __________

B. Sort the jobs into the correct sectors. Then write one more example for each sector on the green line.

doctor
farmer
tour guide
college professor
baker
carpenter
software specialist
fisherman

Jobs in the Four Economic Sectors

Primary Sector	Secondary Sector
Farmer	Baker
Fisherman	carpenter

Tertiary Sector	Quaternary Sector
Doctor	College Professor
Tour guide	Software specialise

C. Answer the questions.

1. What are the similarities among all industries in the secondary sector?

They all make use to raw material to many factor product.

2. In which sector does banking belong? Why?

Banking belongs to the Tertiary sector Because It Provides financial service to People.

3. Which sector do you think employs the most Canadians? Why?

Primary sector Because I see the Mining.

15

Industries in the Cordillera

The Cordillera is located on the west coast of Canada. Its mountainous and irregular topography has given rise to a variety of industries in this region.

A. Name the provinces and territories that lie in the Cordillera. Then unscramble the words to complete the list.

The **Cordillera**

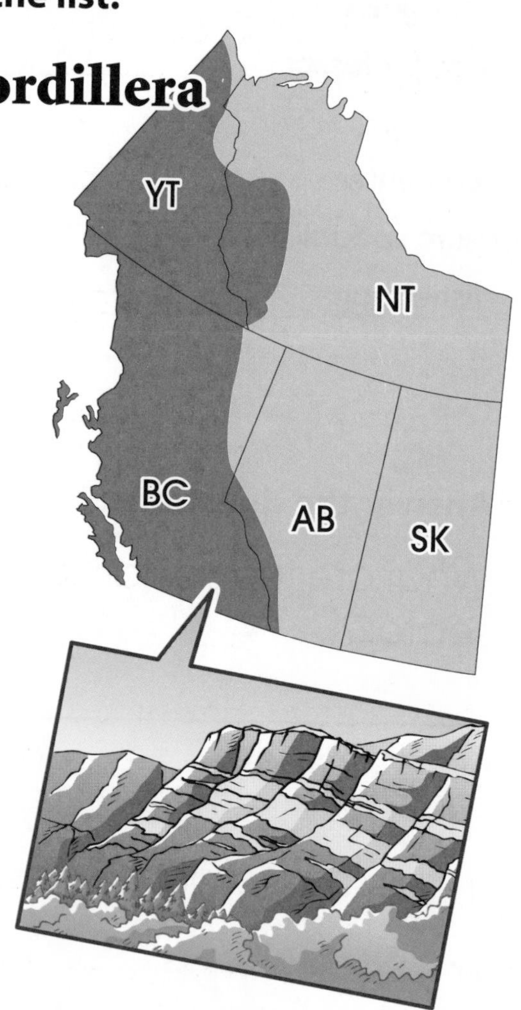

Provinces/Territories

British Columbia

Alberta

Northwest Territories

Yukon

The Cordillera is made up of:

- 1. Plateaus (**p**atealus)
- 2. Bassin (**b**snais)
- 3. Lakes (ke**l**as)
- 4. Rivers (revi**r**s)
- deep 5. valleys (ellay**v**s)
- coastal 6. Islands (la**i**snds)
- high, rugged 7. Mountains (o**m**taunins) covered with 8. Forests (reos**f**ts)

Identify the industries.

Fishing Forestry Mining Agriculture Hydroelectricity

Agriculture The Okanagan Valley in the southern part of the Cordillera is warm but lacks precipitation. Good irrigation systems make the large number of orchards in the region productive.

Mining The Cordillera has rich metal and mineral resources, including copper, iron, lead, and zinc.

Forestry This is British Columbia's largest industry because the mountainous regions are covered with forests. Materials from this industry are used for paper, construction, insulation, and other lumber products.

Fishing This is a valuable industry along the Pacific coast of the Cordillera. It has provided food for this region since people first settled here.

Hydroelectricity British Columbia is on the windward side of the mountains and receives lots of rain. Heavy rainfall and steep mountain slopes make British Columbia Canada's second largest producer of this power.

Answer Kelly's question.

Name one more industry in the Cordillera and explain why the Cordillera favours the development of this industry.

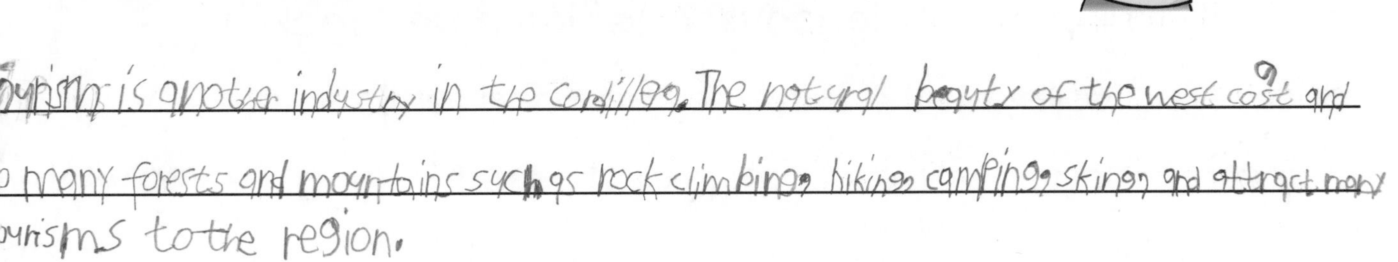

16

Industries in the Interior Plains

Lying to the east of the Cordillera is the Interior Plains, a region made up of sedimentary rock which provides abundant valuable natural resources to the region.

A. Colour the Interior Plains green. Then circle the correct words to describe the characteristics of this region.

The Interior Plains

This region covers:

- *a small part of northeastern* ***Yukon***
- *the middle of the* ***Northwest Territories***
- *the northwestern corner of* ***Nunavut***
- *most of* ***Alberta***
- *the southern half of* ***Saskatchewan***
- *the northeastern corner of* ***British Columbia***
- *the southwestern part of* ***Manitoba***

Characteristics

- rich deposits of oil, gas, and **dinosaur / scorpion** fossils
- many lakes including Canada's **shallowest / deepest** lake – Great Slave Lake
- wide, **flat / barren** lowlands covered by prairie grasslands
- gently rolling hills of **igneous / sedimentary** rock
- low-lying valleys with **thin / deep** and fertile soil
- **short / long** , warm summers and **short / long** , cold winters

B. Fill in the blanks with the given words.

Saskatchewan
hydroelectric
agricultural
Drumheller
Manitoba
Prairies
energy
wheat
coal

1. The southern part of the Interior Plains is commonly known as the Prairies. The flat, fertile land makes this region perfect for the Agricultural industry. This region is one of the largest Wheat producers in the world.

2. The sedimentary rock of the Interior Plains contains large amounts of dinosaur fossils, oil and gas deposits, and non-metallic minerals such as potash and Coal. Drumheller, Alberta, nicknamed "the Dinosaur Capital of the World", attracts many tourists to the region. Alberta is also the main producer of oil and gas in Canada and is known as Canada's " Energy province". Saskachewan is the leading producer of potash for export.

3. Manitoba is also known as "the Land of 100 000 Lakes". The many lakes make this province the major source of Hydroelectric power in the Prairie region.

C. Answer the question.

What makes the Interior Plains, more specifically the Prairies, suitable for large-scale farming?

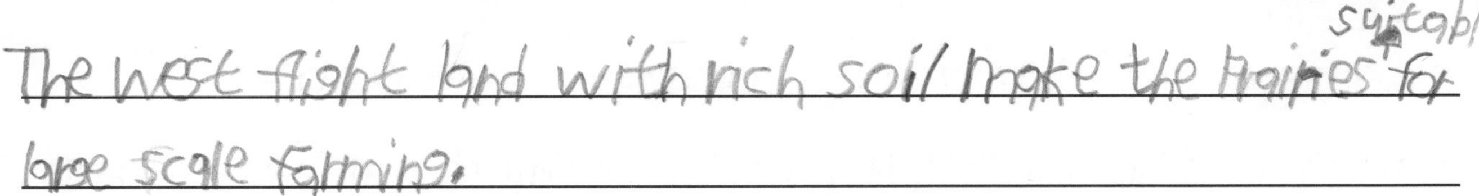

The west flight land with rich soil make the Prairies suitable for large scale farming.

17

Industries in the Canadian Shield

The Canadian Shield is a horseshoe-shaped area that covers almost half of Canada and is the largest physical region. Its plentiful resources of minerals, water, and forests have given rise to various industries.

A. Identify the provinces and territories in the Canadian Shield. Then fill in the blanks to complete the descriptions.

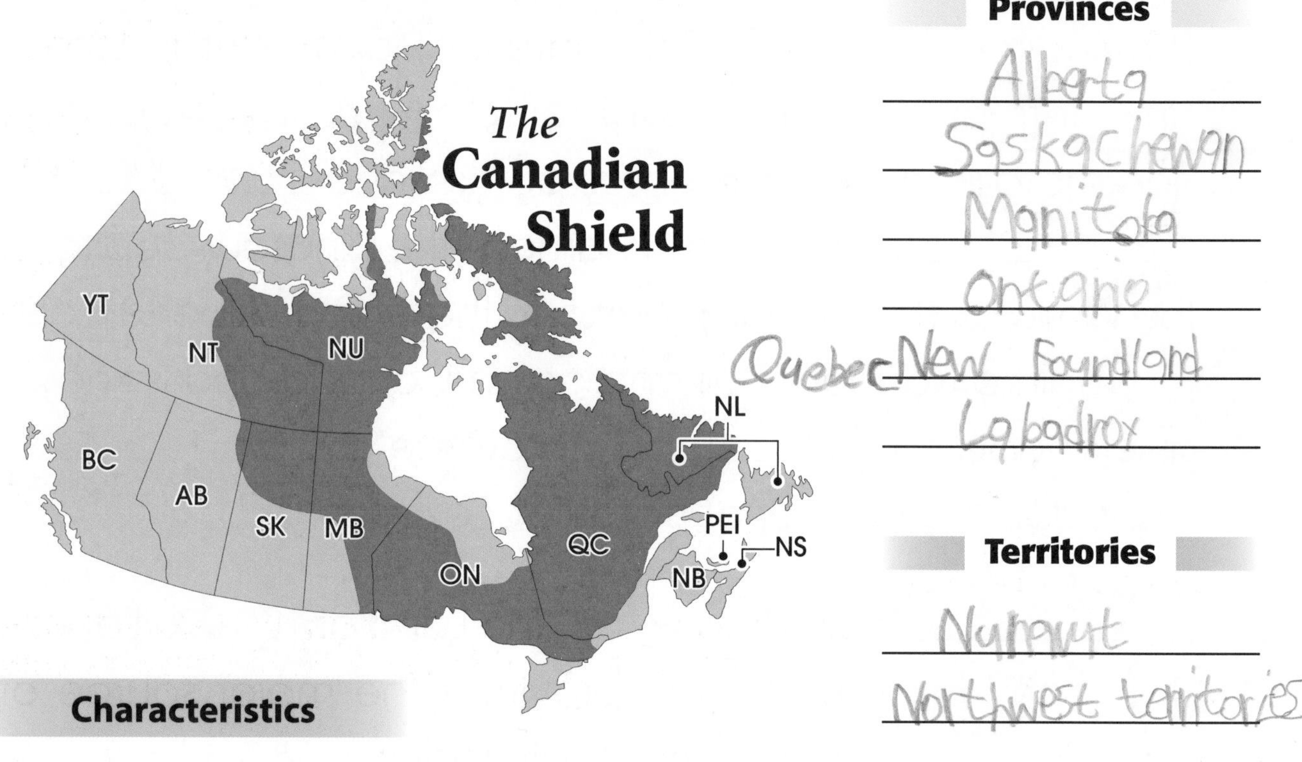

Provinces

Alberta
Saskachewan
Manitoba
Ontario
Quebec New Foundland
Labadror

Territories

Nunavut
Northwest territories

Characteristics

- frozen 1. Tundra in the north
- thick 2. Forests in the south
- various types of 3. Water bodies
- 4. Thin layer of soil on top of the ancient bedrock
- dense soil with 5. Poor drainage in lowland areas
- 6. Coarse soil that does not retain moisture well in some areas

poor thin forests tundra water coarse

B. Identify the natural resources in the Canadian Shield. Then match the facts with the correct resources. Write the letters.

Natural Resources in the Canadian Shield

Rocks Forests Water

Ancient Rocks
- mostly igneous and metamorphic
- large quantities of metallic minerals like gold, iron, and nickel
- fossil fuels

(A) (C)

Water Bodies
- numerous rivers and lakes
- swamps
- waterfalls

(B) (D)

Forests
- dominated by coniferous trees
- some broadleaf trees
- vast boreal forest

(E) (F)

Facts

A *Ontario is one of the world's top ten mineral producers.*

B *One third of the Canadian Shield is covered in water.*

C *Saskatchewan is the world's leading producer of uranium.*

D *Quebec is the largest producer of Canada's hydroelectric power.*

E *About half of Canada's annual wood harvest comes from this region.*

F *Quebec produces more than one third of Canada's pulp and paper products.*

C. Answer the questions.

1. Name four major industries in the Canadian Shield.

Mining, Forestry, Hydroelectricity, and tourisms are 4 major industries in the Canadian Shield.

2. Is agriculture a thriving industry in the Canadian Shield? Why?

Agriculture is not a thriving industry in the Canadian Shield because of the thin and poor soil

Industries in the Great Lakes-St. Lawrence Lowlands

The Great Lakes-St. Lawrence Lowlands is the smallest but most densely populated physical region in Canada. About 50% of Canadians live in this region, and 70% of Canada's manufacturing industries are located here.

A. Name the provinces in the Great Lakes-St. Lawrence Lowlands. Then circle the correct words.

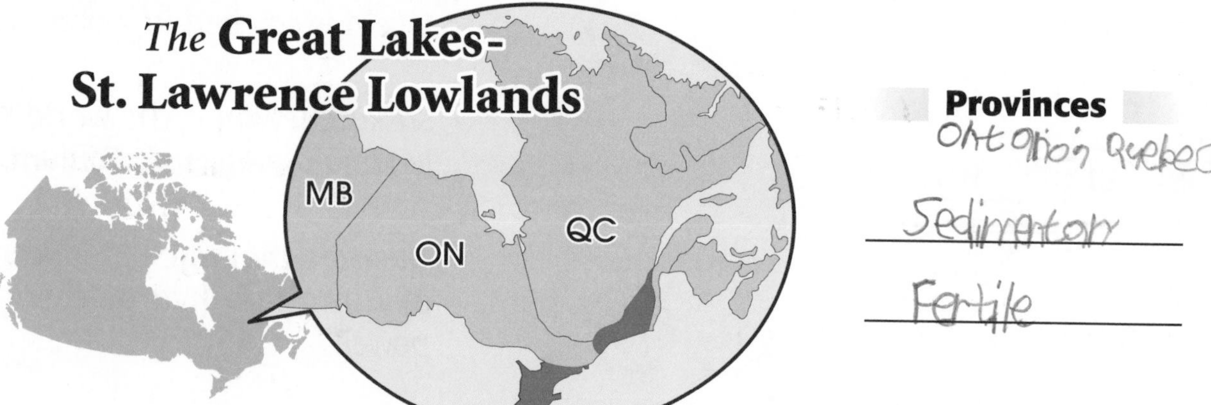

Characteristics

1. Large amounts of deposits carried by tidal waves to the region were compressed into **igneous / sedimentary** rock.
2. The soil in this region is very **fertile / poor** .
3. The region consists of lakes, **raised / flat** plains, rolling hills, and river valleys.
4. The **Great Lakes / St. Lawrence Lowlands** area is where most of the minerals in the region are found.
5. Climate is warm and **dry / humid** in general.
6. Sources of water in the region include the St. Lawrence River, Niagara Falls, and the **Great Lakes / Great Bear Lake** .

B. Write one condition of the Great Lakes-St. Lawrence Lowlands that is favourable for the development of each of the industries below.

1. Mining The rock in the region contain where mineral resources.

2. Hydroelectricity The lakes and falls in the region favour the development of Hydroelectricity.

3. Agriculture The fertile soil and warm humid Climate make the region idel for Agriculture.

C. Write how each of the aspects below has helped make manufacturing the biggest industry in the Great Lakes-St. Lawrence Lowlands.

Manufacturing in the Great Lakes-St. Lawrence Lowlands

1. Proximity to water bodies: Provide easy transportation and Hydroelectricity to power the many fection Plants.

2. Proximity to populated areas: Provide workers for the many Factyring Plants and customers for the Product.

3. Proximity to mineral sources: Provide raw materials needed the many fection for the product plants.

4. Availability of transportation: Transports raw materials to many fection Plants and Product to market.

5. Others: They rocks Provide farm foundation for manufacturing Plants and their heavy machinry.

Industries in the Appalachians

The Appalachians is the easternmost physical region of Canada. This vast mountainous area along the coast, together with the many forests and fertile coastal land, is ideal for the development of a number of industries.

A. Name the provinces in the Appalachians. Then check the six characteristics of this region.

The **Appalachians**

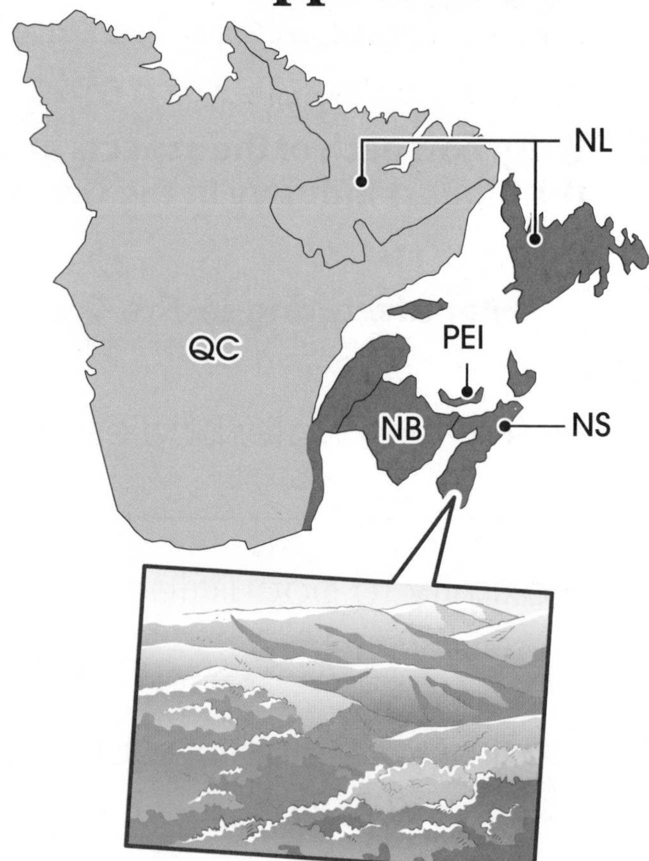

Provinces

Newfoundland and Labrador
Nova Scotia
New Brunswick
Prince Edward Island
Quebec

Characteristics

1. many forests ✓
2. sedimentary rocks ✓
3. permafrost
4. young, rugged mountains
5. lowland areas along the coast ✓
6. many rivers and coastal inlets ✓
7. large coastal bays and deep harbours ✓
8. eroded gentle rolling mountains and rocky cliffs
9. long, hot summers and very cold winters ✓

B. Identify the four major industries in the Appalachians. Then fill in the blanks.

Mining **Forestry** **Fishing** **Agriculture**	valleys lobsters plankton coal temperate ocean metamorphic deciduous potatoes New Brunswick

Industries in the Appalachians

1. Agriculture Industry

- fertile plateaus
- soil rich in nutrients in river Valleys
- rich, red soil ideal for growing Potatoes on PEI

2. Forestry Industry

- rich Deciduous forest areas
- mixed forests of coniferous and Temperate trees

3. Mining Industry

- Coal and salt in sedimentary rock
- iron and zinc in igneous and Metamorphic rocks
- off-shore oil and gas extraction in New Brunswick

4. Fishing Industry

- where two Plankton currents meet
- abundant ocean and microscopic organisms
- rich resources of fish, oysters, Lobsters, and mussels

20

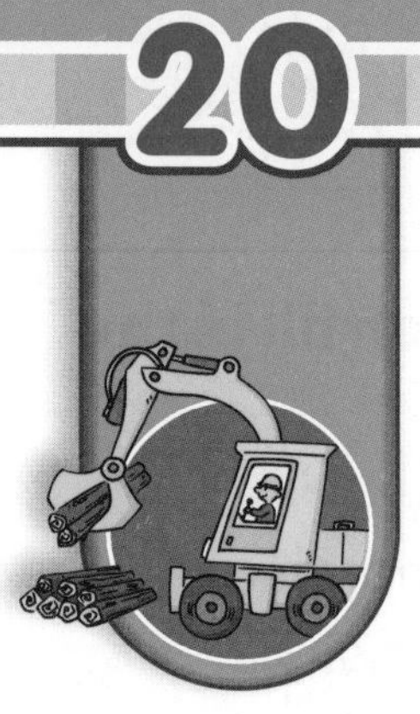

The Hudson Bay Lowlands and the Arctic Lands

The Hudson Bay Lowlands and the Arctic Lands, with their undesirable physical characteristics and harsh climate, are not favourable for the development of most industries.

A. Identify the provinces and territories in the Hudson Bay Lowlands and the Arctic Lands. Then fill in the blanks.

Provinces and Territories

The Hudson Bay Lowlands:

Manitoba
Ontario
Quebec

The Arctic Lands:

Yukon
Northwest Territories
Nunavut

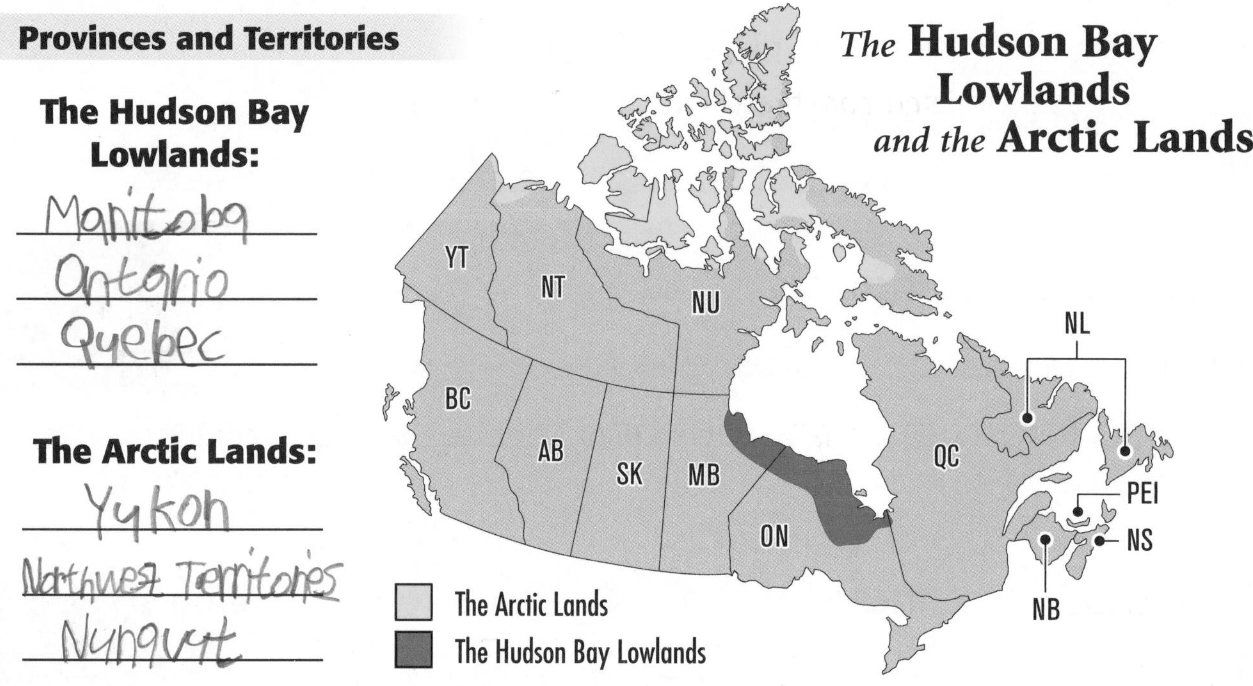

Canadian Shield
James
islands
Innuitian

1. The Arctic Lands include the many Islands in the Arctic Lowlands region and the Innuitian Mountains region.

2. The Hudson Bay Lowlands is located between the Canadian Shield and the southern shores of Hudson Bay and James Bay.

B. Read the descriptions and determine whether they are features of the Hudson Bay Lowlands or the Arctic Lands. Write the letters.

- **A** *very few or no vegetation*
- **B** *forests and tundra*
- **C** *habitat of polar bears*
- **D** *very high and steep mountains*
- **E** *many wide and slow moving rivers*
- **F** *very few people and settlements*
- **G** *summer habitat for migratory shorebirds*
- **H** *flat, poorly drained coastland with lots of swamps*
- **I** *most parts of this region unexplored because of the hostile climate*
- **J** *natural resources including peat, oil, and natural gas*
- **K** *may have large deposits of coal, oil, natural gas, and other mineral resources*
- **L** *low-lying, barren islands consisting mostly of permafrost*
- **M** *wetlands covered in muskeg, which are thick deposits of decomposing dead plants*

Hudson Bay Lowlands	Both	Arctic Lands
B M E J G H	C F	A L D K I

C. Decide if it is possible for the industries below to develop in the two regions. Give one reason to support each answer.

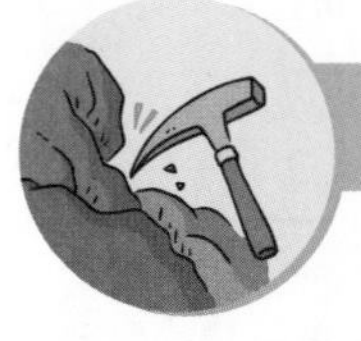

Mining

possible

~~not possible~~

Tourism

~~possible~~

not possible

Agriculture

possible

~~not possible~~

Reason: Extratation Economical.

Mining: The Terrian makes transportation difficult and mineral

Tourism: Polar Bear and Northern area attract tourist to this region.

Agriculture: The Harsh climb and frozen ground make Agriculture Impossible.

21

Recreation, Tourism, and the Environment

The great variety of geographical characteristics of Canada provides ideal locations for recreation and helps foster the development of tourism. However, these human activities can have adverse effects on the natural environment.

A. Name the provinces or territories. Then match the recreation and tourist activities with the locations. Write the letters in the circles.

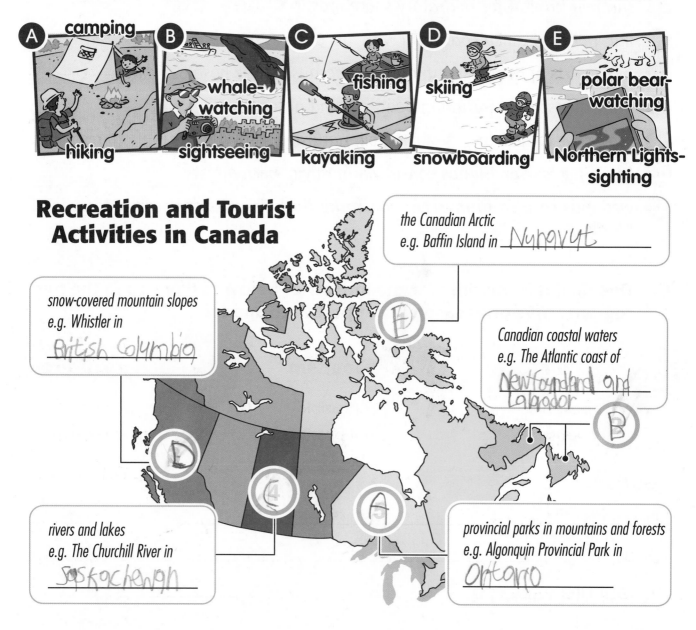

A camping, hiking

B whale-watching, sightseeing

C fishing, kayaking

D skiing, snowboarding

E polar bear-watching, Northern Lights-sighting

Recreation and Tourist Activities in Canada

the Canadian Arctic
e.g. Baffin Island in Nunavut (E)

snow-covered mountain slopes
e.g. Whistler in British Columbia (D)

Canadian coastal waters
e.g. The Atlantic coast of Newfoundland and Labrador (B)

rivers and lakes
e.g. The Churchill River in Saskachewan (C)

provincial parks in mountains and forests
e.g. Algonquin Provincial Park in Ontario (A)

B. Recreation and tourism have strong impacts on the environment. Read each cause and impact. Suggest a possible solution to each problem.

	Cause	Impact
A	construction of recreation and tourist facilities	destroying natural habitats of wildlife
B	increase in visitor/ tourist flow	disturbing wildlife
C	careless and irresponsible visitors/ tourists	land and water pollution; wildfires

A Limit the no. of facilities built.

B Limit the no. of visitor tourists

C Impost strict guideline.

C. Fill in the blanks to show why ecotourism is environmentally friendly.

conservation hike funds workshops respect pollution

Ecotourism is responsible travel with low impact to natural areas. It promotes conservation of the environment and improves the welfare of local communities.

1. Ecotourists Hike or bike to the natural destinations instead of travelling there in cars. This reduces air Pollution and the disturbance to the natural habitats of animals.

2. The tourist fees for entering conservation areas provide Funds for more environmental Conservation efforts.

3. Ecotourists participate in educational Workshops that help build their awareness of and Respect for the environment.

The Impact of Clear-cutting

Clear-cutting is a logging practice in which an entire area of trees is cut down at the same time. In Canada, clear-cutting is the most common method used in harvesting forests. Although forestry provides us with many things we need, the practice of clear-cutting has serious negative impact on the environment.

A. Fill in the blanks with the correct words to show why clear-cutting is practised.

sunlight livestock towns paper healthier pests construction mineral cities

Clear-cutting is practised to...

- make room for the 1. construction of roads.
- regenerate the forest with 2. healthier trees.
- control outbreaks of forest 3. pests and diseases.
- provide 4. paper and wood products needed in every aspect of life.
- allow for the development and expansion of 5. towns and 6. cities .
- foster the growth of specific tree species that need lots of 7. sunlight .
- extract precious 8. mineral and oil resources that lie underneath the forests.
- give farmers land to grow crops and graze 9. livestock .

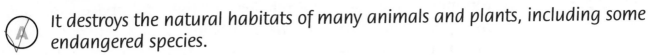

B. Check the impact of clear-cutting. Add one more point with the help of the picture clue.

The Impact of Clear-cutting

- (A) ✓ It destroys the natural habitats of many animals and plants, including some endangered species.
- (B) ✓ Without trees to hold soil together, soil erosion will occur.
- (C) It leads to more frequent earthquakes in the clear-cut regions.

- (D) ✓ Without the shady shield of trees, temperatures in nearby rivers rise, which can cause some fish species to die off.
- (E) ✓ Trees play a significant role in the water cycle and clear-cutting will result in less rainfall.
- (F) ✓ It changes the natural scenery and affects tourism, which is an important industry across Canada.
- (G) ✓ There are fewer trees to absorb carbon dioxide, the key greenhouse gas in the atmosphere.
- (H) Clear-cut areas are more prone to wildfires.
- (✓) The soil dries out because there are no trees to sled it from direct sunlight.

C. Answer the question.

To sustain forest resources, forestry companies replant trees in clear-cut areas. Usually, one or two tree species are chosen. Do you think this is a good way to sustain forests? Why or why not?

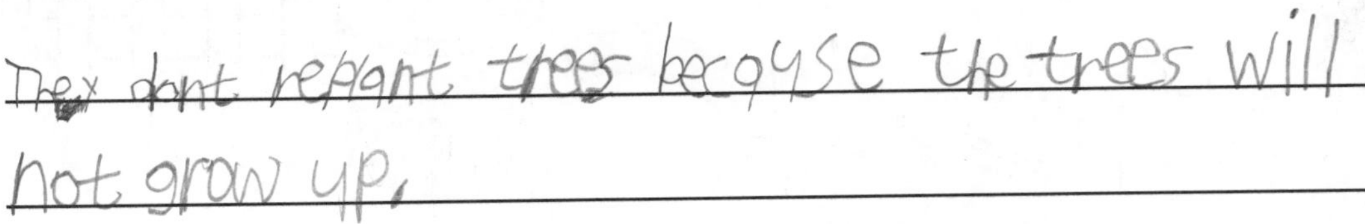

23

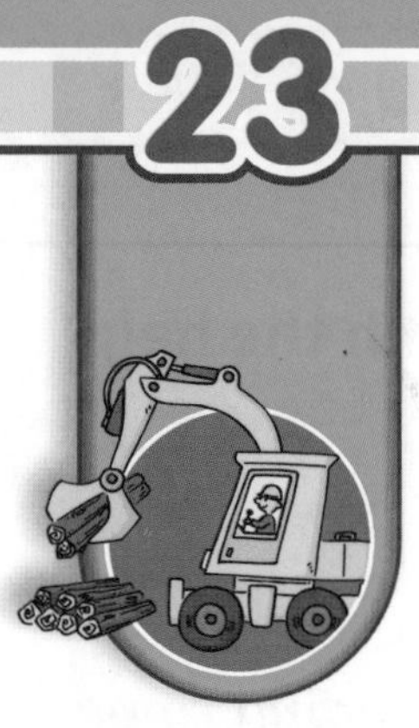

The Impact of Oil Sands

Alberta's oil sands reserves are among the largest in the world. While it has brought positive effects to Alberta's economy, including providing employment in the mining, oil refining, and the local service industries, it has also done great harm to the environment.

A. Write the letters in the circles to show how oil sands are extracted and processed in Alberta.

Extracting and Processing Oil Sands

A *The waste water and sand are sent to tailing ponds.*

B *Mining shovels dig up huge chunks of oil sand ore.*

C *The bitumen is diluted and processed into crude oil.*

D *A large area of the boreal forest is removed to expose the oil sands beneath it.*

E *The mixture is put in a tank, where the bitumen is separated from the sand and water.*

F *The oil sand ore is crushed into smaller pieces, mixed with warm water to form a slurry, and transported through pipelines to an extraction plant.*

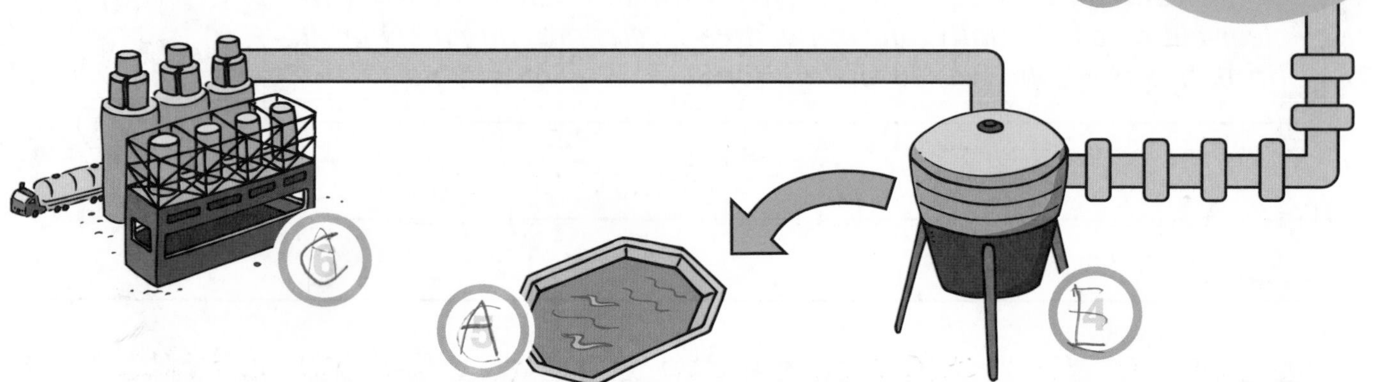

B. Fill in the blanks to complete the sentences. Then add one more point for each aspect to show the negative impact of the development of oil sands in Alberta.

The Impact of the Development of Oil Sands in Alberta

sick deforestation toxic water greenhouse

Land

- Large areas of the boreal forest in Alberta are levelled.
- The landscape is permanently altered.
- Large toxic tailing ponds are created.
- 1. Deforestation leads to soil erosion.

Wildlife

- The boreal forest's natural habitats for many animals, including the threatened woodland caribou, are destroyed.
- Animals die from drinking the highly 2. Toxic water.

Air

- Large amounts of 3. Greenhouse gases are emitted throughout the process.

Water

- Large amounts of 4. Water from the Athabasca River are used in the warming of oil sands and the separation process.

Human Beings

- Human beings get severely 5. Sick from drinking the polluted water.

The negative impact on each aspect:

Land: Deforestation and soil erosion may lead to land slice.

Wildlife: Fish and other equatic life cannot servive in the polluted river in the lakes.

Air: The increase in greenhouse gas imission contributes in global warming.

Water: leaching from telling ponds pollutes nearby rivers and lakes.

Human Beings: Toxic pollutends in the food chain will sickin people for generation.

24

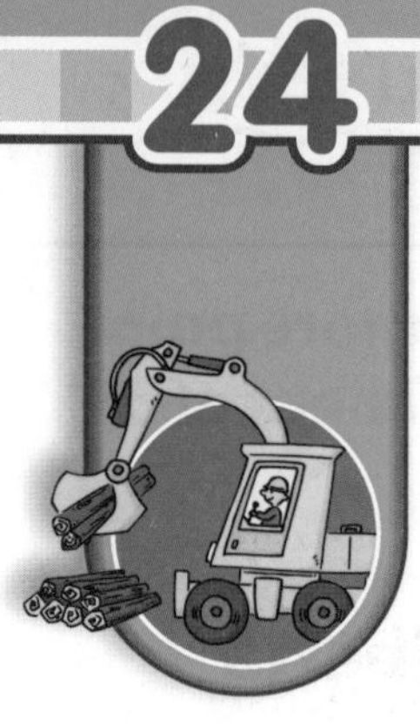

Energy Source

Canada produces energy from different sources. Some are renewable and some are not. Using hydro power is one way Canada generates electricity. It has both advantages and disadvantages. When deciding on the construction of a hydroelectric dam, everyone's voice needs to be heard before steps are taken.

A. Look at the chart and put the energy sources in order. Then answer the questions.

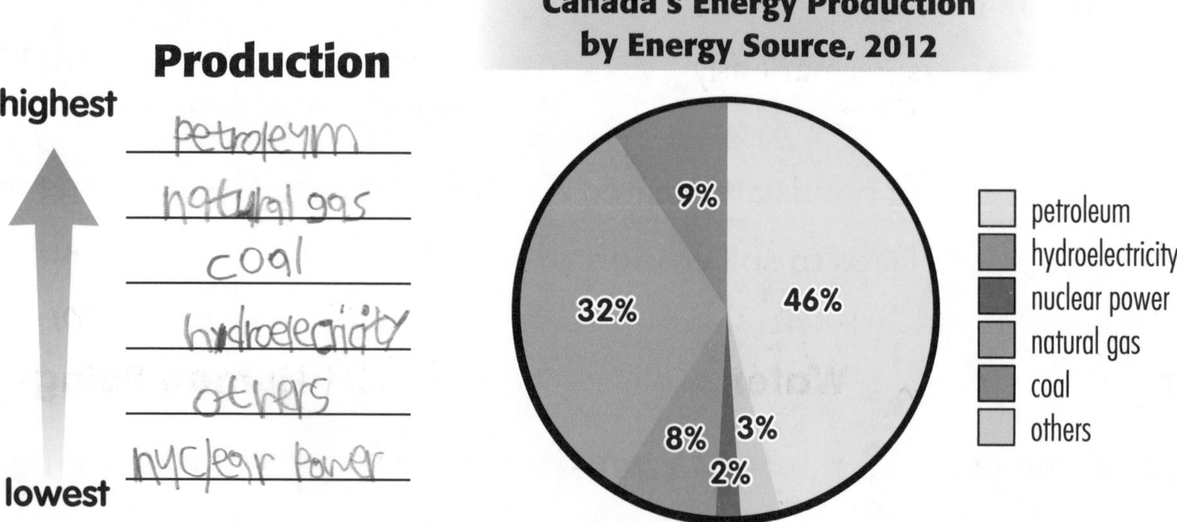

1. Between hydroelectricity and nuclear power, which one do you think is better? Why?

   Others include wood and woods waste.

2. Which energy source do you think is the most harmful to the environment? Why?

   Petroleum is the most harmful to the environment.

3. What energy sources do you think "others" include?

   Others include wood and woods taste.

B. There is a plan for building a hydroelectric plant near a town. Read what the people from the community say. Then complete the decision-making chart and answer the question.

I'm a businessman. The hydroelectric plant is a good idea for our community and our province. It will create more jobs and we'll make money from selling the electricity generated here.

I'm an environmentalist. I think the hydroelectric plant is a very bad idea. It will destroy the habitat of some fish species. Also, gas emissions from the generator will contribute to greenhouse gases.

I'm a farmer. I'm looking forward to the building of the hydroelectric plant here because it will provide more water for my crops.

I'm a resident in this town. I don't want a hydroelectric plant here. Many of us will have to move houses to make way for a dam.

Building the Hydroelectric Plant

Pros
Job for People in the community clean source of energy more money for the community.

Cons
destory fish habbit more green house gases residents have to move house.

Not Building the Hydroelectric Plant

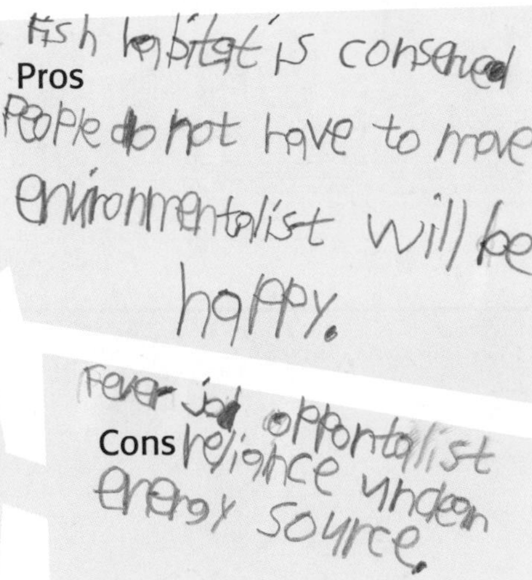

Pros
Fish habitat is conserved
People do not have to move
environmentalist will be happy.

Cons
Fewer job opportunities
reliance unclean energy source.

If you were the mayor of the town, would you build the hydroelectric plant? Why or why not?

No because i did not build the plant.

CONGRATULATIONS

24

SOCIAL STUDIES

S

SOCIAL STUDIES COMPLETE

SCIENCE

1

Habitats

- *A habitat is a place where plants and animals live and grow.*
- *Plants and animals must have everything they need for health in their habitats.*

A. Look at the favourite food and things of the animals. Write the animals' habitats on the lines.

wetlands cave carpet desert savanna underground

Trumpeter Swan

Food:
aquatic plants, snails

Things:
grassy areas, water

Habitat:

1. Wetlands

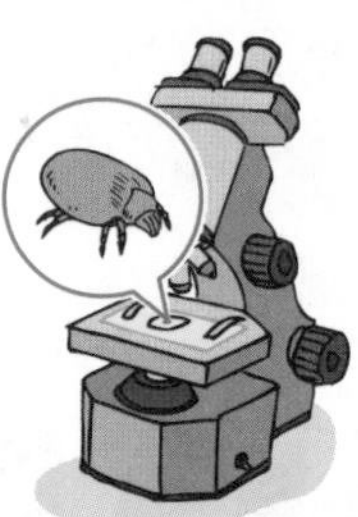

Dust Mite

Food:
human skin flakes

Things:
warmth, humidity

Habitat:

2. Carpet

Mole

Food:
worms

Things:
dark, damp places

Habitat:

3. Underground

Roadrunner

Food:
lizards, insects

Things:
space to run

Habitat:

4. Dessert

Giraffe

Food:
tree leaves, grass

Things:
dry, open space, tall trees

Habitat:

5. Savanna

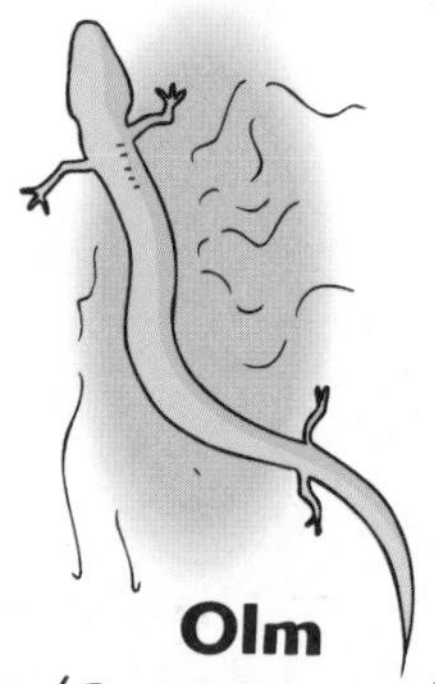

Olm
(Cave Salamander)

Food:
worms, can go years without food

Things:
dark, wet places

Habitat:

6. Caves

B. Help the zookeeper prepare the correct habitat for each animal. Put a check mark in the correct boxes.

	Polar Bear	Black Bear
Ice floes	✓	
Chilly water	✓	
Forest		✓
Shrubs and berries		✓
Fresh fish and seal meat	✓	
Fish streams	✓	✓
Large space to roam	✓	✓

C. Draw lines to match the descriptions with the habitats.

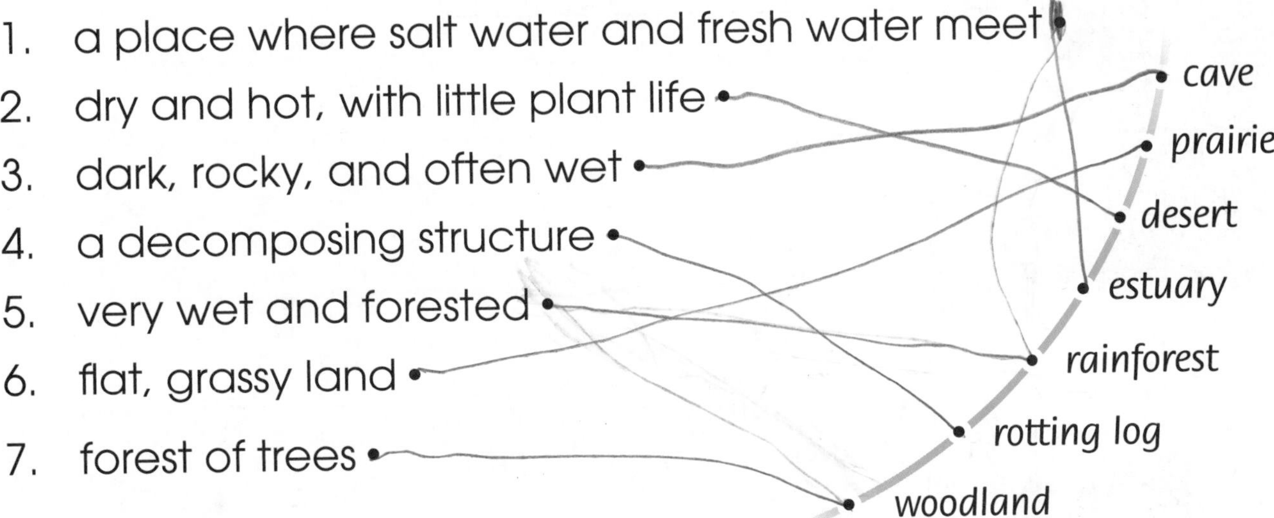

1. a place where salt water and fresh water meet
2. dry and hot, with little plant life
3. dark, rocky, and often wet
4. a decomposing structure
5. very wet and forested
6. flat, grassy land
7. forest of trees
cave
prairie
desert
estuary
rainforest
rotting log
woodland

Science Fact

The habitat of an insect can be as small as a space in your backyard, while the habitat of a whale can be as large as all the world's oceans.

Producers and Consumers

- *Living things are either producers or consumers.*
- *Animals can be grouped by the type of food they eat.*

A. Read what they say. Help them fill in the blanks with the words in bold. Then sort the things by writing the letters in the circles and draw one more item for each group.

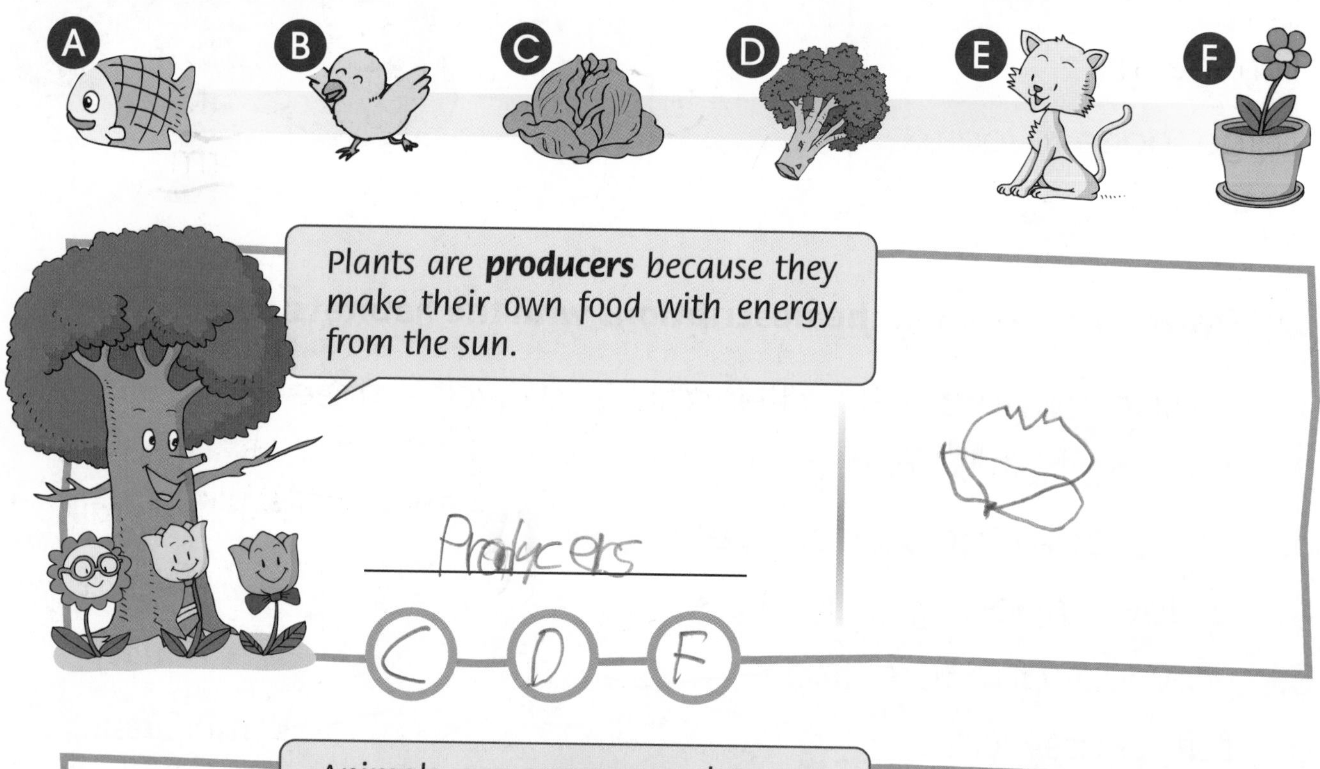

A
B
C
D
E
F
Plants are **producers** because they make their own food with energy from the sun.

Animals are **consumers** because they get their energy by eating plants or other animals.

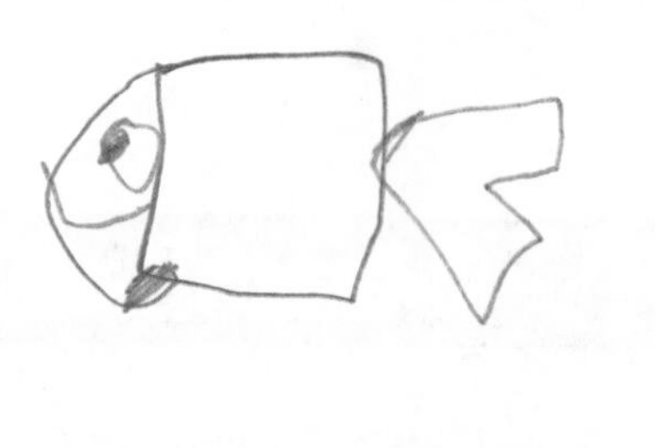

B. Fill in the missing letters to complete the words. Then help the animals find their favourite food. Circle the answers.

carnivore herbivore omnivore

Types of Animals

H__ __b__ __o__e
(eats plants only)

__ar__ __ __or__
(eats animals only)

__m__ __ v__r__
(eats both plants and animals)

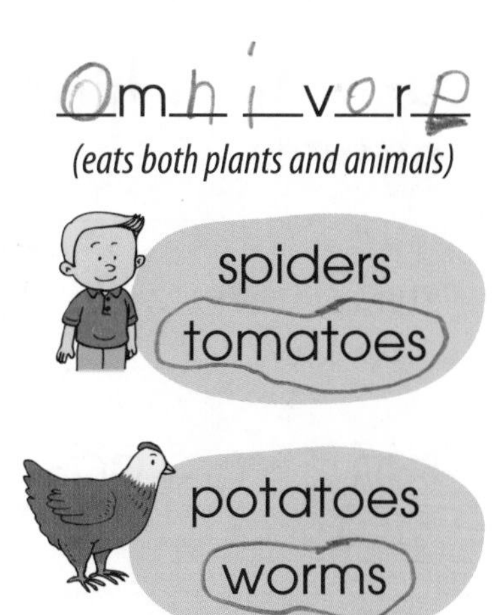

C. Colour the dinosaur that was probably a carnivore.

Most carnivorous dinosaurs had strong, sharp teeth for tearing flesh. They could run quickly to catch their prey and grasp them with strong claws.

Brachiosaurus

Stegosaurus

Tyrannosaurus rex

Triceratops

Science Fact

A panda bear is physically a carnivore, though it behaves like a herbivore by eating only plant material.

3

Food Chains

- *A food chain shows the order that animals eat plants and other animals.*

A. Draw the missing link in each food chain with the help of the given pictures.

1. sun ➔ [ ] ➔ cow
2. sun ➔ algae ➔ [ ]
3. sun ➔ leaf ➔ [ ] ➔ small bird
4. [ ] ➔ grain ➔ hen ➔ human

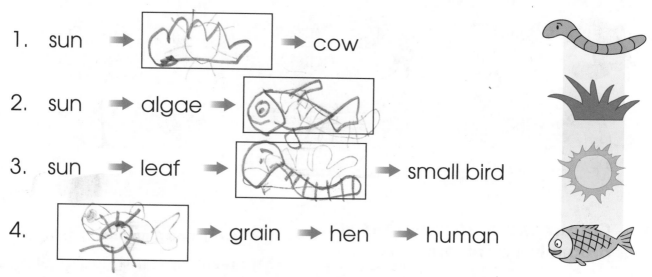

B. Circle the correct words to complete the sentences.

1. Every food chain starts with the plant / sun .

2. The link following the sun in any food chain is the producer / consumer .
3. The arrow (➔) in a food chain means "provides food for" / "eats" .
4. In any food chain, the animals are always producers / consumers .

C. **Find the animals that eat the salmon at its different life stages. Write the letters.**

As salmon go through their life cycle, their habitat changes. As their habitat changes, they become a part of different food chains.

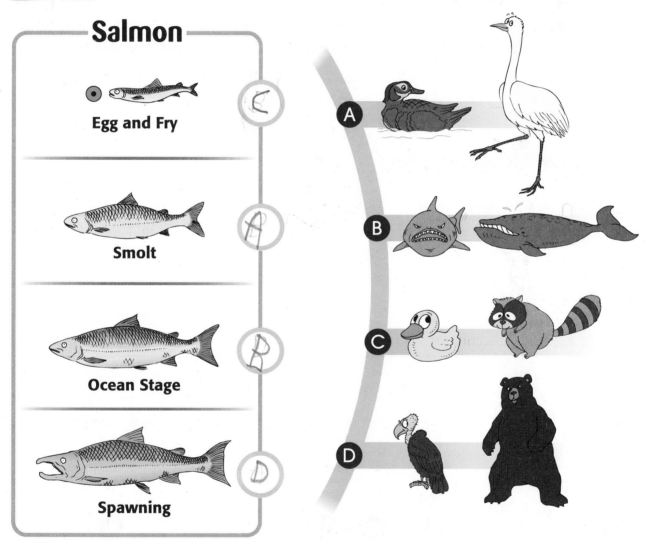

Salmon

Egg and Fry C

Smolt A

Ocean Stage B

Spawning D

A

B

C

D

Science Fact

A food chain can be thought of as a cycle. As the consumers die and provide food for decomposers like fungi, they in turn provide food for new plants.

4

Adaptations

- *Adaptations are traits animals or plants develop to survive in a habitat.*
- *An adaptation can be physical or something about the way an animal or a plant behaves.*

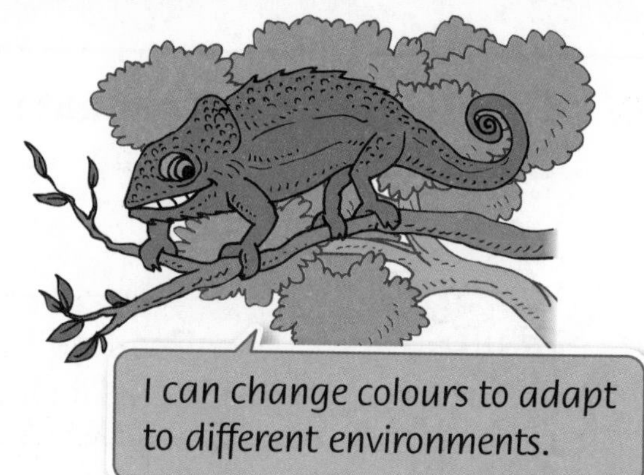

I can change colours to adapt to different environments.

A. Fill in the blanks with the given words to tell the reasons for adaptations. Then find the animals that show these kinds of adaptations.

defence **movement** **feeding**

Reasons for Adaptations

- Defence – to protect themselves against predators and extreme weather

  e.g. A and E

- Feeding – to find and reach the available food easily

  e.g. B and D

- Movement – to get where they need to go easily

  e.g. C

A  fur changes to colour of snow in winter

B  long beak can reach nectar

C  long toes help move on mud

D  stores water for drier times

E  small horns on head protect when fighting

B. Read the poem. Tell what each line describes. Fill in the blank with "behavioural" or "physical".

Why do geese travel in groups?
Why do bees fly loop-the-loop?
Why do sea lions' nostrils close?
Why do some birds have only three toes?

- 1st line: the Behavioural adaptation of geese
- 2nd line: the Physical adaptation of bees
- 3rd line: the Physical adaptation of sea lions
- 4th line: the Physical adaptation of some birds

C. Draw lines to match the sentences with the correct feet.

1. An eagle can grasp and carry a fish from the water to its nest with its feet.
2. A duck moves well in water.
3. A finch can rest on the thinnest tree branch.
4. A chicken is unable to fly or swim, but it scratches for food on the ground.

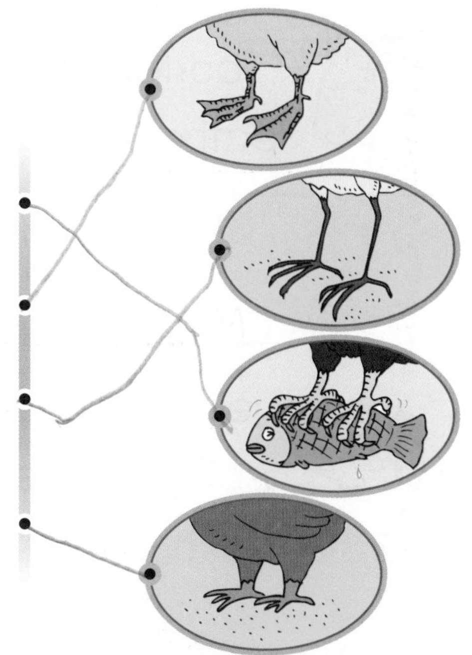

The web-footed gecko's webbed feet are adapted not for swimming, but for staying atop a sandy desert.

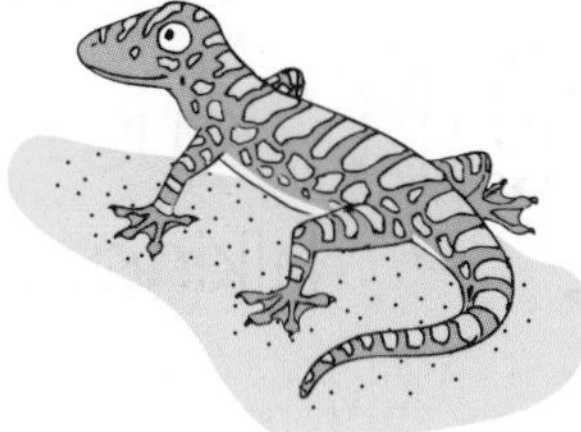

5

Habitat Destruction

- *Humans depend on plants and animals and their habitats.*
- *When we take things from nature, habitats can be harmed or destroyed.*
- *We recognize and categorize the plants and animals at risk of disappearing.*

A. See how we use animals, plants, and their habitats in our lives. Fill in the blanks with the correct words. Then cross out the one that does not belong in each group.

Building Material Clothing Energy
Food Medicine Recreation

1. Clothing

cotton fur
leather ~~plastic~~

2. Energy

oil ~~cup~~
natural gas coal

3. Medicine

~~jello~~ ginseng
aspirin aloe gel

4. Building Material

rock quarry hay
lumber wheat

5. Recreation

skiing boating
hiking ~~cleaning~~

6. Food

wheat meat
~~pencil~~ corn

B. Find the different ways human activities can harm or destroy different habitats. Match the pictures with the descriptions. Write the letters.

Loss of habitat due to human activity:

- (E) Oil extraction
-  Oil spill
-  Hydroelectric dam
-  Air pollution
-  Development
-  Logging

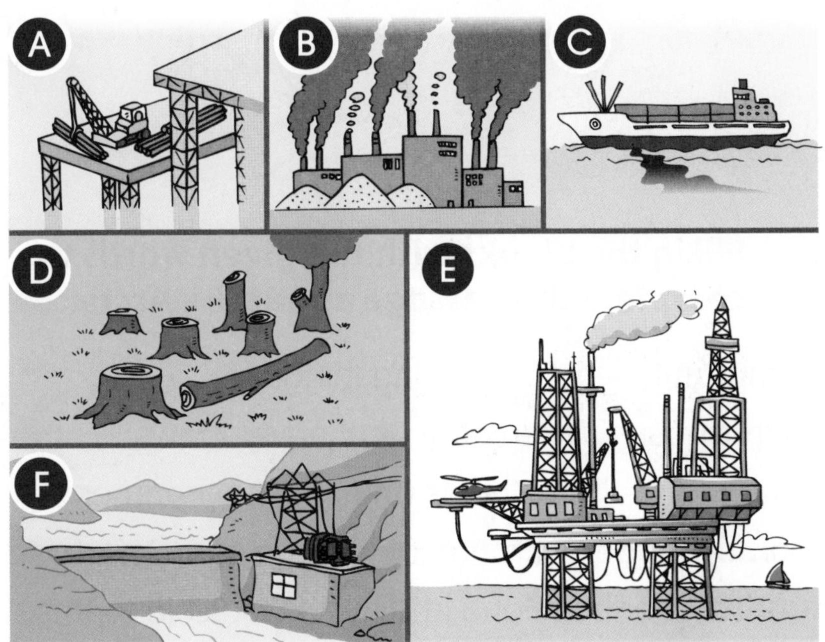

C. See how we define the different levels of danger for species at risk. Write the words in bold on the lines to complete the chart.

Endangered species:
This species is facing future extinction or extirpation.

Species of special concern:
Something has happened to put the species at risk.

Extirpated species:
This species no longer exists in Canada.

Threatened species:
Something must be done to prevent this species from becoming endangered.

Least at Risk

Species of special concern

Threatened species

Endangered species

Extirpated species

Most at Risk

Extinct species
(This species no longer exists in the world.)

Science Fact

Landfills take up space and habitats. Reduce your garbage to help save the homes of some plants and animals.

The Arctic

- *The Arctic is a habitat for animals and plants adapted to cold weather.*
- *A food web can show the relationships among Arctic animals.*

A. Fill in the blanks with the given words to complete the passage about the Arctic.

community – group of living things
permafrost – frozen earth that never thaws
ecosystem – living things and their environment
biome – large environment with the same characteristics
tundra – northern land in climates too cold for most plants
ecological niche – the role a living thing has in its ecosystem

Much of the Arctic is treeless 1. tyndra . There is little soil for plants and the temperature is extremely cold in the dark winter. Even so, a large community of perfectly adapted animals and plants thrives in the Arctic 2. biome . The permanently frozen ground beneath the shallow soil excludes deep-rooted plants, but shallow-rooted plants grow happily above the 3. permafrost . Birds, insects, and many marine and land animals are also part of the Arctic 4. commqnity . Food is abundant in the summer, and the long daylight hours give plenty of time for hunting and growing. All living things in the Arctic have a role to play: an 5. ecologicalniche that drives the Arctic 6. ecosystem .

B. Read the clues. Complete the Arctic food web and answer the questions.

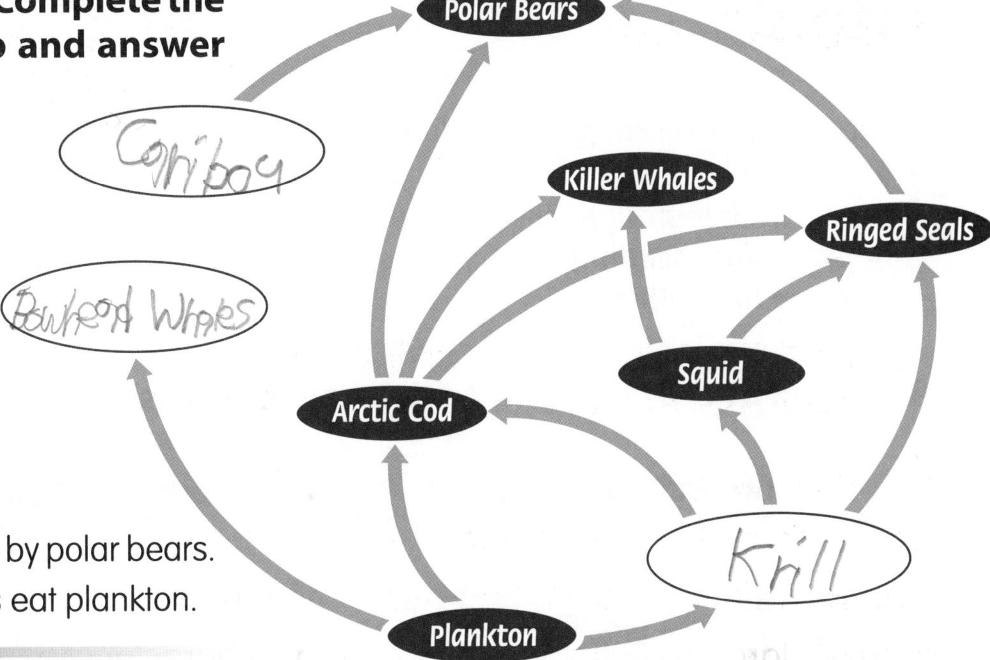

Arctic Food Web

- Squid eat **krill.**
- **Caribou** are eaten by polar bears.
- **Bowhead whales** eat plankton.

1. Killer whales and ringed seals both eat: Arctic Cod and Squid
2. Plankton is eaten by: Arctic Cod, Krill, and Bowhead Whales

C. Match the descriptions with the things that humans wear in similar weather.

1. Caribou have wider hooves than their southern relatives, better for walking on snow.
2. Polar bears have an extra eyelid to help prevent snow blindness.
3. The Arctic fox is a short-eared fox. A body part that sticks out is one that loses heat fast.
4. The long, thick coat of a musk-ox will get it through the worst winter storm.

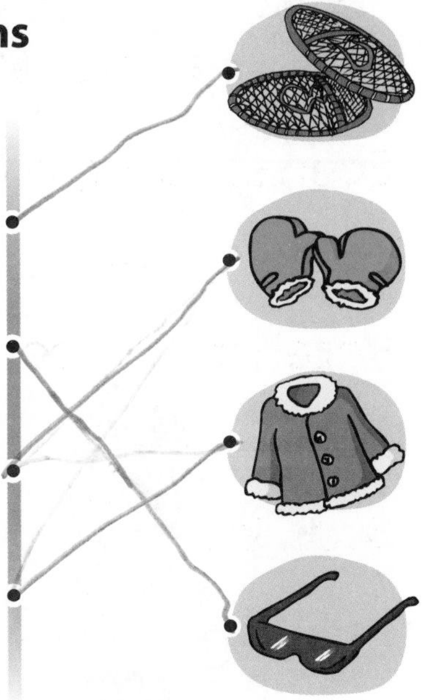

Science Fact

The reindeer of northern Europe is the same species as the caribou of northern Canada.

7

Light

- *Light is a form of energy that is found naturally or artificially in the universe.*
- *Light travels in straight lines, reflecting off some objects, and bending as it passes from one medium to another.*

A. Look at the "light" in each picture. Classify it with the given words.

natural / artificial **light producer / light reflector**

1.

Moon:
Natural ; Light Producer

Cat:
Natural ; Light reflector

Flashlight:
Artificial ; Light producer

Lightning:
Natural ; Light Producer

2.

Sun:
Natural ; Light producer

Water:
Natural ; Light reflector

Candle:
Artificial ; Light producer

Sunglasses:
Artificial ; Light reflector

B. Read the properties of light. Then draw lines to match them with the movie posters that illustrate the properties.

Properties* of Light

* Properties are the special things or powers that an object has.

"Ken the Thief"

The Reflective Moon

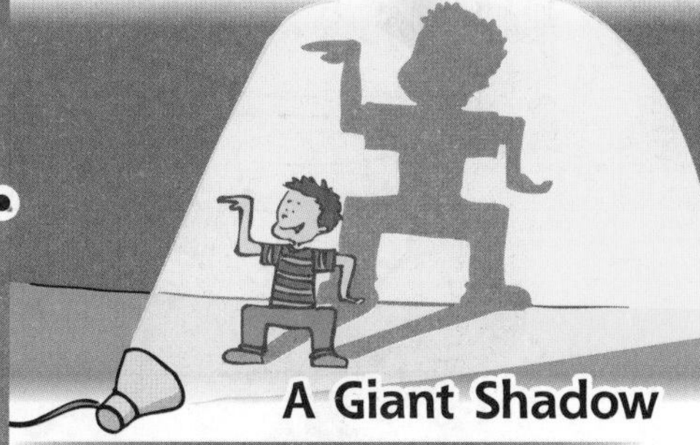

A Giant Shadow

"Bendy Spoon Bendy – A Magician's Life"

Light travels in straight lines.

Light can pass through some things but not others.

Light can be reflected by shiny objects.

Light bends as it passes from one medium to another.

Light travels at more than one billion kilometres an hour.

Light – Reflection and Refraction

- *We can see something because light is bouncing or reflecting off that thing.*
- *Lenses bend light, or refract it, making objects appear smaller or larger.*
- *Some devices use reflection and refraction to help us see things better.*

A. Colour the objects that reflect green and the objects that refract red.

B. The names of the children are reflected in a mirror. Put a mirror along the grey lines to find out their names in normal form and write them on the lines.

My name is NANCY.
My name is BRIAN.

C. Read the clues and fill in the missing letters to complete the names of the devices. Then draw lines to match the devices with their images.

kaleidoscope microscope telescope

1. _ a _ _ id _ _ cope
mirrors

2. _ _ le _ _ op _
lenses

3. _ _ cr _ _ _ op _
mirrors and lenses

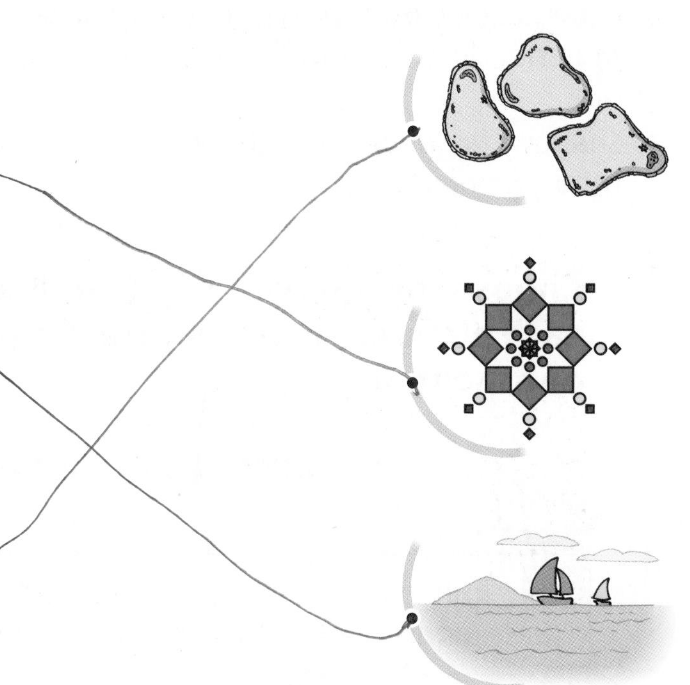

Experiment – Fun with Refraction

Put a nickel into a soup bowl on a table. With the bowl in front of you, sit down and slouch in your chair so that when you look at the bowl, the nickel is just barely out of sight. Then, without changing your position or moving your head, pour water into the bowl. What do you see?

____

____

Science Fact

A periscope makes it possible to see things from a hidden position. It is widely used on submarines.

Light – Transparency

- *Materials that allow all light to pass through are said to be transparent. A translucent material allows some light to pass through, while an opaque material doesn't allow light to pass through it at all.*
- *Shadows are a result of light not being able to pass through objects.*

A. Choose the best word to describe the material being talked about in each picture. Then give an example that has the same property as the one mentioned.

transparent   translucent   opaque

1. This unit provides the total darkness that these plants need, at least for the time being.

Opaque

Example: Rock

2. I can see the clothes clearly through this clean and nice window.

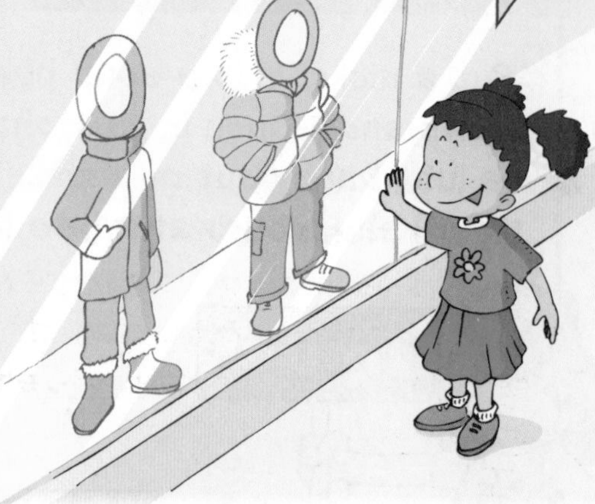

Transparent

Example: Fish bowl

3. This weave will allow just the perfect amount of late afternoon light to enter your lovely living room.

Translucent

Example: [illegible]

B. **Read what Judy says. Look at the location of the shadow in each picture. Put a check mark in the circle if it is correct; otherwise, put a cross and draw the correct one in the picture.**

Light travels in a straight line and opaque objects absorb light. Therefore, the length of the shadow of an opaque object depends on where the light is coming from in relation to the object.

Experiment – Shadow Puppets

Take a flashlight with you into a dark room. You should stand about 1 m away from a clear wall and make different puppets with your hands in front of the flashlight. Look at the shadows cast on the wall.

Science Fact

The sundial was an ancient timepiece that used the shadow cast by the sun to tell time. As the sun travelled across the sky, the shadow would move and mark the time of day on the dial.

10

Light and Colour

Spectral Colours

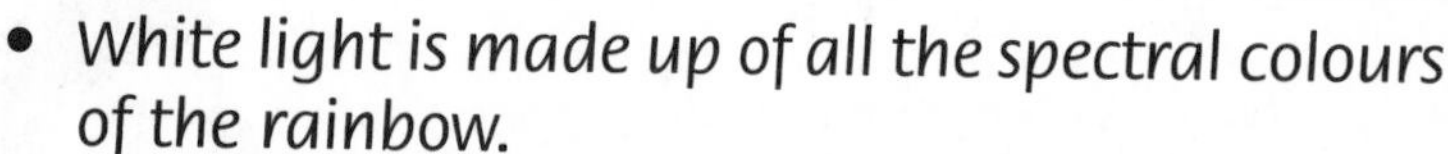

- White light is made up of all the spectral colours of the rainbow.
- We can see the colour of an object because the object absorbs all the other colours of the spectrum, except the one seen. The colour seen is the colour reflected.
- Colours can be mixed to produce other colours.

A. Read what Judy says. Help her colour the spectrum.

The glass prism has bent the beam of light into the spectral colours that make up white light. The order of the colours is the same as the one in the rainbow.

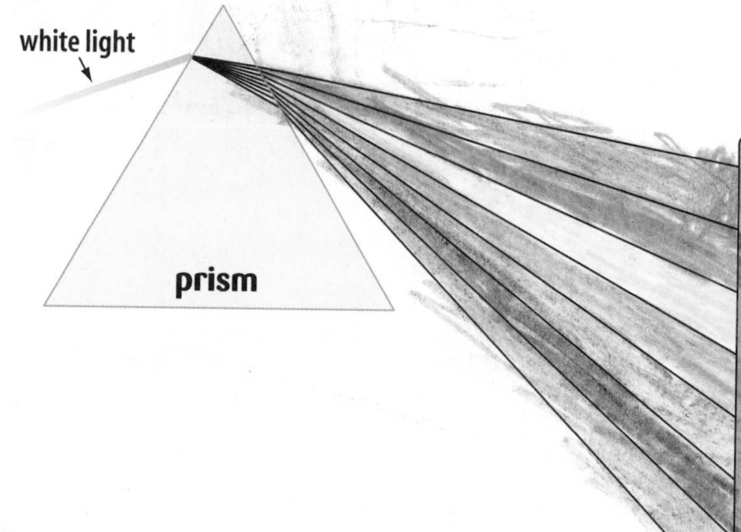

B. Fill in the blanks with "absorbs" or "reflects" to complete the sentences.

1. The grass looks green because it absorbs all colours except green.
2. A black cat is black because it absorbs all the colours that make up light.
3. A clean, white shirt appears white because it reflects all the spectral colours of the rainbow.

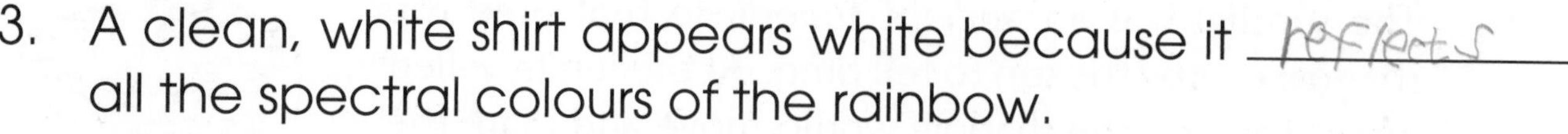

C. Colour the circles with acrylic paint. Then write what colours you can see in the overlapping area.

- red + yellow = Orange
- red + blue = Purple
- yellow + blue = Green

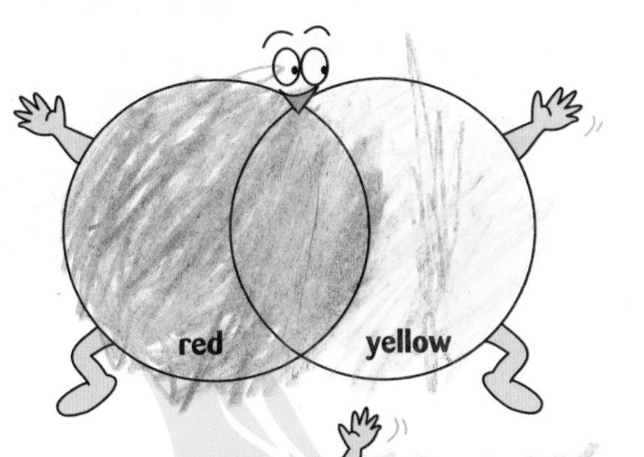

red
blue

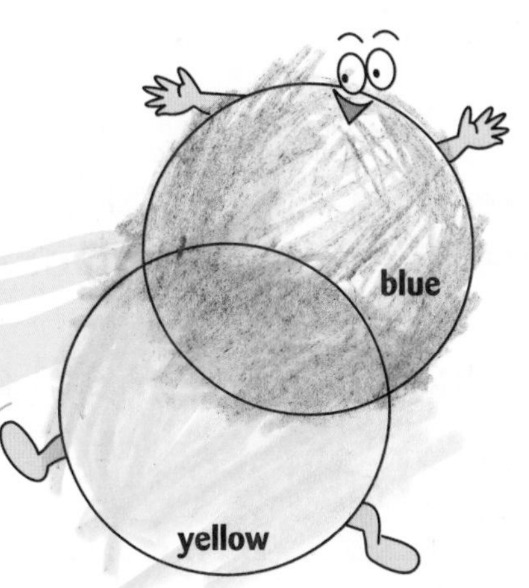

Try this

Trace the circles with tracing paper. Colour each section with a different colour in the given order. Cut out the whole thing and glue it on a cardboard. Use a sharp pencil to pierce the cardboard wheel through the centre, and place the pencil point on a table. Then spin it like a top.

Order of the colours: (from outside to inside)
red, orange, yellow, green, blue, indigo, violet

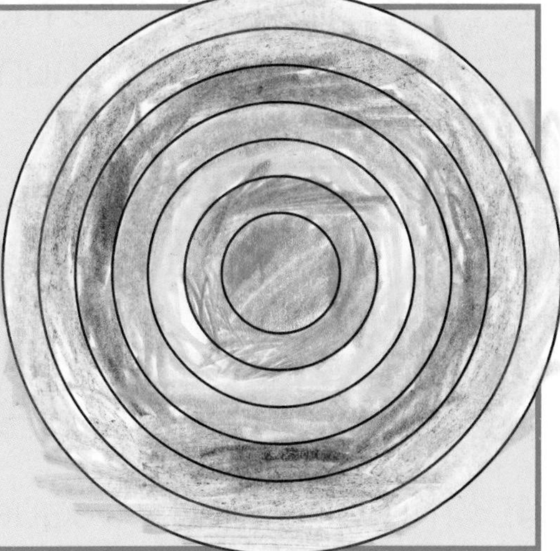

Science Fact

The light that we see is the "visible" part of something known as the electromagnetic spectrum (a bunch of types of radiation). Infrared light is often thought of as heat, and ultraviolet light is the invisible light that gives us sunburns if we stay too long in the sun.

11

Sound

I like the low pitch of your drum.

- *Sounds are caused by vibrations. The faster something vibrates, the higher the pitch is.*
- *The stronger it vibrates, the louder the sound is.*
- *The human ear is a complex organ designed to detect vibrations, thus giving us information about our environment.*

A. Identify the animal that makes the sound. Tell whether the pitch is high or low.

Fruit Bat
African Elephant
Bottle-nosed Dolphin
Saint Bernard Dog
Humpback Whale

1. This very large pet does not bark very much.

   Saint bernard dog ; low pitch

2. The clicking noise that this flying mammal makes allows it to "echolocate". It hunts and captures its food by using sound.

   Fruit bat ; high pitch

3. Sounds made by this animal travels through the ground to tell family group members of its whereabouts.

   African elefant ; high pitch

4. This animal uses squeals to communicate emotions as well as clicks to echolocate.

   Bottle-nosed dolphin ; high pitch

5. *This water animal can make sounds, called "songs", that can be heard several hundred kilometres away.*

   Humpack whale ; low pitch

B. Fill in the blanks with the words given in the diagram.

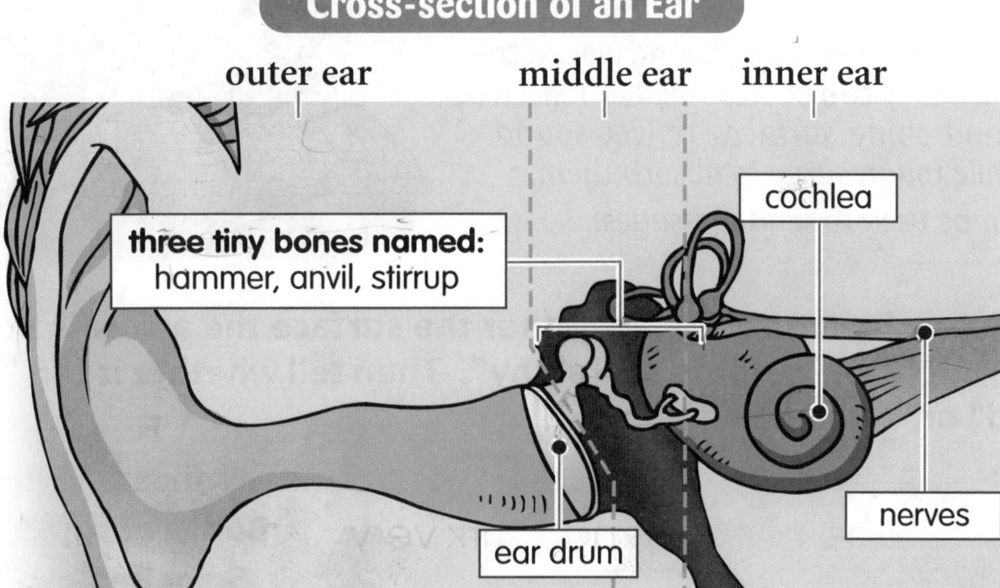

Sound is collected by the 1. Outer ear, which is made up of an earflap and a tunnel that leads to the 2. Ear drum, a thin-skinned structure. There are three tiny little bones in your 3. Middle ear. These bones, the 4. Hammer, 5. Anvil, and 6. Stirrup, make the vibrations larger and send these vibrations to the 7. Inner ear. It is in this part, the 8. Cochlea, where the motion of the vibrations is changed into signals that are carried by 9. Nerves to your brain.

Science Fact

Vibrations cause sound, and the colliding of air molecules transmits the sound to us. There is no sound in space because there are no air molecules there.

12

More about Sound

- Sound travels in waves. When sound waves strike other things, they can be absorbed or reflected. Smooth and shiny surfaces reflect sound waves, while rough surfaces absorb them.
- Sound can be used to send messages.

A. Look at each picture. Tell whether the surface the arrow is pointing at is "rough" or "smooth and shiny". Then tell whether it can "reflect sound" or "absorb sound".

1.

Smooth and shiny ; Reflect sound

2.

Rough ; Absorb sound

3.

Rough ; Absorb sound

4.

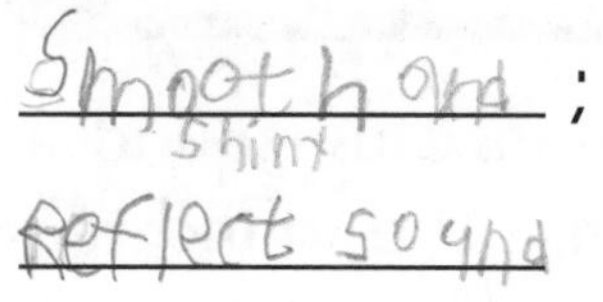

Smooth and shiny ;

Reflect sound

5.

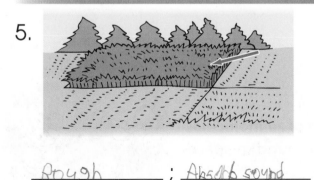

Rough ; Absorb sound

B. Sound can be used to convey messages. Match the sounds with the correct messages.

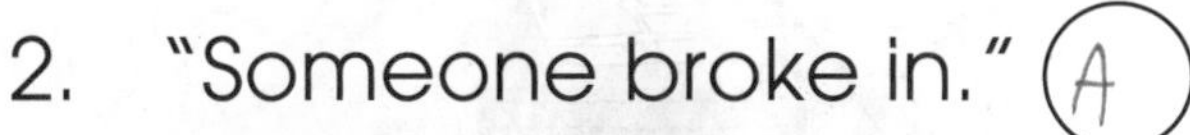

1. "Wake up!" (D)

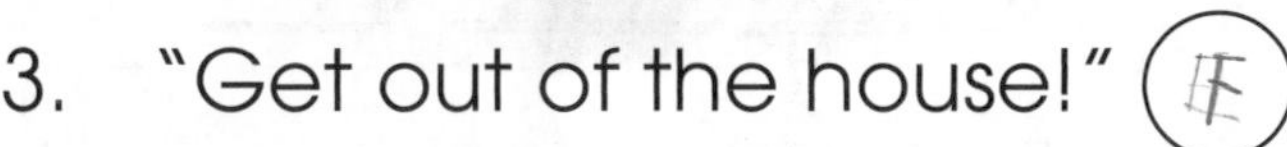

2. "Someone broke in." (A)

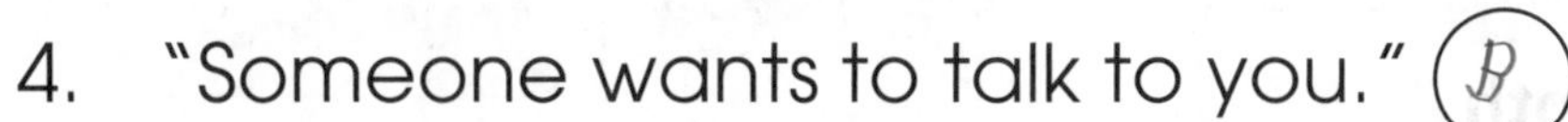

3. "Get out of the house!" (F)

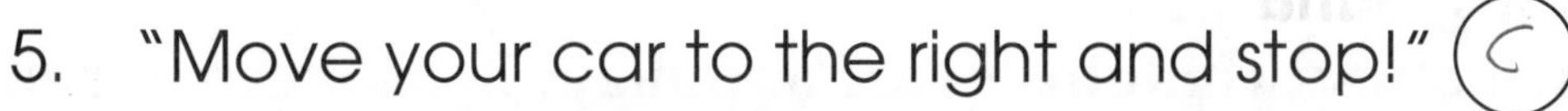

4. "Someone wants to talk to you." (B)

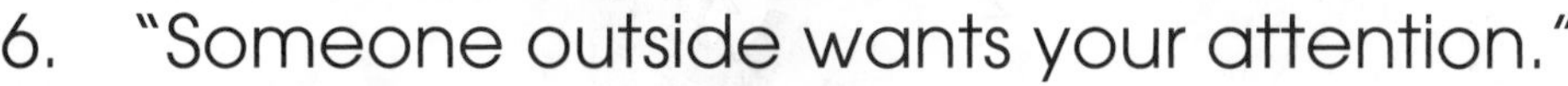

5. "Move your car to the right and stop!" (C)

6. "Someone outside wants your attention." (E)

Experiment

You can do this experiment to see how well different materials absorb sound.

Things needed:

- *1 shoebox with lid*
- *a tick-tock clock*
- *paper strips, dish towels, wood chips, etc. to use as insulators*

1. Put the shoebox on the table with the clock inside it and close the lid.
2. Open the box and fill it with one of the packing materials. Close the lid.
3. Stand back 1 metre and take note of how the loudness of the ticking of the clock has changed. Test with the other materials.

Science Fact

Sound travels at about 340 m/s. In 1947, Air Force pilot Chuck Yeager broke the sound barrier using a rocket-powered Bell X-1. This flight marked the first time a plane moved faster than the speed of sound. This speed resulted in a crashing sonic boom.

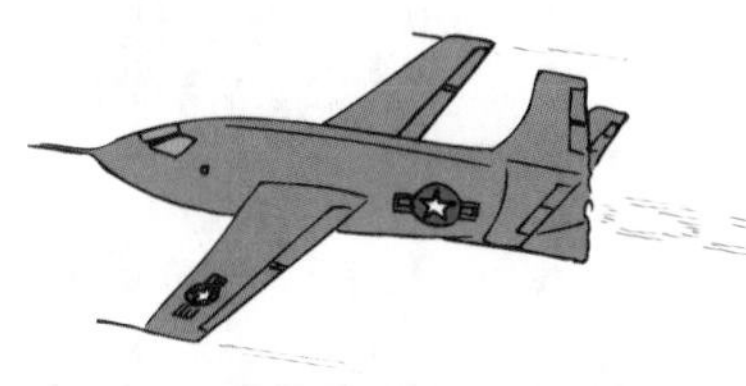

13

Special Wheels – Gears and Pulleys

- *Gears and pulleys are wheel-like simple machines that make our work easier. Gears have teeth and a pulley has a groove.*
- *When gears are linked together, they can change the speed and direction of movement.*
- *Sometimes we make our work easier by changing the direction of movement with the help of pulleys.*

We make the work a lot easier.

A. Tell whether each object contains gears or pulleys in its mechanism. Write "gears" or "pulleys" on the line. Leave it blank if the mechanism contains neither.

1. Gears

2. ______

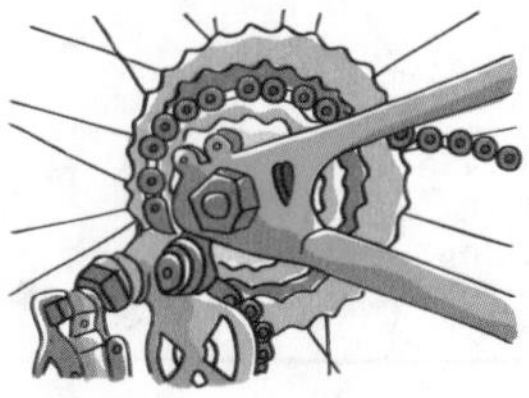

3. Gears

4. pulleys

5. ______

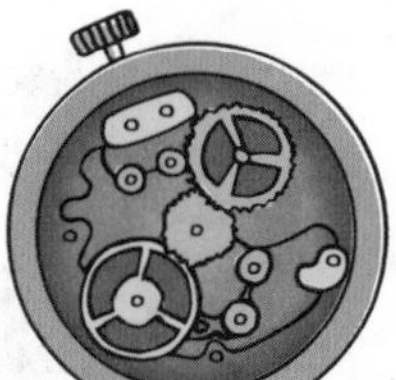

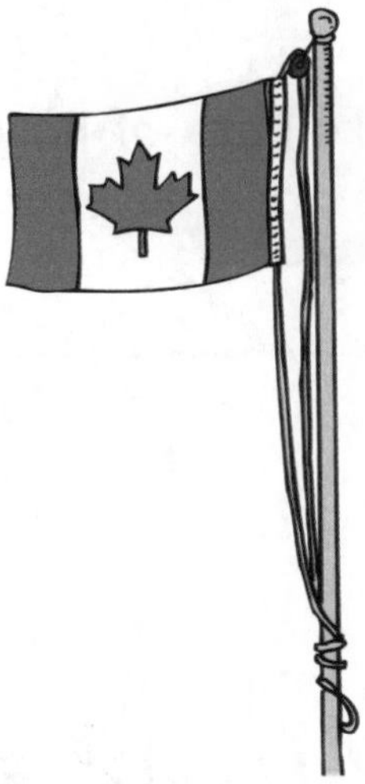

6. Pulleys

7. Pulleys

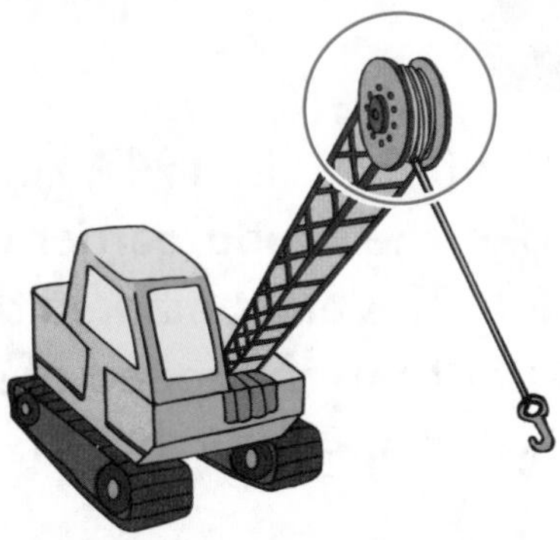

B. Look at the gears. Draw arrows to show the directions that the blue gears will turn. Then use the given words to describe the turns.

as fast as **faster than** **slower than**

1. 

It turns Faster than the one on the left.

2. 

It turns As fast than the one on the left.

3. 

It turns Slower than the small blue gear.

C. Look at the picture. Answer the question.

How are the pulleys helping the mouse?

The pulleys are helping the mouse allowing him to use his on weight to lift the heavy crat of the ground

You can consider my weight.

Science Fact

The world's tallest flagpole is in Saudi Arabia. It is 171 m tall, and the flag at the top of it weighs 570 kg.

14

Minerals

- *Minerals are non-living, solid substances that occur naturally.*
- *Minerals are what rocks are made of.*

A. Fill in the blanks with the given words.

non-living inorganic lead tools shapes mineralogists colours minerals heaviness hardness diamond food

Salt, gold, 1. Diamond, and 2. Lead are all examples of minerals. They are different from plants and animals because they are 3. Non-living. Because they have never been alive, we call them 4. Inorganic. Minerals come in different 5. Shape, 6. Colours, 7. Heaviness, and 8. Hardness. These are just some of the ways that 9. Mineralogists use to compare and identify minerals. 10. Minerals are commoner in our lives than we may think. They are the ingredients of rocks, which can be made up of one or many minerals. From rocks, we mine minerals and use them for 11. Food, jewellery, 12. Tools, and many more.

B. Fill in the missing letters to complete the names of the minerals. Then colour the precious minerals the colour they are most often prized for.

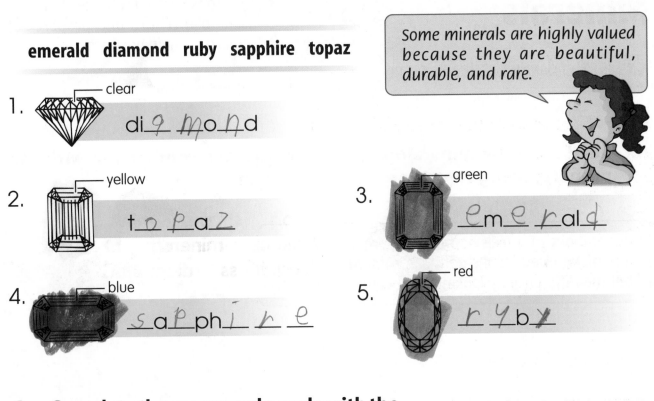

emerald diamond ruby sapphire topaz

Some minerals are highly valued because they are beautiful, durable, and rare.

1. 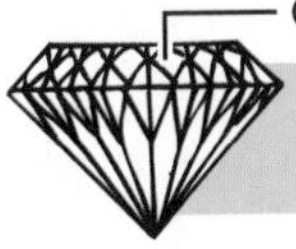 clear — di__ __o__d
2.  yellow — t__ __a__
3.  green — __m__ __al__
4. 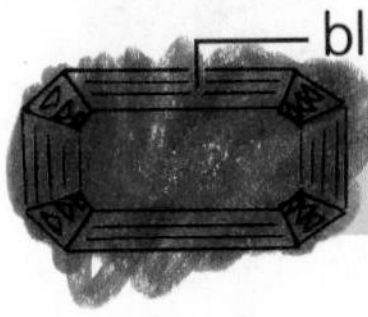 blue — __a__ph__ __ __
5. 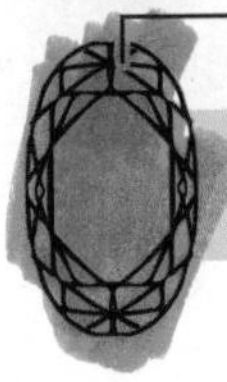 red — __ __b__

C. Complete the crossword puzzle with the given rocks.

In many rocks, the mineral crystals are large and easy to see. Some rocks have more than one mineral.

Rock: quartz, granite, diabase

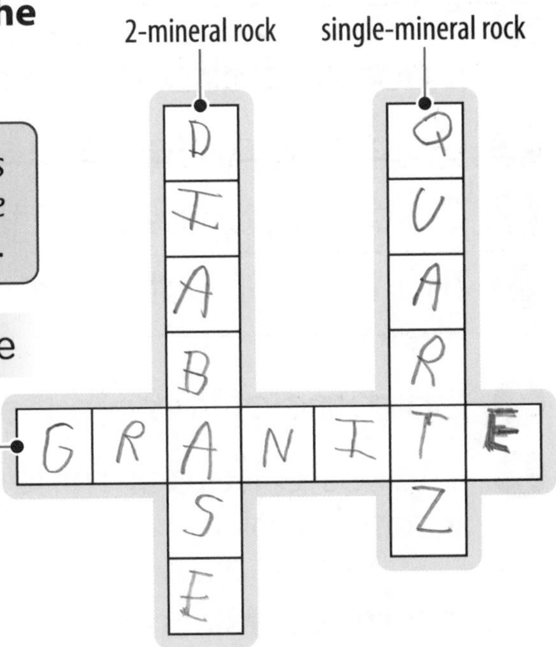

2-mineral rock

single-mineral rock

3-mineral rock

Rubies and sapphires are different coloured specimens of the same mineral: corundum.

More about Minerals

It's hard. I think it's quartz.

- Minerals are identified by their physical properties.
- The Mohs Scale of Hardness is a tool used to measure one property of minerals: their hardness.

A. Read what the mineralogist says. Match the comparison with the property being compared. Write the letter.

Pyrite looks and feels so much like real gold that it is nicknamed "fool's gold". A mineralogist can tell the difference by looking at special properties.

Gold and Pyrite

- **A** Pyrite leaves a black streak of powder when rubbed on a piece of unglazed porcelain. Real gold leaves a yellow streak.
- **B** Gold and pyrite have similar shades of yellow.
- **C** Gold is much heavier than a similar sized sample of pyrite.
- **D** The look of both pyrite and gold is not dull or waxy, but metallic.
- **E** Gold and pyrite are both opaque.
- **F** It takes a harder mineral to scratch pyrite than it does to scratch gold.

Properties of Minerals

(B) colour	(F) hardness	(C) specific gravity
(D) lustre	(A) streak	(E) transparency

B. Use arrows to place the minerals in the "Mohs Scale of Hardness" chart. Then answer the questions.

1.

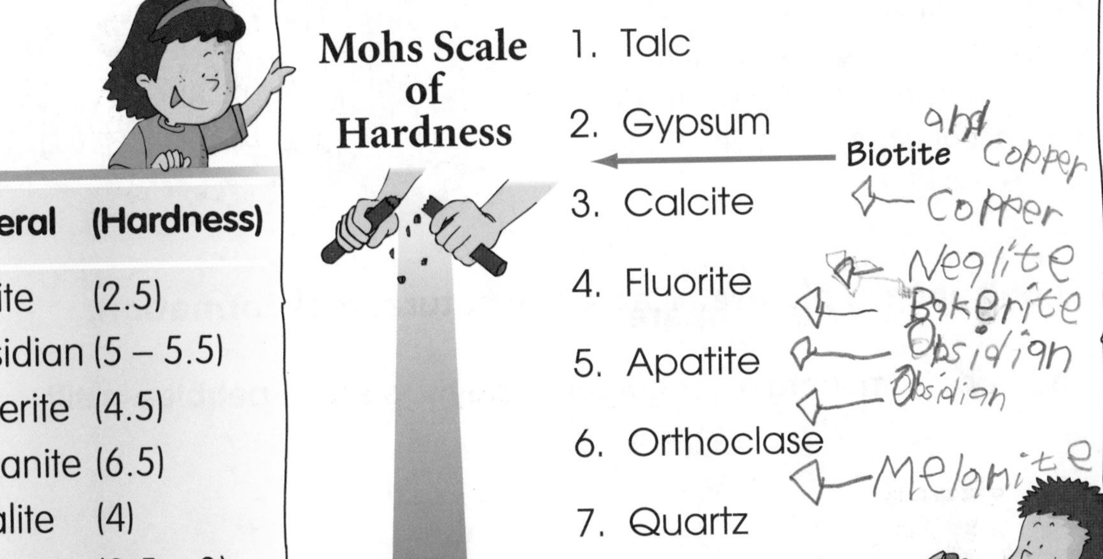

Mohs Scale of Hardness
1. Talc
2. Gypsum
3. Calcite
4. Fluorite
5. Apatite
6. Orthoclase
7. Quartz
8. Topaz
9. Corundum
10. Diamond
Biotite and Copper
Copper
Nealite
Bakerite
Obsidian
Obsidian
Melanite

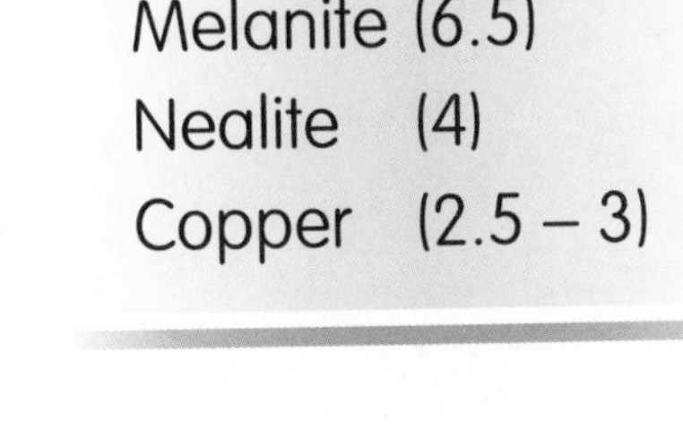

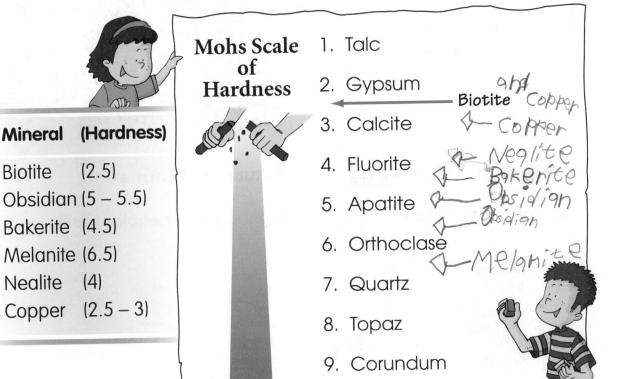

Mineral	(Hardness)
Biotite	(2.5)
Obsidian	(5 – 5.5)
Bakerite	(4.5)
Melanite	(6.5)
Nealite	(4)
Copper	(2.5 – 3)

2. Name two minerals that

a. can cut copper. Obsidian and Melanite

b. can be scratched by a diamond. Topaz and Corundum

c. are softer than apatite. Talc and Gypsum

d. are harder than calcite but softer than quartz. Apatite and Orthoclase

Science Fact

Mercury does not have a hardness rating. Because of its unusual characteristic of being liquid at room temperature, mercury cannot scratch or be scratched.

Rocks

- *Rocks are all around us.*
- *Almost all rocks are solid and made from non-living substances on Earth.*
- *Many people study rocks and things to do with rocks.*

A. Look at each picture. Name the natural rock formation.

bedrock mountain boulder clay sand pebbles silt rock

1. Clay
2. Mountain
3. pebbles
4. Rock
5. Sand
6. Silt
7. Bedrock
8. Boulder

B. Draw a line to match the unusual rock with the definition.

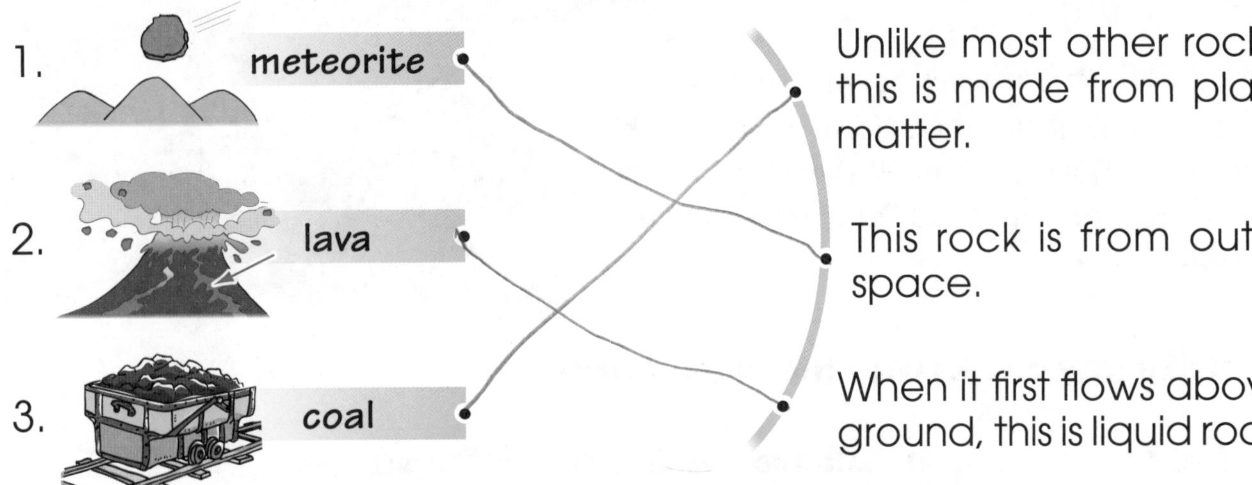
1. meteorite
2. lava
3. coal
Unlike most other rocks, this is made from plant matter.
This rock is from outer space.
When it first flows above ground, this is liquid rock.

C. How do we name the people who work closely on minerals? Write the letters.

- **A** gemologist
- **B** geologist
- **C** mineralogist
- **D** paleontologist
- **E** petrologist
- **F** prospector
- **G** rock hound
- **H** volcanologist

One who...

1. studies fossils (D)
2. studies rocks (E)
3. studies minerals (C)
4. studies volcanoes (H)
5. searches for minerals 
6. studies precious stones 
7. collects rocks or minerals 
8. studies features of the Earth and its history 

Science Fact

Liquid rock is called magma when it is below the Earth's surface. Above the surface it is called lava, even after it hardens.

Igneous Rocks

- *Igneous rocks form when hot molten lava cools.*
- *Intrusive igneous rocks form beneath the Earth's surface. They are exposed by erosion.*
- *Extrusive igneous rocks form from volcanic eruptions.*

A. Fill in the blanks with the given words.

in above extrusive intrusive

- Intrusie igneous rock – forms In the ground

Hot molten magma below the Earth's surface gets trapped in an underground pocket. It is slow to cool, but when it finally hardens, it is igneous rock.

- Extrusive igneous rock – forms Above the ground

Hot molten magma is forced from the inside of the Earth through a volcano or opening in the crust to the Earth's surface. When it is above ground, it is lava. Hot molten lava cools quickly, and another kind of igneous rock is formed.

B. Complete the chart with the names in bold to tell whether each formation of igneous rock is intrusive or extrusive.

1. The stripe of **diabase** in this rock is called a dike. It seeped into a crack in the rock, hardened, and after millions of years of erosion, it is exposed.
2. **Obsidian** is a rock that is smooth as glass. It cools quickly, so no crystals have a chance to form in the rock.
3. This **basalt** formed when magma seeped through an opening in the ocean floor.
4. This **granite** cliff is easy to see now, but it was once underground! After this earth was forced upward to make a mountain, soft rock around it eroded, exposing the granite.

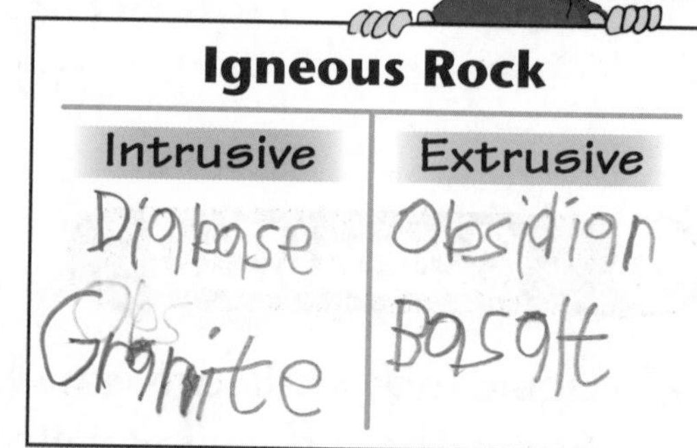

Igneous Rock

Intrusive	Extrusive
Digbase	Obsidian
Granite	Basalt

C. **Colour the igneous rock words to find the path leading to ground surface.**

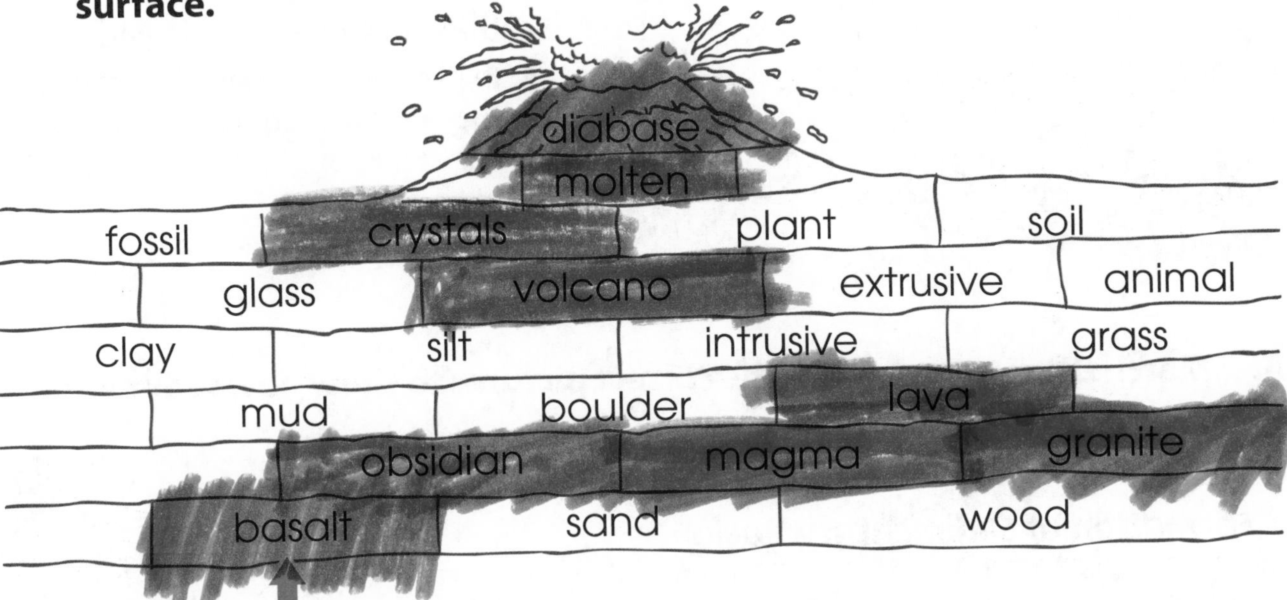

Experiment *What makes hot molten magma rise?*

Things needed:

- *a large, clear jar*
- *a small jar*
- *a long string*
- *food colouring*
- *hot and cold water*

Steps:

1. Tie a long string to the top of a small jar and fill the jar with hot water.
2. Add a few drops of red food colouring to the small jar.
3. Slowly immerse the small jar into the large jar filled with cold water.

What happens to the coloured hot water?

The volcano is coming from the ground

Science Fact

Can rock look like long thin strands of hair? An igneous rock called Pele's hair looks just like that. It forms when lava flies through the air under the right conditions.

Sedimentary Rocks

- *Small pieces of rock break off from bigger rocks and are carried through water as sediment.*
- *In time, with chemicals from water, they become sedimentary rocks.*

A. Match the sentences with the correct pictures to show how sedimentary rocks are formed.

Formation of Sedimentary Rocks

1. Rivers tumble sand into the sea.
2. Sand builds up over thousands of years.
3. Chemicals in sea water cement grains together.
4. Sandstone layers are revealed as sea recedes.

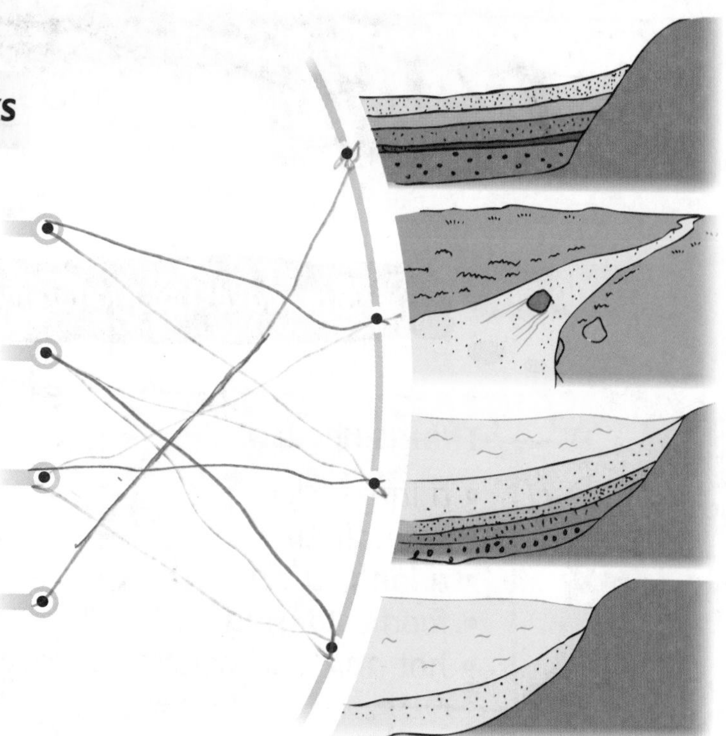

B. Fill in the blanks to find the origins of the sedimentary rocks.

Origin		Sedimentary Rock
1. sand	→	sandstone
2. mud	→	shale
3. shells	→	limestone
4. river pebbles	→	conglomerate

* rich in a chemical substance called calcium carbonate

C. **Where do sedimentary rocks form? What kinds of sedimentary rocks are there? Write the names of the rocks and draw the correct pictures.**

Place				Sedimentary Rock
shells	muddy water	flowing river	dry seabed	rock salt conglomerate limestone shale

1. Minerals in water provide the cement for this rock.

Conglomerate

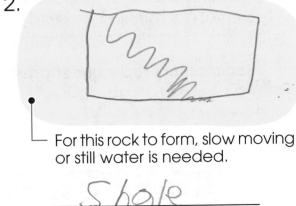

2. For this rock to form, slow moving or still water is needed.

Shale

3.

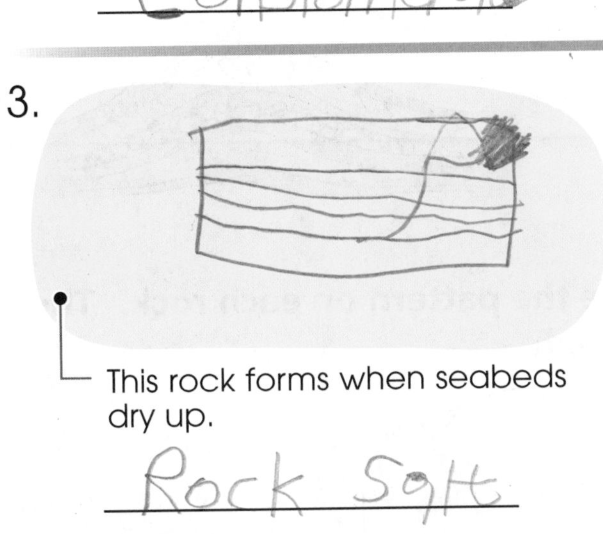

This rock forms when seabeds dry up.

Rock Salt

4.

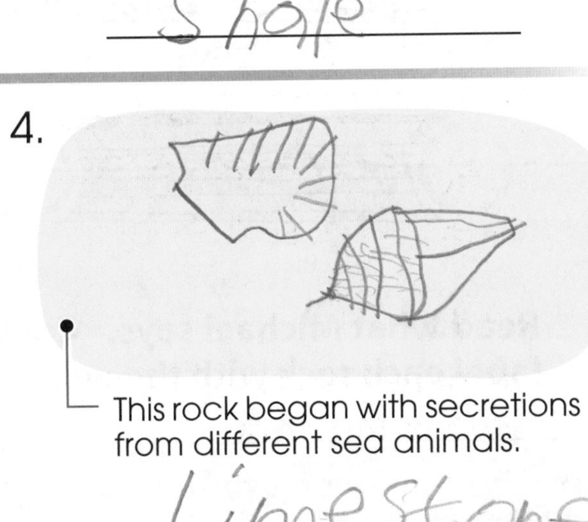

This rock began with secretions from different sea animals.

Limestone

Science Fact

Limestone is an exception to the rule that rocks are made from inorganic (non-living) substances. It is formed from the crushed shells of living animals.

19

Metamorphic Rocks

- Metamorphic rocks are made from extreme heat or pressure in the Earth.
- The rock cycle shows the relationship among the different rock types.

A. Read what Susan says. Draw an arrow in each circle to show the direction of pressure.

The right amount of heat and pressure below the Earth's surface can change a rock into another kind of rock.

Sedimentary rocks under pressure | **Metamorphic rocks formed**

1.

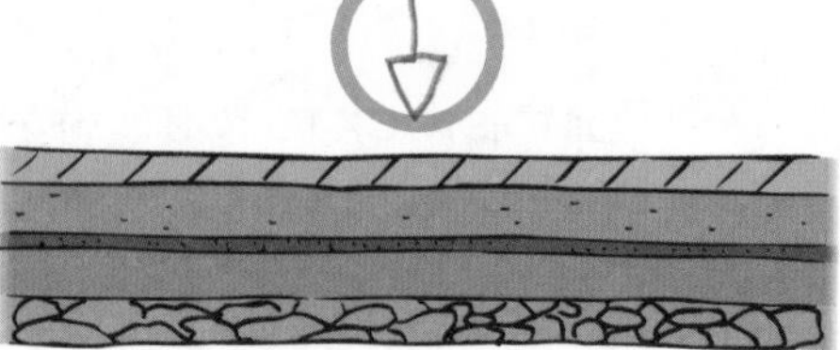

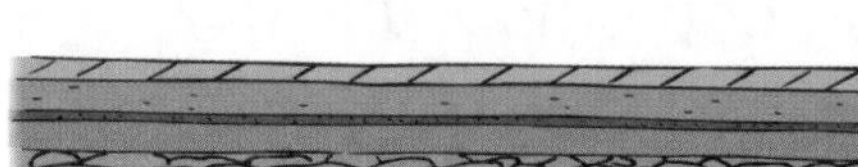

2.

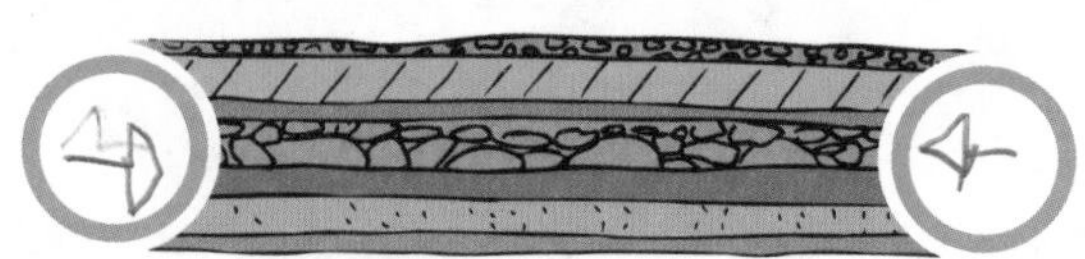

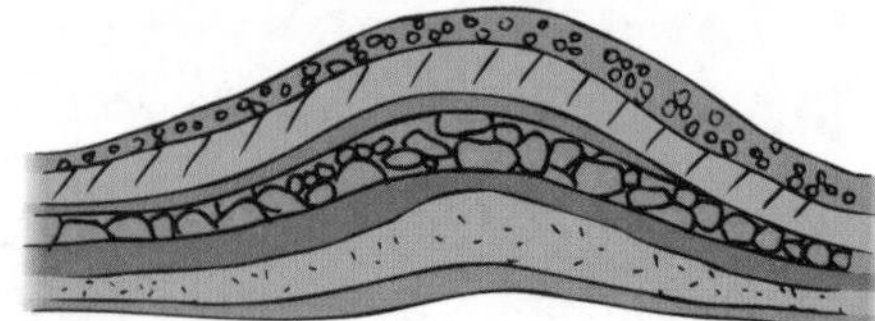

B. Read what Michael says. Complete the pattern on each rock. Then label each rock with the words in bold.

The igneous rock **granite** changes to the metamorphic rock **gneiss** when it is under extreme heat or pressure.

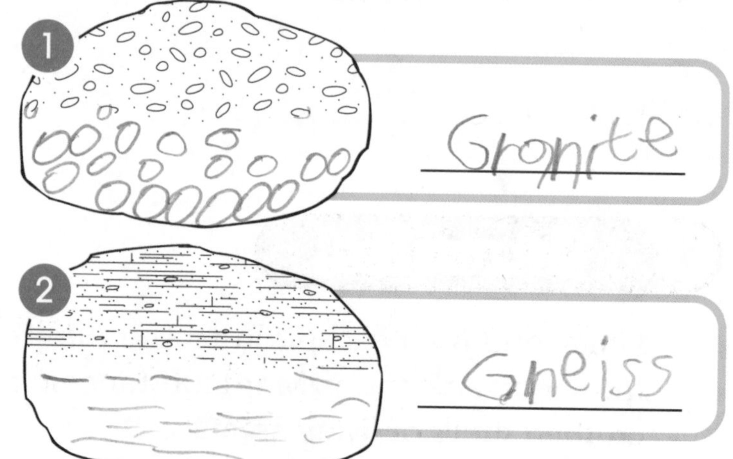

C. **Fill in the missing letters to find out what type of metamorphic rock the given rock will turn to under the right amount of heat and pressure.**

Metamorphic Rock

- *slate*
- *gneiss*
- *marble*
- *quartzite*

1. sandstone ➡ __ __ar__ __i__ __
2. shale ➡ __ __at__
3. granite ➡ __ne__ __s
4. limestone ➡ __a__b__ __

D. **Look at the rock cycle. Fill in the blanks.**

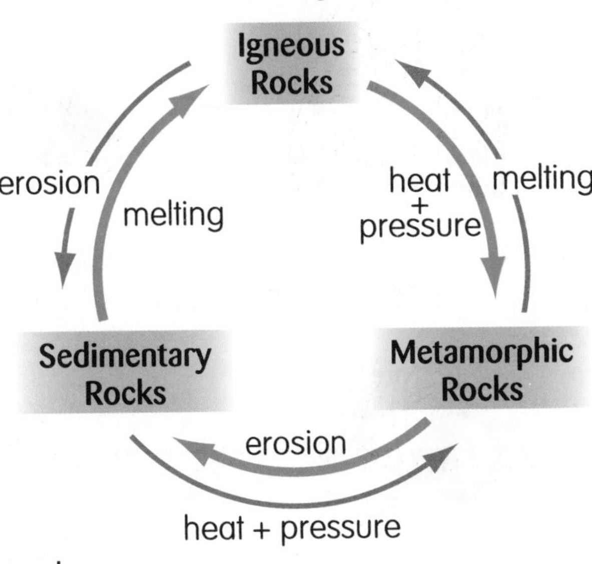

1. Metamorphic rocks can become __________ when they melt into hot molten magma.

2. When __________ and __________ undergo intense heat or pressure, they become metamorphic rocks.

3. Metamorphic rocks may become __________ when they break down into small pieces and are carried off into the sea.

Science Fact

Conditions can be too extreme for metamorphic rocks to form. If temperatures are high enough, rocks will turn to hot molten magma instead.

How We Use Rocks and Minerals

- *Rocks and minerals are used in almost every aspect of our lives.*

A. Colour the things that are made of rocks and minerals.

1.

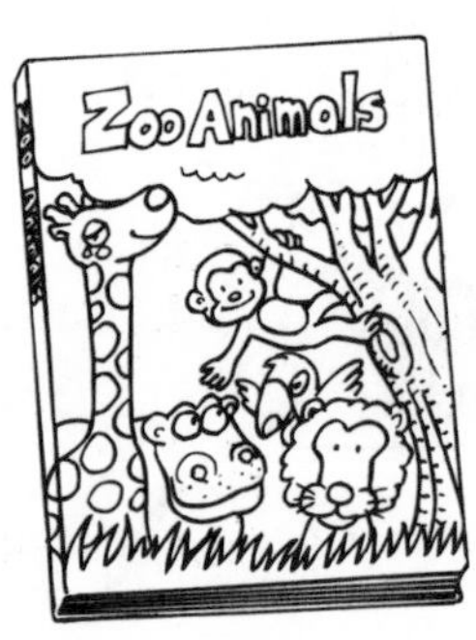

2.

3.

4.

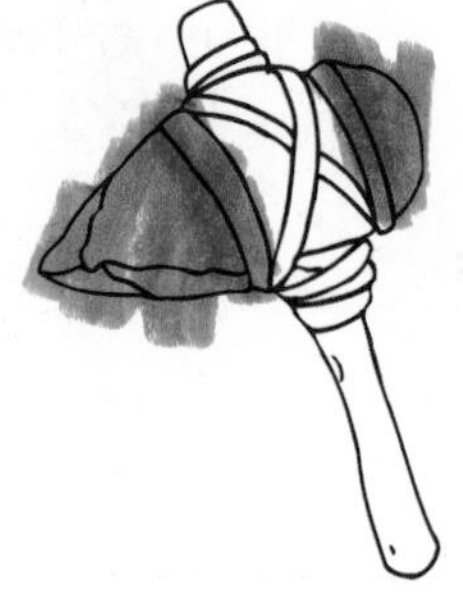

5.

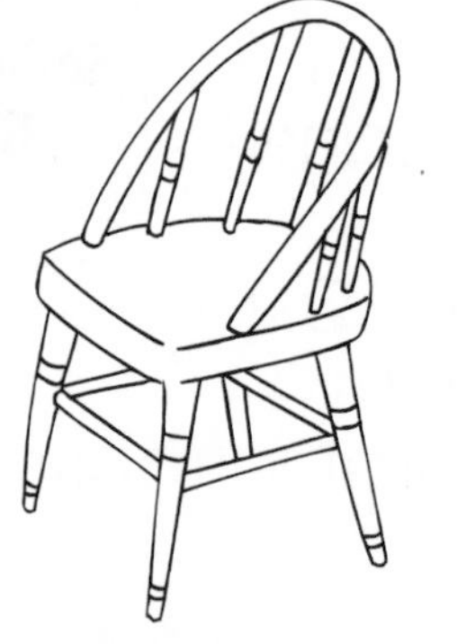

8.

6.

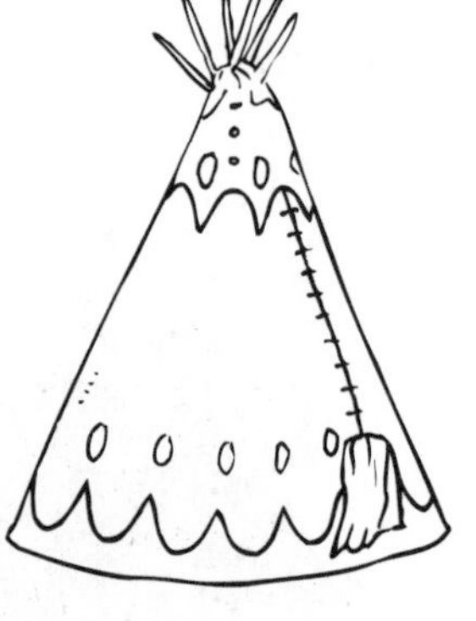

7.

B. Use the rock-based materials to make a house. Draw it in the box and label the materials you use.

Materials:

concrete (made from crushed limestone and pebbles)

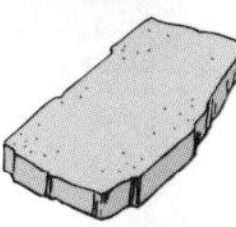
granite

slate sheets

stones

bricks (made from sand)

glass (made from sand)

steel bars

C. Read the descriptions to find the colours of these minerals.

Minerals are often a source of colour pigments.

Minerals

- Hematite – Red
  (colour of an apple)
- Azurite – Blue
  (colour of the sky)
- Malachite – Green
  (colour of grass)
- Charcoal – Yellow
  (colour of a shadow)

Science Fact

Sometimes, minerals can be dangerous to us. Asbestos is a mineral with qualities that make it very useful. Unfortunately, it also causes serious lung diseases.

Erosion

- *Erosion causes rocks to break off, break down, and move to another place.*
- *Erosion has many different causes.*

A. Fill in the blanks to show the progress of erosion.

sand
rock
mountain
silt

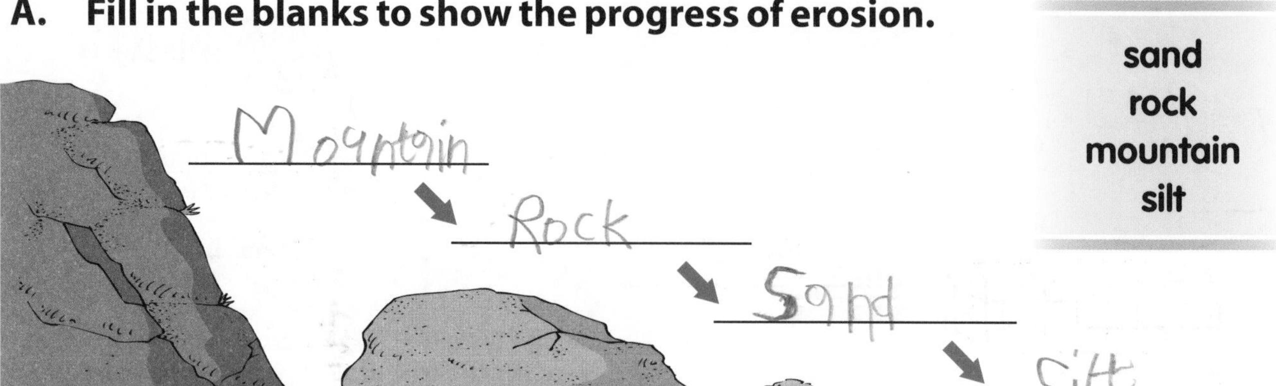

B. Tell what type of erosion occurs in each picture. Write "ice", "wind", or "moving water" on the line. Then draw a line to match each type of erosion with another example.

Types of Erosion

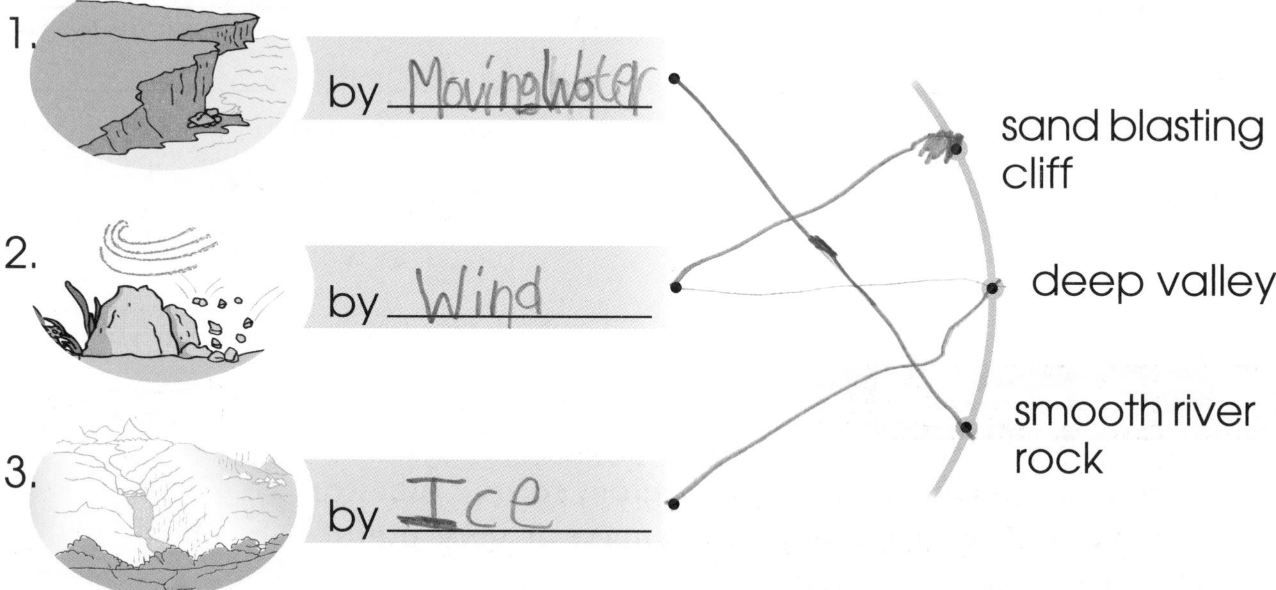

C. **Read the descriptions. Draw lines to show the causes of erosion. Then fill in the blanks to tell what the causes are.**

glacier landslide tide plant roots

Causes of Erosion

1. Rock will not stop it from growing.

2. The twice-a-day rise and fall is powerful enough to break down rocks.

3. This will slowly carve valleys between mountains.

4. The erosion of this mountainside happened in minutes, not thousands of years.

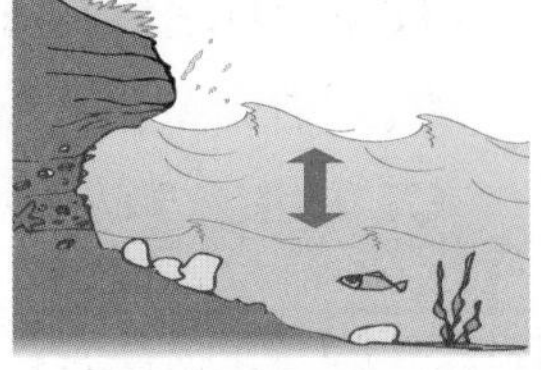

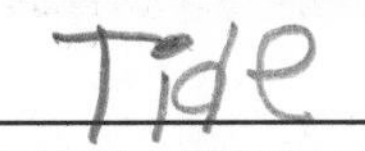

One of the most disastrous consequences of a drought is soil erosion. With no plants to keep the soil together, and lack of rain causing the soil to dry, winds easily carry good soil away.

Fossils

- *Fossils are traces of things that lived in prehistoric times.*
- *Fossils can be the preserved bodies of plants or animals, or imprints of them.*

A. Put the formation of each fossil in order. Write the letters.

Ammonite fossil formation:

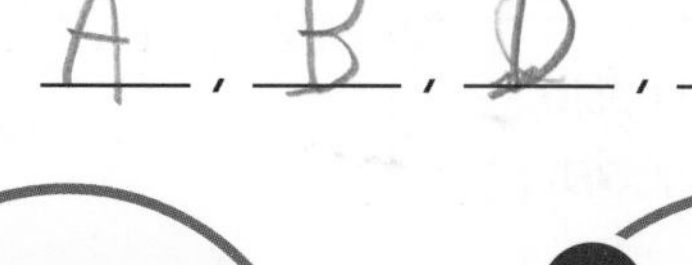

A , B , D , C

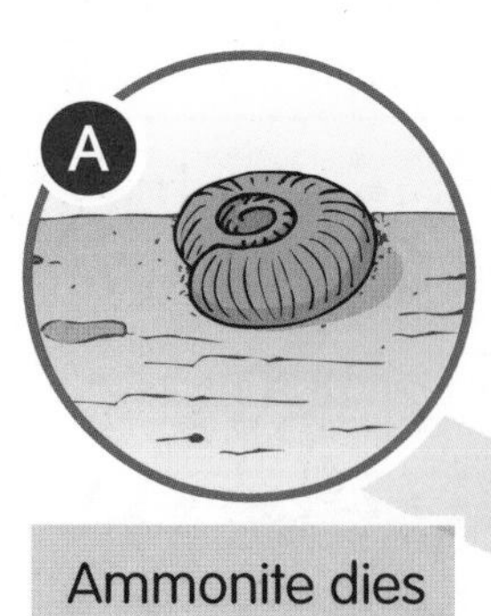

Ammonite dies

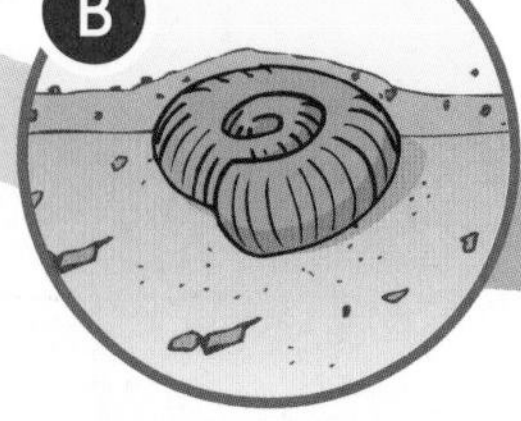

Covered by sediment

Erosion exposes fossil

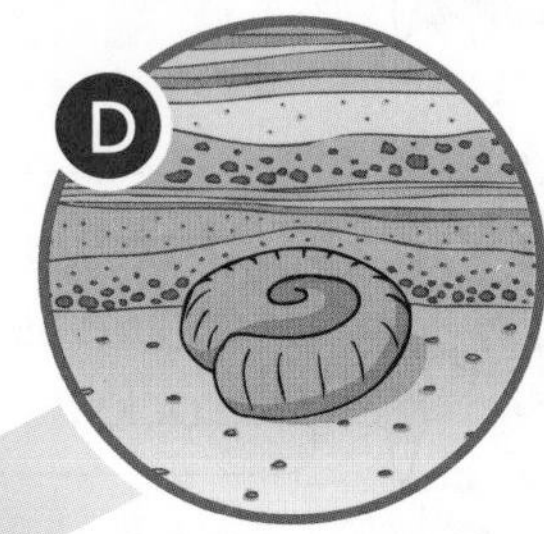

More layers of sediment – ammonite is mineralized and rock forms from sediment

Leaf imprint fossil formation:

R , P , Q , S

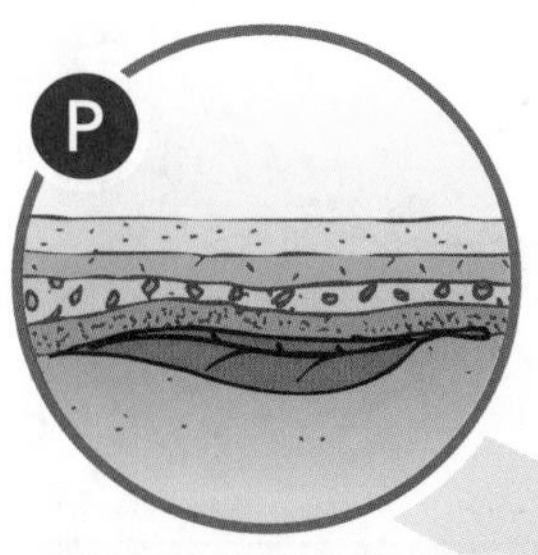

Buried in more mud and sand

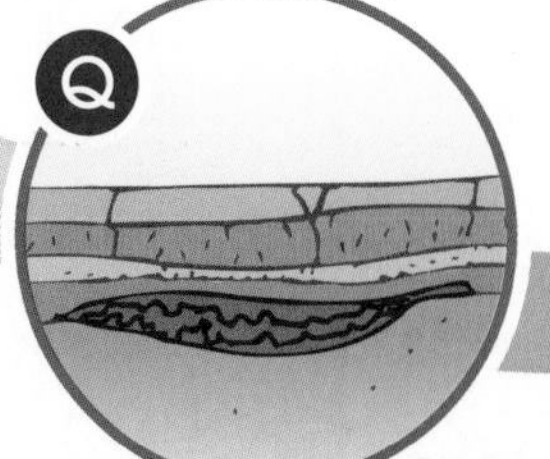

Leaf decomposes as surrounding mud hardens

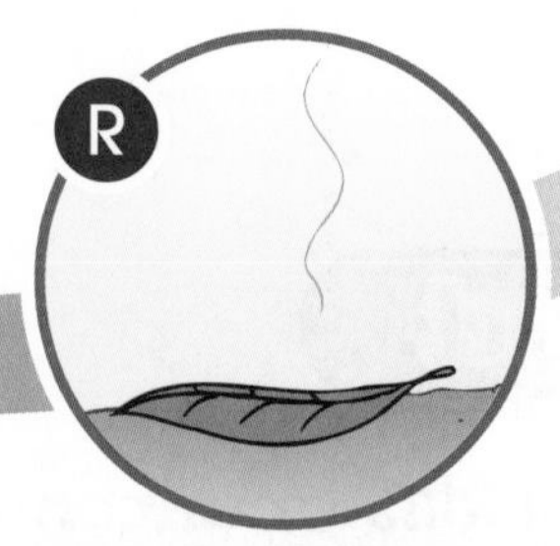

Leaf falls on muddy riverbank

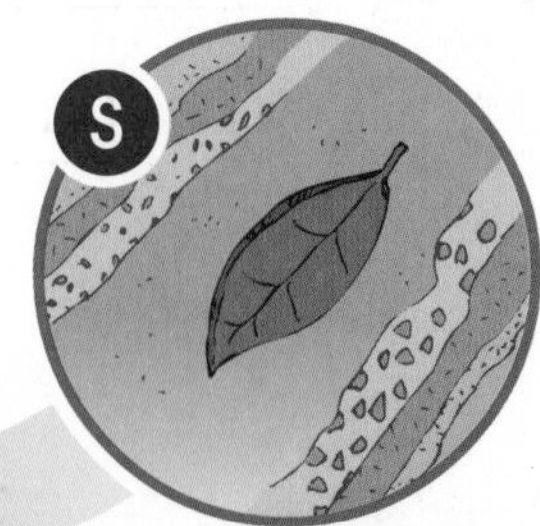

Sediment fills space of leaf to make a mold

B. Label the fossils with the given words. Then tell which fossils are used to find out the following about each animal.

bones teeth tracks egg nest dung

1. **Fossil**

Tracks

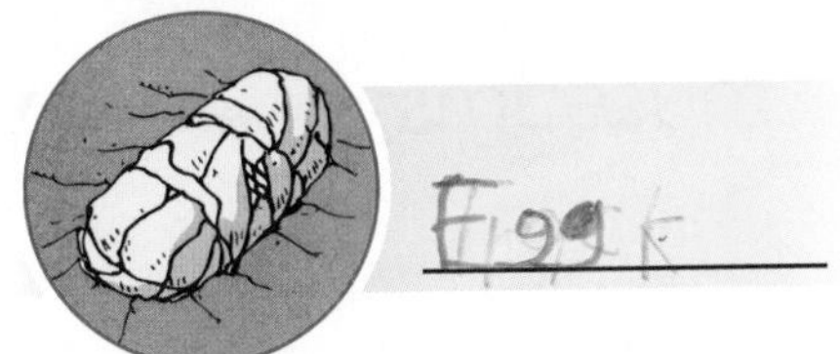
Egg

Dyng

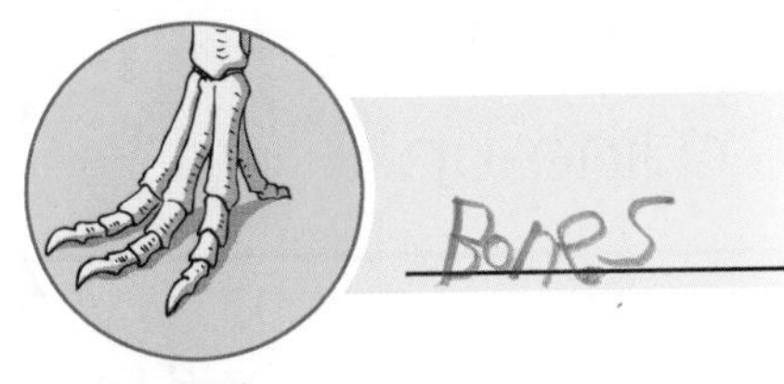
Bones

Teeth

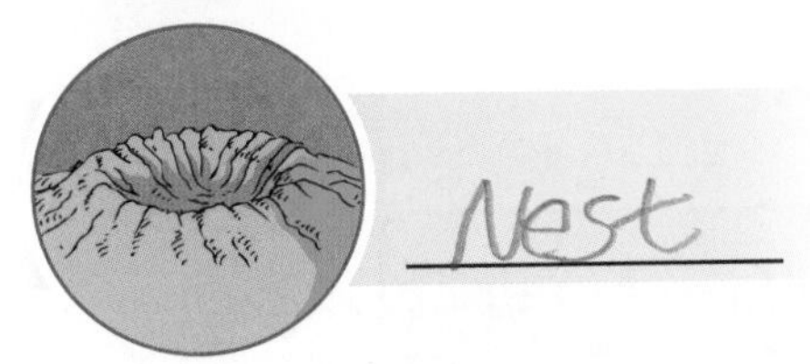
Nest

2. Which fossils tell us

a. if the animal walked on two legs?
Tracks ; Bones

b. how an animal defended itself?
Bones ; Nest

c. what an animal ate?
Dyng ; Teeth

d. that an animal was a carnivore?
Dyng ; Teeth

e. how an animal moved?
Tracks ; Bones

f. the size of a baby animal?
E99 ; Nest

Fossils of dinosaur droppings that are bigger than a small dog have been found. Scientists call these fossils coprolites.

More about Fossils

- Fossils are only found in places where the conditions were right for making fossils.
- Most fossils are never discovered. The ones we find are exposed through erosion or quarrying.

A. Where are fossils found? Circle the correct answers.

1. Fossils are most often found in A.

   sedimentary rocks   magma   museums

2. Insects are sometimes found in amber, which is fossilized C.

   apples   seeds   tree resin

3. Some fossils are from animals that got stuck in B.

   a tree   tar pits   a line-up

4. The Burgess Shale is rich in fossils. Once in the tropics at sea level, it is now at the top of the A.

   Rocky Mountains   Swiss Alps   CN Tower

5. 

   Sometimes, fossilized animals are found in dry desert C.

   air   water   sand

B. Read what the archaeologist says. Help him circle the correct tools for removing fossils from rock.

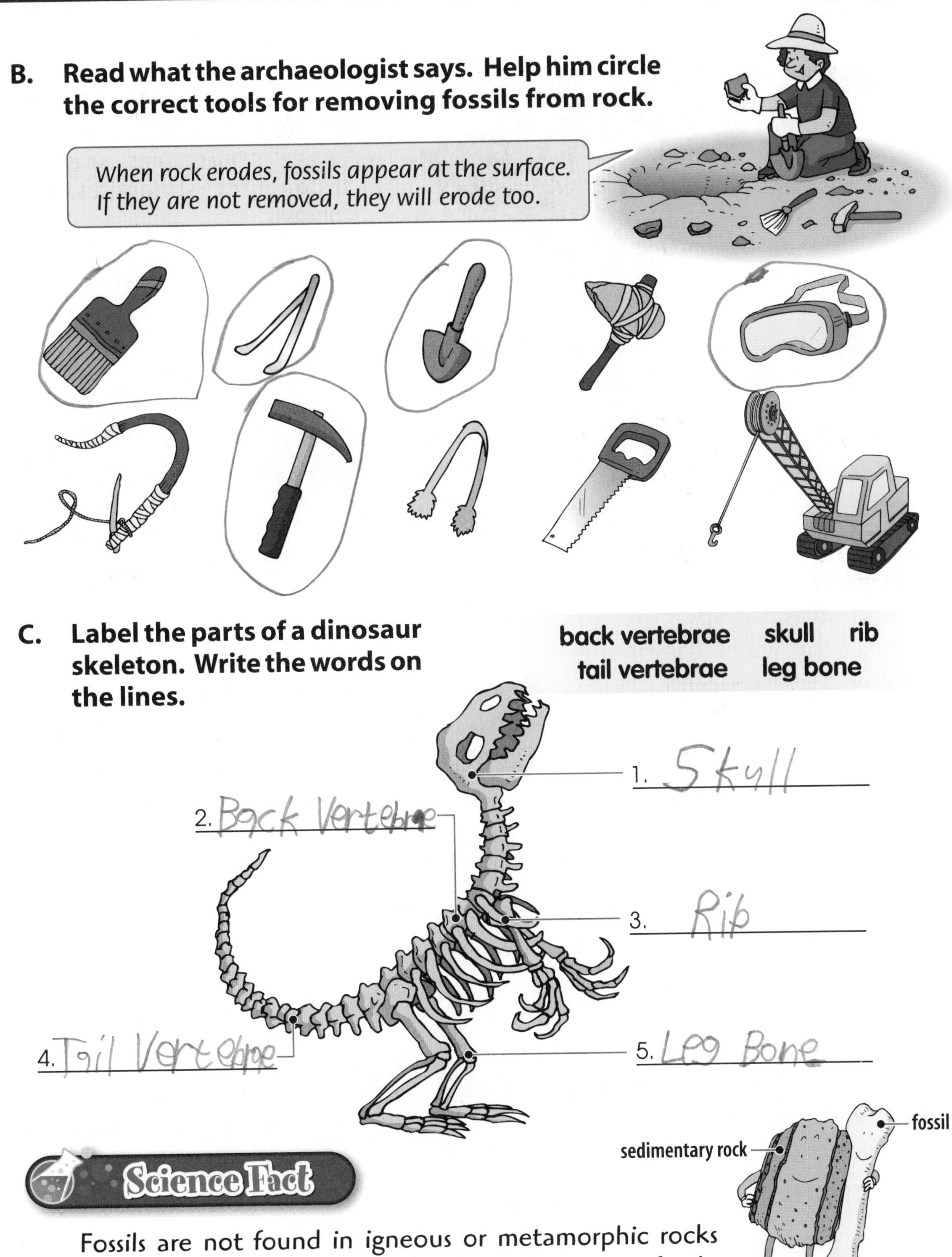

C. Label the parts of a dinosaur skeleton. Write the words on the lines.

back vertebrae skull rib tail vertebrae leg bone

Science Fact

Fossils are not found in igneous or metamorphic rocks because the heat that creates the rocks destroys the fossils.

Caves

- *The special environment of caves allows unique structures to form over many thousands of years.*
- *These structures include stalagmites, stalactites, and columns.*

A. Read the passage. Then write a word to match each description.

Water flowing or dripping over limestone gradually erodes the soft rock. In fact, most caves are formed exactly because of this. Limestone caves with flowing water develop speleothems, or decorations, caused by water dissolving limestone and then letting it collect when the water evaporates. With each drip from a cave's ceiling, a stalagmite grows higher. Mineral deposits also build from the dripping point, and a stalactite grows downward. If the two ever meet, they form a column of the mineral calcite.

1. What cave "decorations" are called Speleothems
2. A mineral that stalactites and stalagmites are made of Calcite
3. A speleothem growing down from the cave ceiling stalagmite
4. A speleothem growing up from the cave floor Stalactite
5. A kind of rock that most caves are made from Limestone
6. A structure that is formed when a stalagmite and a stalactite meet Column

B. Label the structures in the cave.

stalagmite **stalactite** **column**

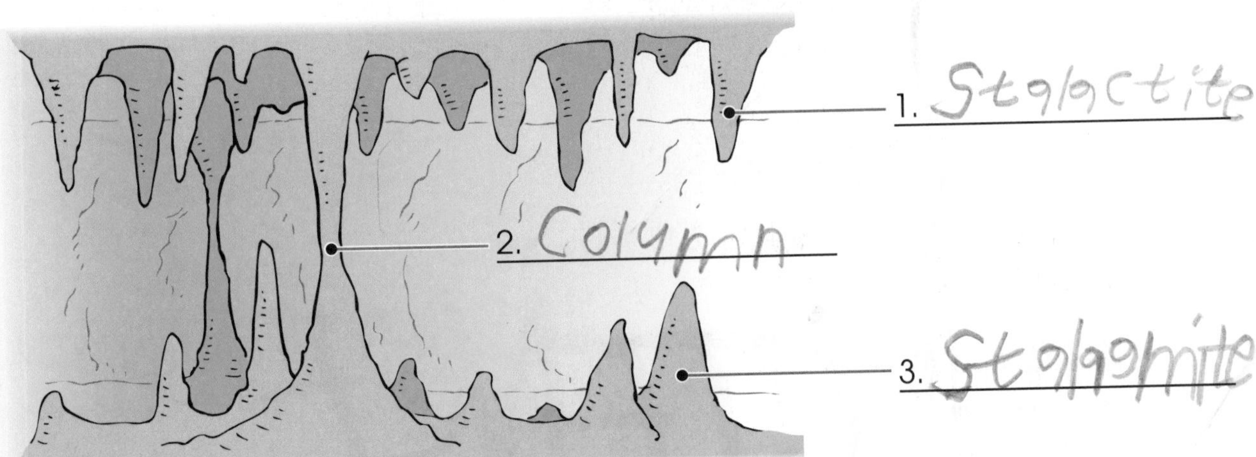

Experiment – Making Stalagmites

Things needed:

- *2 jars*
- *washing soda*
- *hot water*
- *a small plate*
- *a cotton string*

Steps:

1

Fill the jars with hot water to about $\frac{3}{4}$ full. Stir in washing soda until it no longer dissolves.

2

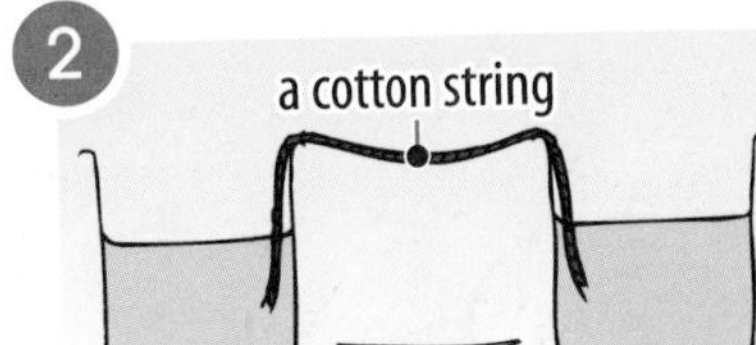

Let one end of the string hang in one jar of water, and the other end in the second jar. Allow the string to hang just above the plate.

3 *Soon it will start to drip. If left alone, stalagmites and even stalactites will form.*

Science Fact

Other speleothems made from calcite are found in caves too! "Soda straws" and "drapes" hang from ceilings, and flowstone can take the shape of ice cream scoops.

CONGRATULATIONS

24

SCIENCE

S

SCIENCE COMPLETE